BEFORE
the
IRONCLAD

BEFORE *the* IRONCLAD

Warship Design and Development
1815–1860

D K Brown, RCNC

Seaforth
PUBLISHING

Frontispiece:
This depiction of the bombardment of Acre (3 November 1840) shows a typical mixed fleet of the period. The principal ships of the line are the 72-gun *Benbow* and *Edinburgh*, both completed at the end of the Napoleonic war. However, the latter – here displaying Seppings's round stern – was to become one of the prototype steam battleship conversions. In the foreground are the paddle sloops *Vesuvius*, *Phoenix* and *Stromboli*, demonstrating their real value in naval warfare for the first time during this campaign. (*© National Maritime Museum neg 7019*)

Copyright © D K Brown 1990

This edition first published in Great Britain in 2015 by
Seaforth Publishing,
Pen & Sword Books Ltd,
47 Church Street,
Barnsley S70 2AS

www.seaforthpublishing.com

British Library Cataloguing in Publication Data
A catalogue record for this book is available from the British Library

ISBN 978 1 84832 258 5

Typeset and designed by Stephen Dent
Printed and bound in China by Imago

Contents

Introduction:
The Navy's Industrial Revolution

It will always be said of us with unabated reverence, 'They built ships of the line'. Take it all in all, a ship of the line is the most honourable thing that man, as a gregarious animal, has ever produced.

Ruskin, Harbours of England

IN THE NINETEENTH CENTURY, as now, the big warship was the most complicated and most expensive item in the defence budget. This book tells the story of the successive technical changes which led to the wooden ship of the line, first, vastly growing in size, then gaining in mobility through the power of steam

and, finally, quite quickly being replaced by the iron-hulled, armoured battleship.

The first great change came when Robert Seppings used scientific method in the design of wooden hulls, an approach which led to a rapid growth in the line-of-battle ship. The heavy and inefficient steam engine driving a paddle wheel was first introduced in auxiliaries to tow the sailing warship in calms or contrary winds. These paddle steamers soon grew, acquired an armament and became effective fighting ships themselves, though with some severe limitations.

The screw propeller overcame many of the problems

Virago towing the 110-gun *Queen* out of Grand Harbour, Malta, on 16 January 1844, demonstrating one of the earliest naval roles for steamers. *(© National Maritime Museum PY0891)*

Valorous. A second-class paddle frigate, the last major paddle fighting ship built for the Royal Navy. *(© National Maritime Museum neg 6845)*

of the paddler – and introduced a few new ones – and it could be fitted to many existing ships. Only a decade after the screw was proved, the Victory Review at the end of the Crimean War saw a fleet almost entirely consisting of wooden screw steamers.

Heavy steam engines and the vibration from the early propellers required a strong and rigid hull which had to be made of iron. The first attempts at iron hulls were not successful, for wrought iron was not, and is not, a suitable material for warship construction. With the strong but brittle iron hull protected by armour, the way was open for the iron-hulled, armoured screw battleship *Warrior*. She was just as much the culmination of the developments of an earlier era as she was the prototype for the next generation and like most transitional designs was very soon obsolete herself.

These major changes in the ships of the Navy took place in little more than a generation and yet all too often 'the Admiralty' of 1815–60 is portrayed as reactionary, opposed to all change. There was indeed a proper conservatism which was seen as a reluctance to render valueless by unnecessary change the investment already made in the world's largest fleet. The initiation of change could safely be left to others, since Britain's industrial might could quickly and easily retake any

temporary lead elsewhere. The quotation below comes from Sir Baldwin Walker's case for the radical introduction of the *Warrior* at the end of the era, but is implicit in much of what had gone before.

> Although I have frequently stated that it is not to the interest of Great Britain – possessing as she does so large a navy – to adopt any important change in the construction of ships of war which might have the effect of rendering necessary the introduction of a new class of very costly vessels, until such a course is forced upon her by the adoption by foreign powers of formidable ships of a novel character requiring similar ships to cope with them, yet it then becomes a matter not only of expediency, but of absolute necessity…

One often reads that the design of a particular early-nineteenth-century warship was copied from another, usually in the context that British ships were copies of foreign prizes. While there is some truth in such statements, they ignore other more important factors. On a more general level, it is true that the French first developed the big two-decker and the Royal Navy followed.

Designers of the period attached undue importance to the lines of the ship; indeed, the lines were William

Official half-model of *Duncan*, the final development of Edye's brilliant design of *Agamemnon* and the only one of the class completed as an unarmoured ship. *(© National Maritime Museum L0818)*

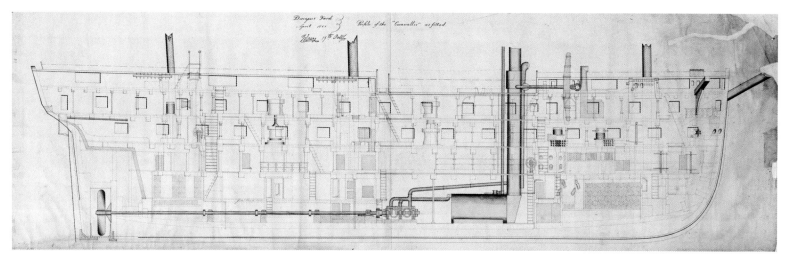

Admiralty profile draught of the *Cornwallis*, as converted to a screw 'blockship' or Steam Guard Ship. Beginning in 1845, this programme was the first to apply steam propulsion to ships of the line. *(© National Maritime Museum J2677)*

Symonds's only claim to be a designer, as he left the structure to his very able deputy, John Edye. In fact, as discussed later, the shape of the ship was so constrained by the need to provide buoyancy at the ends that all forms were far removed from the hydrodynamic ideal, and the small differences between rival designs can have had no effect on performance. In structural design the British were far in the lead, thanks to Seppings. He was the first to understand fully the nature of the loading on a ship at sea and he developed a light and durable structural style to meet these loads. It is wrong to say that *Ganges* was a copy of the captured French *Franklin* (HMS *Canopus*) merely because Seppings used the French lines; the shape of the bow and stern and the structural style were more important, and were all Seppings's.

Admiral Sir Baldwin Walker in the uniform of the Turkish navy in which he served from 1838 to 1845. He later became a distinguished Surveyor of the Navy from 1848 to 1861. *(© National Maritime Museum neg 9572)*

The notion of a reactionary Admiralty is so deeply entrenched that it is essential to quote at some length from contemporary reports and documents which demonstrate a determination to seek the whole truth and an ability to appreciate future potential, as well as to warn of immediate difficulties. After all, it has well been said, 'Of what use is a newborn baby?'

For this reason, prominence has been given to the trials of such ships as the HEICoS (Honourable East Indian Company Ship) *Nemesis*, the first iron warship; of *Archimedes* and *Rattler*, the early screw ships; of the 'blockships', the first steam battleships, and the full-scale tests of armour. The only significant opportunity for these ships to be proved in action was during the Crimean War, whose technical aspects are discussed in some depth. It was the first naval war in which fleets of steamships were deployed, and the first in which significant use was made of shells, mines, armour and other modern systems. The effects of this war were important, too, for the merchant navy, as steamships increased rapidly in numbers due to favourable charter rates. However, despite novel production methods, the war led to the collapse of the shipbuilding industry on the Thames, due mainly to wage inflation.

Some of this new technology was created within the Admiralty service, such as Seppings's structural scheme and George Airy's work on correcting the deviation of compasses in iron hulls which alone made iron seagoing ships possible. Much more was developed in industry, but it will be shown that the Admiralty was usually among the leaders in the utilisation of such inventions.

All too often it is forgotten that an organisation such as the Admiralty is not an impersonal and homogeneous entity, but consists of a number of all-too-human individuals, widely differing in their outlook, united only in their dedication to the cause of the Navy. To all these people the well-being of the Navy mattered and there were a few cases in which technical differences crossed the border into very bitter personal feuds. Some of the people involved were both innovators and highly competent (and these qualities are not the same); others were less so, but from 1815 to 1860 the Admiralty was blessed with many outstanding servants.

Among the politicians, Sidney Herbert and Henry Corry stand out. Corry seems to have been a leader in the complex dealing which led to the blockships completing as seagoing battleships rather than as semi-mobile batteries. Later, he was one of those who recognised the need for *Warrior* to be an iron ship. For many years the senior civil servant (Second Secretary) was John Barrow, an early advocate of steamships, whose advice helped Smith greatly in winning acceptance for his screw propeller.

Admirals Cockburn and Baldwin Walker were most prominent among naval officers, but perhaps even more impressive is the way that time and time again an officer, often undistinguished, would be called on to report on a new type of ship, engine or weapon, and would produce a balanced and comprehensive report which stands up to the penetrating scrutiny of hindsight. The seaman officer was not the reactionary so often portrayed. In particular, the Board of Admiralty maintained a wise balance between innovation and well-tried practice in using resources which were very limited.

Within the service, there were many outstanding engineers. In this writer's opinion, Thomas Lloyd, engineer-in-chief at the time of *Warrior*, was one of the great engineers of the century, possessing a breadth of vision matched only by Marc, Isambard and Henry Brunel, George and Robert Stephenson, and a very few others.

Isaac Watts, designer of some of the largest wooden ships ever built and then responsible for their successor, the *Warrior*, must rank only a little behind. These men were supported by a number of distinguished naval architects such as Fincham, the Langs, Edye, Large, Morgan, Creuze and, of course, Seppings. With a few exceptions, all these Admiralty constructors were graduates or staff of the first School of Naval Architecture, opened at Portsmouth in 1811. Almost accidentally, the final success of the graduates of this school has become an underlying theme of this book.

By 1860, the majority of master shipwrights in the Royal Dockyards were also graduates of this school. The role of the master shipwright, his background and status, is often misunderstood. They were the managing directors of the largest industrial concerns in the country, usually of middle-class background, well educated and from whose ranks would be chosen the Surveyor who was usually knighted as, indeed, were some master shipwrights. They were certainly not mere uneducated craftsmen. The most promising young men rose rapidly through the junior ranks, and as assistant masters would be given a chance to show their managerial skills in a small yard. If successful, a larger yard and promotion to the well-paid rank of master would follow. In the nineteenth century career development was less formal than it is today; knowing the right people

The first iron warship to see service was the *Nemesis*, belonging to the Honourable East India Company. She is in action here against Chinese war junks on 7 January 1841. *(© National Maritime Museum PY8893)*

Thunder. A wooden-hulled, armoured battery of the Crimean War.

counted – and still does – so that reality was not as simple as that sketched above.

There were many more who made major contributions, such as Thomas Blomefield on gun-making, John Hay on the fouling of iron ships and Airy, the Astronomer Royal, whose work on compass correction made the seagoing iron ship possible. Airy also made studies into the efficiency of steam engines, justifying the Admiralty's choice of manufacturers, outstanding among whom were Penn and Maudslay.

The Admiralty deserved great credit for the way in which the transition from *Victory* to *Warrior* was handled. Looking back, one can see only a very few aspects in which they could have moved a little faster, and even fewer in which they moved too fast. They had some excellent engineers within the service, and were quite willing to work with the great men outside the service.

Sources

There are few readily available and reliable books covering the technical aspects of the period and not many on more general topics. For the political and economic background, Bartlett is invaluable. Lavery deals well with the sailing ship, as does Lambert with the steam battleship. Fincham, a master shipwright, is the only contemporary writer of history to be of much value, and he is reliable only when writing of his own experience. There is no good history of marine engines nor of gunnery (*pace* the various works quoted). This is a history of ships themselves and cannot adequately cover engines or guns, though their implications for the ship designer must be mentioned. The major sources are the searching Parliamentary Enquiries of the day.

Acknowledgements

Above all, I must thank the late George Osbon, who showed me the way ahead some sixteen years ago and gave me so much statistical data. Then, too, the staffs of various libraries: the Naval Library (particularly Miss V Francis), the PRO, Ship Department and A E W Haslar. Dr Tom Wright of the Science Museum and his colleague Joe Roome, Dr N A M Rodger, PRO, and David Brown, my namesake, Naval Historical Branch, have given most valuable assistance, as have Cdr Trevor Shaw PhD, Terry Davis and David Lyon. Steve Roberts and John Campbell have not only made the result of their own studies available to me but have been friendly but searching critics. Thanks are due also to Robert Gardiner, whose suggestion that *Warrior* be included brought the whole story into focus; and to the many others, too numerous to mention, who have contributed.

Finally, my thanks to my former secretaries, Sheila and Edwina, and to my wife Avis for their help and forbearance.

David K Brown, RCNC
1989

Publisher's note

Since the above was written, there have been a number of significant publications in this area: indeed, *Before the Ironclad* might be seen as the work that encouraged, if not inspired, a more positive interpretation of the Royal Navy in this period. The ships are now covered in great detail in *The Sail and Steam Navy List* by David Lyon and Rif Winfield, and the 1817-1863 volume of Winfield's *British Warships in the Age of Sail* series. Andrew Lambert's pioneering work *Battleships in Transition* was followed by a far larger study entitled *The Last Sailing Battlefleet: Maintaining Naval Mastery 1815-1850* and two books on the Crimean War, as well as a monograph on HMS *Warrior*. Professor Lambert also contributed the section on Brunel, HMS *Rattler* and the introduction of the screw propeller into the Royal Navy to *Brunel's Ships* with Denis Griffiths and Fred Walker. A broad account of the period is *Steam, Politics & Patronage: The Transformation of the Royal Navy 1815-54* by Basil Greenhill and Ann Giffard.

Steam at Sea by Denis Griffiths filled the need for a good general history of marine engineering, but there is still no satisfactory history of guns and gunnery in the first half of the nineteenth century.

Illustrations

In the first edition D K Brown wrote:

> These present some special difficulties in that photography had been barely invented during the period covered, and illustrated journals were not common until well into the period. Only in the Crimean War did illustrations become common and hence that chapter is much more generously decorated than others. Originals are hard to find and copies of copies lose their quality. However, thanks to individuals, museums, etc (listed below), I hope that something of the quality of this forgotten fleet is presented.
>
> I am particularly grateful to the Trustees of the Science Museum for permission to use many of their photographs, especially those of their beautiful models of marine engines.

After his death in 2008 the author's picture collection was dispersed, so it was necessary for the publishers to reconsider the illustration of the book. Fortunately, the vast collections of the National Maritime Museum were able to supply many of the original illustrations, but in higher-quality formats that benefit from modern digital technology. Furthermore, the cooperation of the Museum made it possible to include additional images from parts of the collections – like the original draughts – which were almost impossible to access when the book was first written. In this context, the publishers would like to extend special thanks to Jeremy Michell, Andrew Choong and the staff of the Museum's Brass Foundry

outstation, and Emma Lefley and her colleagues in the Picture Library.

We are also happy to acknowledge specific help from William Mowll, Dr Stephen S Roberts, and from Major Grant Walker of the Beverley R Robinson Collection, US Naval Academy Museum.

Some terms used

Displacement The actual weight of the ship and its equipment. By Archimedes' principle, weight equals buoyancy and buoyancy is the weight of the water displaced by the underwater hull when floating.

Entrance The forward part of the underwater hull, up to the largest section.

Horsepower A very difficult subject, covered in full in Appendix 1, but in brief:
NHP (nominal horsepower) was a measure of the geometry of the engine and bore little relation to the real power. Modern convention is to use lower case letters for horsepower and this has been adopted except for NHP where capitals are used to make it clear that it is not power.
ihp (indicated horsepower).The power available in the steam, not all of which could be used to drive the propeller.
shp (shaft horsepower). The power put into the screw.

Line-of-battle ship The usual contemporary abbreviation was 'liner', which is used here, as well as 'battleship'.

Run The after part of the underwater form.

Tonnage Given in 'builder's measurement' (bm) or, from the mid-1830s, strictly 'builder's old measurement', since a new definition of tonnage was introduced for merchant ships; it was rarely used for warships. It was a measurement of volume, given by

$$\frac{(LB - \tfrac{2}{3}B) \times B/2}{94}$$

Trials Trial speeds quoted were generally the average of several runs over a measured distance in opposite directions. This procedure eliminated the effect of tide, but not necessarily that of wind. With care, the procedures then in use should give a speed, *on the day*, accurate to about ¼ knot; the three decimal places often quoted are an arithmetical quirk of the averaging process and should be forgotten. Methods to correct for the effects of fouling, which could be several knots, or for changes in displacement, did not exist. The Admiralty published very detailed tables of the trials results of screw ships; data for paddle ships are less abundant and much less reliable.

One | Victory 1793–1815

DURING THE REVOLUTIONARY and Napoleonic wars the Royal Navy achieved the most overwhelming series of victories in the history of naval warfare. The main fleets of France, Spain, Denmark and The Netherlands were captured or destroyed – in some cases more than once – and there were innumerable successes in single-ship actions. After Trafalgar, the British battlefleet was not seriously challenged. These repeated victories gave the Royal Navy an arrogant self-confidence which helped it greatly to win against the odds, even as recently as the Second World War.

Written in the form of a scoreboard, the results of this war at sea seem almost incredible. The figures in Table 1.1 are inevitably imprecise, since some older or smaller ships had only a marginal claim to be classed as line-of-battle ships, and it is not always clear whether individual losses were due to damage in action at sea, bad weather, military action against a port, or a combination of causes.

In summary, in fighting at sea, the Royal Navy lost five battleships and sixteen frigates, and the enemy navies lost some 92 battleships and 172 frigates. It should be noted that only about 20 per cent of losses in action involved the destruction of the enemy by fire or

flood. The wooden fighting ship was hard to sink by cannon fire; for example, take the well-documented case of *Impregnable* at Algiers in 1816. She was struck by 268 shot, of which fifty hit below the lower deck, including three 68pdr balls below the waterline, yet she was able to sail to Gibraltar for repairs.[2] The large number of captured ships helped augment the output of hard-pressed British building yards.

Table 1.2 **Accidental Losses**

		Wreck	Founder	Fire	Total
Royal Navy	Line of battle	15	3	8	26
	Frigates	59	3		62
France	Line of battle	6	4	1	11
	Frigates	10	1	1	12
Netherlands	Line of battle	1			1
	Frigates	1			1

Considering the relative number of ships at sea, the figures in Table 1.2 demonstrate the superb seamanship of the Royal Navy, the result of long years at sea and a strict discipline. It is worth noting that five of the liners lost were the old and unsatisfactory 64-gun ships, a high proportion of such vessels (it is possible that they had less efficient officers). The number of vessels lost by fire suggests that the improvements made after the war to magazine safety were long overdue.

The British success in battle was primarily due to leadership and to seamanship. Sea officers had learnt much from the War of American Independence and had polished their skills in the opening years of the new war. On the other hand, the majority of the French officers of the old navy were killed or deposed in the Revolution. The high rate of fire maintained by British gun crews was another important factor in victory. In part, the ability to fire at least three rounds as against two from the French was a result of training, but it also owed much to the technology of British gunfounders, an aspect discussed later.

The overall superiority of the Royal Navy in battle, due to gunnery and seamanship, is clear from Table 1 and it seems unlikely that the ships themselves were inferior to those of the enemy. It is strange, therefore, that virtually all British writers insist that British-built ships were poor in comparison with those built in other countries. Naval officers and the new generation of professional naval architects were in agreement on the virtues of foreign, and in particular, French ships. British designs were said to be smaller and slower, with cramped gun decks too close to the waterline. Their designers

Table 1.1 **British and Enemy Losses 1793–1815**

		At sea		Port	
		Captured	Destroyed	Captured	Destroyed
Royal Navy	Line of battle	5			
	Frigates	16			
France	Line of battle	46	10	13	10
	Frigates	110	25	15	4
Netherlands	Line of battle	8	10	3	1
	Frigates	8	1	5	1
Spain	Line of battle	17	2	3	1
	Frigates	16	3	1	2
Denmark	Line of battle	1	17		
	Frigates	1	8		
Turkey	Line of battle	1			
	Frigates	1	4		
Russia	Line of battle	1			
USA	Frigates	3			
All enemy	Line of battle	79	13	43	14
	Frigates	139	33	29	7

Notes

1. Figures from James, *The Naval History of Great Britain*.[1]

2. Line-of-battle ships under sixty guns ignored.

3. Ships which ran ashore in battle and were then destroyed count as destroyed at sea.

4. Ships scuttled in port to avoid capture are listed as destroyed in port.

The battle of Algiers, 1816. Like much naval warfare of the period 1815–1860, this action involved ships attacking forts, usually successfully. (© *National Maritime Museum BHC0617*)

were said to be mere tradesmen with none of the science of French naval architects.

There are innumerable accounts by officers of the RN, accepted by historians such as James[3] and Brenton,[4] and by later writers, extolling the merits of captured ships and few indeed put a different viewpoint. By 1816 one-ninth of the battleships in commission were prizes, as were about a ninth of smaller vessels. A large proportion of British-built ships were based, to some extent, on the designs of captured enemy vessels.

Actual evidence in support of these views is less easy to come by. One may use the subjective impressions of ships' captains and officers, but even today such evidence is considered unreliable because of the strong emotional bond between a captain and his ship. Unless she breaks his heart, a captain will always swear that his present ship is the best ever. Admiral Nelson, during the brief period in which the *San Joseph* was his flagship, told Lord Spencer that she was the finest ship in the world, yet he had never been to sea in her at that time. Brenton, too, commends the *San Joseph* in his book:

> The *San Joseph*, of 112 guns, taken in the battle off Cape St Vincent in 1797, was long admired in the British Navy, uniting all the superior qualities of a ship of the line with the sailing of the fastest frigate: her lower deck ports were higher out of the water with all her sea stores in than was ever known in any other ship of the line; she could carry her guns run out when few British ships would have ventured to open a port; she stowed 500 tons of water and we had nothing that compared with her as a ship of war.[5]

San Joseph may have been a fine ship, but English builders, who were not in any way reluctant to copy the best of foreign designs, chose *Victory* as the model for the smaller three-deckers.

Before considering such allegations in detail it is necessary to set out the desirable qualities of a warship. British resources of all kinds were limited, yet the Royal Navy had to provide several large fleets, as well as smaller squadrons worldwide. The enemy could bide his time and strike in one area only, a difference summed up today by comparing a sea *command* navy with a sea *denial* navy.

Britain was short of building slips and of shipwrights; timber was increasingly difficult to obtain, as were naval stores such as hemp. Seamen, too, were scarce and all these problems forced the Admiralty and Navy Boards

1. W James, *The Naval History of Great Britain 1793–1820*, London (1822).

2. Ibid.

3. Ibid.

4. E Brenton, *Naval History of Great Britain*, London (1823).

5. Ibid.

San Josef. This captured Spanish three-decker was much praised by naval officers but did not influence British ship design. *(© National Maritime Museum J1945)*

to build the smallest ships with the minimum capability to do the job. As Sir Robert Seppings was to say in 1830:

> It is a fact which cannot be controverted, that in point of experience, whether considered in respect of building and first equipment or in reference to the subsequent wear and tear of the hulls of ships and their stores, the smaller they are to carry the number of guns prescribed and to secure the necessary seagoing qualities, the more advantageous they will be to the country. [6]

The 'rate' of a ship depended on the number of guns it carried and it is obvious that a bigger ship would carry a set number of guns more effectively, would be more seaworthy, and hence would be considered superior. Later in the century, displacement was the base line for comparison and the 'best ship' was the one carrying most guns on a given tonnage.

The first paper read to the Society for the Improvement of Naval Architecture in 1791 was, unfortunately, anonymous but contained a reasoned critique of British design.[7] The author (possibly Captain Sir John Warren) suggested that British ships were at a disadvantage when 'sailing by the wind' and in the angle of heel produced by the wind. Both these problems related to lack of stability affecting mainly the smaller three-deckers and the 64-gun ship, already obsolete by 1815. The bigger frigates (1791) of thirty-six and thirty-eight guns were 'admirable ships'.

A limited study of contemporary French writing suggests that they had a different view of the performance of their ships vis-à-vis those of the Royal Navy. M Bouvet, writing of French ships, says:

> They have never, by any chance, taken or preserved any advantage over their adversaries, or succeeded in eluding or flying from a disastrous engagement. Our ships of all rates, whether in company or alone, have rarely escaped pursuit of those of the enemy that have fallen in with them while cruising … The fault may in great measure be attributed to the French ships being too sharp and constricted at their extremities; they are not what is

termed good sea-boats; this peculiarity, which has been imagined to lead to superiority in point of swiftness, has produced a contrary effect, at least in rough seas.[8]

The most common allegation by British writers against British designs is that they were slower than those of all other navies. Direct evidence on relative speed is both hard to find and hard to interpret. Study of James's history has identified only fifty-eight chases in which it is clear that one ship, or groups of ships, was faster than its opponent. It must be noted that these fifty-eight chases almost all led to an engagement and there must have been many inconclusive pursuits. However, the number identified is sufficient and probably sufficiently unbiased to give meaningful results. This evidence is examined in detail by the author elsewhere.[9]

Table 1.3 **Comparison of Ships in Chase**

Frigates and above				
Faster ship		*Slower ship*		
Built in	*Manned by*	*Built in*	*Manned by*	*Number*
Britain	Britain	France	France	40
France	France	Britain	Britain	6
France	Britain	France	France	8
Spain	Britain	Britain	France	1
Britain	Britain	Denmark	Denmark	1
Britain	Britain	Russia & Sweden	Russia & Sweden	1

The problem of comparing the performance of two or more groups of ships of different designs with crews of different ability and under very different conditions of sea state is not easy (Table 1.3). There will always be two different categories of influence at work: the systematic advantage of better seamanship, skill in trimming ballast and rig and of better hull design, as against the random effects of fouling and the strength and direction of both wind and sea. The latter effect was clearly shown on 26 July 1798 when HMS *Brilliant* was being caught by the French ship *Vertu* but, when the wind changed, *Brilliant* proved the faster.

6. R Seppings, letter to *United Services Journal*, vol 1 (1830).

7. Anon, 'Remarks on the forms and proportions of ships'. *Collection of papers on naval architecture, European Magazine*, London (1800).

8. M Bouvet, quoted by 'Nauticas' Veritas', *Naval and Military Magazine*, vol III (1828).

9. D K Brown, 'Speed of sailing warships', 'Empires at war and peace', Conference, Portsmouth (1988).

Table 1.4 **Relative Speed of British-Manned Ships**

Built in	Won	Lost
Britain	42	6
Abroad	10	0

Some further insight can be gained by comparing the performance of British-manned ships, built at home or abroad (Table 1.4). This table suggests that there was a slightly greater chance of foreign-built ships winning a chase, but any such advantage was small and swamped by random effects.

From the mid-eighteenth century onwards, captains of British ships were required by the Navy Board to report on the sailing qualities of their ships, answering a standard list of questions.[10] The key questions concerned the maximum speed attained with different wind speeds and directions during a whole commission. Such reports provide a somewhat more objective assessment of a prize than that given in the moment of victory.

Fouling affected all ships but it is not clear that they were affected equally. Copper sheathing was tried in the Royal Navy in 1763, and by 1782 all problems had been overcome and some three hundred British ships were sheathed. During the War of American Independence this usually gave British ships a speed advantage of up to 1½ knots.[11] By 1793 all navies were using copper sheathing and, if it was in good condition, no one ship would have had an advantage. However, due to shortages, the French used very thin copper, which was easily damaged or eroded, leading to rapid growth of fouling on the unprotected areas. Even when the copper was sound, it would form a green patina after about a year in seawater and lose much of its anti-fouling properties. British ships on blockade duty, long out of dock, did suffer from such fouling and would be slow in comparison with ships fresh out of dock. It is thought that French dockyards were so dilatory that their navy reaped little benefit. Overall, the effect of fouling is seen as random, making difficult the comparison between forms.[12]

It was also suggested, notably by the new generation of naval architects, that French forms were faster because of their superior understanding of hydrodynamics. The drag of hulls of the size, shape and speed of nineteenth-century warships was primarily due to viscosity, a topic almost totally ignored by the science of the day. Since a fluid lacking viscosity produces no drag at all, scientists from Isaac Newton onwards fudged the answer by considering flow over the fore body only. This incorrect assumption led them to direct their attention to the form of the entrance and the shape of the midship section, contrary to the empirical knowledge that the shape of the run was

10. B Lavery, *Ship of the Line*, vol I (Appendix XI), London (1983); see also n9.

11. R J B Knight, 'The introduction of copper sheathing into the RN 1779–86', *Mariner's Mirror*, vol 49 (1963).

12. Brown, op cit.

Hibernia. A 110-gun ship designed by Henslow and launched in 1804. Reconstructed in 1819–1825, she was highly regarded and enjoyed a long career – seen here at sea in the 1840s. (© *National Maritime Museum PW5999*)

vital to good performance. It is no wonder that the master shipwrights were unimpressed by such science.

Morgan made a very careful analysis of the characteristics of hull forms from many navies in *Papers on Naval Architecture* in 1826.[13] His tables show little difference between the proportions of rival designers. There was, perhaps, a tendency for British ships to be marginally narrower than most, which would lead to slightly greater heel in a strong wind. Morgan appreciated that, once a ship heels, its underwater form is unsymmetrical, always increasing the drag, and usually causing the ship to fall away to leeward as well as bringing the gunports nearer the water.

Like his contemporaries, Morgan believed that the shape of the midship section had a major influence on sailing. Today, it is clear that the section shape could have had no influence on speed and little on rolling. Section shape could have affected the ability to hold a course, but the effect must have been very small within the practical limits of the shape.

The effect of an extreme and certainly quite impractical change of shape has been examined by G S Baker, superintendent of the Froude Ship Tank.[14] He compared the resistance of the *Victory* with that of a 'modern' sailing ship of the same displacement but 69ft longer and 12½ft narrower. This dramatic change in form led to a reduction in resistance of some 30 per cent, which would lead to a 1–1½-knot advantage to the longer ship. In comparison, the very small differences between ships of rival navies can have had no observable effect.

In fact, the hull form of the wooden warship of all navies was dominated by the problem of keeping the load on the hull down to a level which could be accepted by the structure.[15] The side planking was not effectively joined at the seams or at the ends of the planks and could move under load. Such relative movement led to the whole hull bending, an effect known as 'hogging' or 'breaking the sheer'. In order to reduce the loading due to the sea to an acceptable level, it was necessary to arrange that the buoyancy at any section along the length was roughly equal to the weight of that section. In particular, the weight of the heavy bow and stern chasers had to be supported by full underwater sections, very different from the fine ends which would be selected by a modern naval architect. The hull form of warships was so far from the ideal that small differences in shape can have had no measurable effect.

The evidence that there was little difference in hull

13. W Morgan, 'Brief sketch of the progress of naval architecture', *Papers on Naval Architecture*, vol I, London (1826).

14. G S Baker, 'Development of the hull form of merchant vessels' (8th Andrew Laing lecture), *Transactions, North East Coast Institution of Engineers and Shipbuilders*, vol LIV (1937).

15. J F Coates, 'Hogging and breaking of frame built wooden ships', *Mariner's Mirror*, vol 71 (1985).

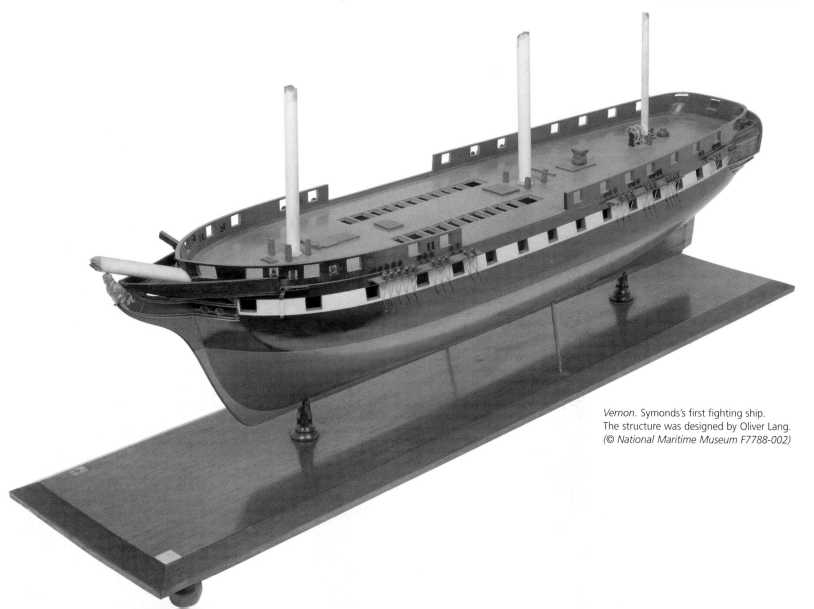

Vernon. Symonds's first fighting ship. The structure was designed by Oliver Lang. (© *National Maritime Museum F7788-002*)

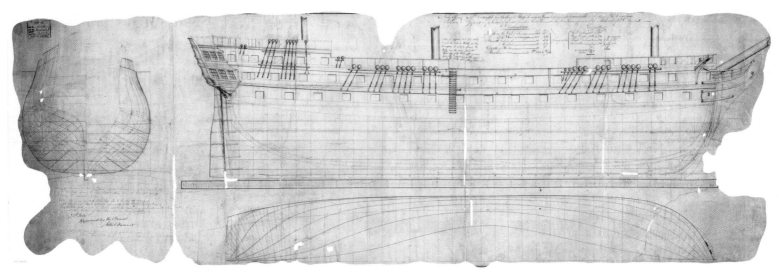

form or in speed between different national styles seems conclusive. One must ask why the almost unanimous British view was to the contrary. First, there was the excitement of the chase which always leads the hunter – and perhaps even more, the hunted – to exaggerate. In this case there was an even better reason to praise the qualities of a capture, since prize money depended on the value of the ship which had been taken. Naval architects, too, had reason to support the myth of French superiority. They wished for more attention to be given to the scientific study of their subject and it was convenient to attribute the apparent superiority of enemy ships to their superior science. True or false, the Admiralty acted in several ways to remedy what they perceived as British inferiority.

For many years the Admiralty, the Navy Board and the master shipwrights had used the lines of some captured French ships as the basis for new British designs. This practice was by no means universal; the big three-deckers owed little to foreign influence and Slade's *Victory* was seen as a form worth copying well into the nineteenth century. The big two-deck Second Rates were a French speciality and the form, but not the structure, of such ships was usually based on *Canopus*. Third Rates had a more mixed ancestry, with some French input, much modified by the surveyors.[16] French influence was more closely seen in the form of frigates. The two most numerous classes of Fifth Rate were based on the *Presidente* captured in 1806 and the *Leda* in 1782. It is surprising that the 44-gun *Presidente* was chosen as a model since she was caught after a twelve-hour chase by the 18-gun brigantine *Despatch*, a vessel not well regarded for speed. Despite the ease with which both these ships were caught, they were highly praised for their sailing qualities and their lines were used for large classes of RN ships. (*Leda*, incidentally, was similarly prized in the French navy, large numbers of this Sane design being built well into the nineteenth century.)

There were real, if small, differences between the design philosophies of the two rival navies. Gardiner has summed up the practical consequences of the French philosophy as follows:[17]

a. Light construction which may have given a slight advantage in speed when new. However, lack of strength led to rapid distortion of the hull, causing a loss of speed.
b. A high speed in optimum conditions, usually on one point of sailing only.
c. Less stability at large angles of heel and hence able to carry less sail in high winds but able to 'ghost' in light breezes.
d. Relatively leewardly.
e. Lower firepower than British ships of the same size.

It will be seen later that these differences persisted at least until 1830. It should be emphasised that the foregoing remarks are not intended to show that British ships were 'better' than their French equivalents, but merely different to a very small degree. To sum up, the words of Sir Phillip Watts, who designed much of the First World War fleet, seem appropriate. 'They were weather-beaten craft, often in poor repair, but they did their work with extraordinary persistence.'[18]

The firepower of RN ships was enhanced by the high rate of fire which they could achieve. To a considerable extent, this rate was due to the skill of British gunfounders and, in particular, to Thomas Blomefield.[19] He was appointed Inspector of Artillery and Superintendent of the Royal Brass Foundry in 1780, with the rank of major, where he remained until his death as a general in 1822.

During the War of American Independence attempts had been made to achieve a higher rate of fire but too many guns had cracked or burst. Blomefield introduced new methods of testing (proof), better instruments for inspection and required a more exact adherence to contracts. In addition, he redesigned the guns for greater strength. Progress was slow but steady and, by about 1796, British iron guns were reliable and could be fired faster than those made elsewhere. Indeed, British guns were highly valued abroad and sought energetically. Initially, his insistence on getting everything right led to a shortage of guns, but as new contractors appeared to accept his challenge this problem was soon remedied.

Formidable. This draught for an 84-gun ship of 1815 is annotated 'on the lines of the *Canopus*', a French prize, but the design was later altered to include Seppings's structural improvements and his round stern. *(© National Maritime Museum J2310)*

16. Lavery, op cit.

17. R Gardiner, 'Frigate design in the 18th century', *Warship* 9, 10 and 12 (1984).

18. P Watts, 'Ships of the RN as they existed at the time of Trafalgar', *Trans INA*, vol 47, Pt 11 (1905).

19. H A Baker, *The Crisis in Naval Ordnance*, National Maritime Museum, Monograph 56, London (1983).

Two | Science, Seppings and the School

THE FRENCH DEVELOPMENT of the theory of naval architecture owed much to an initiative by Jean Baptiste Colbert, Minister of Marine to Louis XIV. In 1681 he summoned many of the leading scientists of France to a conference in Paris, where the problems of warship design were outlined to them and their help invited in finding solutions. The Academy of Science encouraged these studies by offering prizes for the best papers submitted on naval architecture. By the end of the seventeenth century papers had been published on the theory of sails, manoeuvring, etc. In 1697 Paul Hoste, Professor of Mathematics at the Royal Seminary at Toulon, wrote that unless the fundamentals of naval construction were fully understood, design would continue to be a process of trial and error.

During the eighteenth century many books were published of increasing value to the profession. The most famous is Bouguer's *Traité du Navire* (1746), but there were other important works from Euler, Jorge Juan and Chapman. The state of naval architecture at the end of the century was summarised in Chapman's works, discussed later.

The only British contribution to theory, but a most valuable one, was that by George Attwood on the stability of ships at large angles of heel, presented in two papers to the Royal Society in 1796 and 1798. However, the length and difficulty of the calculations required for a direct solution of Attwood's equations meant that they could not be used in ship design until Barnes produced a simplified method some seventy years later.

It was left to a bookseller named Sewell to take the initiative in raising the standard of naval architecture in Britain.[1] In visits to naval ports he had heard much talk of the inferiority of British warship designs, and he set aside the covers of the *European Magazine*, which he published, for correspondence on the subject.

As a result of the interest aroused, Sewell called a meeting at the Crown and Anchor in the Strand on 14 April 1791 which led to the formation of the Society for the Improvement of Naval Architecture. By June the Duke of Clarence, himself a naval officer and later King William IV, had agreed to become president of the society, which had a distinguished membership including the Earl of Stanhope (a naval innovator of note), Lord Mulgrave (First Lord), Sir Joseph Banks (President of the Royal Society), Admiral Sir Charles Middleton (a former controller, later Lord Barham) and Sir Charles Knowles (a hydrodynamicist). The vice president was Captain Sir John Warren, distinguished both for his intellect and his fighting record. By the following year some 270 had paid their subscription of two guineas (£2 2s).

The principal object of the society was stated to be 'the improvement of naval architecture in all its branches'. The society intended to offer awards of up to £100 for work on the theory of floating bodies and their resistance to motion, to obtain plans of various ships and calculate their capacity, position of the centre of gravity, tonnage, etc. The society also intended to carry out its own experimental work.

The papers of the society were published by Sewell in 1800 and it can be seen how well they lived up to their aim of studying all branches of the subject.[2] The first paper was by an anonymous naval officer (possibly Warren himself), entitled 'Remarks on forms and proportion'. As well as the general comparisons of British and foreign ships quoted in the previous chapter, it discussed problems of stability and described how de Romme had measured the metacentric height of the *Scipio* in 1779 by running out the guns on one side only and then moving the crew across to the low side. Finding the stability inadequate, de Romme had the ship girdled, adding a foot each side to the beam.

The author then describes how he carried out three similar inclining experiments, moving fourteen guns, each weighing 3 tons, through 3ft and measuring the heel. From this he was able to deduce the metacentric height (see Table 2.1). He found that the *Bombay Castle* was stiff enough, perhaps even a little too stiff, while the other two needed more ballast to improve their stability. The full theory of the inclining experiment was given by Chapman in the same volume.

Table 2.1 **Metacentric Heights**

Ship	Displacement (tons)	Metacentric height (ft)
Formidable	3,150	3.42
Barfleur	3,360	3.77
Bombay Castle	2,700	4.47

A lengthy paper by Gabriel Snodgrass, discussed later, gave his views on the strength of wooden ships, and Attwood's classic work was republished. More practical articles covered the curing of beef, stowage of drinking water and life saving, and Clerk's well-known book on tactics was reviewed.

The most famous work by the society was the series of model tests on the stability and resistance of various forms carried out by Colonel Beaufoy, a member of the council. Between 1793 and 1798 he completed some 1,700 successful runs in Greenland Dock, London. These tests and their results are described in Appendix 2,

1. A W Johns, 'An account of the Society for the Improvement of Naval Architecture', *Trans INA*, vol 52 (1910).

2. Anon, 'Remarks on the forms and properties of ships', *Collection of papers on naval architecture (European Magazine)*, London (1800).

but it is clear that Beaufoy was close to a solution to the problem of estimating resistance of full-size ships, finally solved by William Froude some seventy years later. In particular, he appreciated the importance of friction, neglected by most previous workers.

The society came to an end in about 1799, but it had a lasting effect on the progress of warship design in Britain. In particular, Lord Barham had come to believe in the need for a better-educated class of naval constructors within the Admiralty service. He had probably noticed that few, if any, Admiralty naval architects belonged to the society. It is, however, interesting to note that many years later Morgan, a product of Lord Barham's new school and an outstanding man, was to dismiss the society as 'amateurs'.[3] Although he admitted that a few of the papers were valuable, he dismissed others as 'totally devoid of scientific knowledge' and saw Beaufoy's work as inferior to that of the Royal Academy of Paris. Though there is an element of truth in his comments, similar criticism could be levelled at his own *Papers on Naval Architecture*. There was undoubtedly considerable ill-feeling between the society and the Admiralty constructors.

The work of Sir Robert Seppings

Many of the critics of the supposed lack of science in British design are themselves lacking in understanding of scientific method and confuse science with mathematics. Scientific method involves setting out a general explanation of cause and effect and then testing the application of the new theory. Viewed in this light, British work on the design of structures was original, scientific and useful.

With few exceptions, wooden warships up to the end of the Napoleonic wars had a structure of transverse frames covered with longitudinal planking. Seppings described such a structure as like a five-bar gate without the diagonal member, in that there was little resistance to prevent the planks sliding past each other, turning rectangular bays into lozenges. Such movement in the side planking of a ship caused what is referred to as hogging, or breaking the sheer. The ends of the ship would droop and the seams would slip and open, leading to a further weakening of the structure as the damaged joints filled with water, causing rapid rotting of the wood.[4] The widely-held belief at the time that the flexibility of a wooden ship made it better able to resist the force of the sea is totally fallacious. Study of hogging can be confusing, since hogging in the context of a modern steel ship is a somewhat different phenomenon in which the whole ship bends as a homogeneous beam.[5]

The nature of the problem was beginning to be understood towards the end of the eighteenth century and attempts were made in several countries to introduce the diagonal members in the side needed to resist shearing forces.[6] Several French and Spanish experimental ships were captured by the Royal Navy and

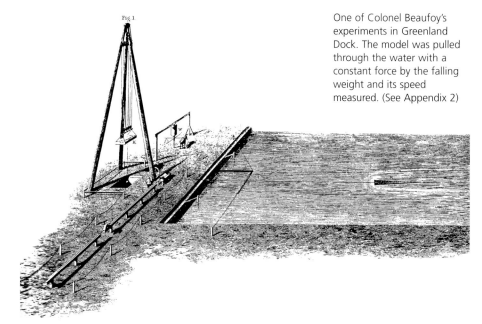

One of Colonel Beaufoy's experiments in Greenland Dock. The model was pulled through the water with a constant force by the falling weight and its speed measured. (See Appendix 2)

found to be no more rigid than were traditional structures. During the wars, Gabriel Snodgrass joined the Admiralty from the East India Company, where he had been chief surveyor. His prime task was to make emergency repairs to ships whose structure had already failed. In many of the ships that he had to repair, the transverse sections had distorted, which he cured by diagonals in that plane. His short-term cure for lack of sheer stiffness in the planking was to add further thick planks on the outside. This provided a bigger area of caulking which helped, by friction, to prevent relative movement. Snodgrass's structural philosophy is clearly expressed in a letter of 1796, republished by the Society for the Improvement of Naval Architecture, and shows that he was well aware of the loads which are imposed on a ship in a seaway and of the disposition of structure needed to resist them.[7]

3. W Morgan, 'Brief sketch of the progress of naval architecture', *Papers on Naval Architecture*, vol 1, London (1827).

4. J F Coates, 'Hogging or "breaking" of frame built wooden ships', *Mariner's Mirror*, vol 71, Part 4 (1895).

5. J E Gordon, *The New Science of Strong Materials*, London (1968).

6. D K Brown, 'The structural improvements to wooden ships instigated by R Seppings', *The Naval Architect*, Pt 5 (1985).

7. G Snodgrass, letter to H Dundas, printed in *Collection of papers on naval architecture*, London (1800).

Loading in a seaway

1. When the ship is floating in still water, the weight of guns, hull structure and supports for the sails at the bow and stern will be greater than the support provided by the buoyancy of these narrower sections. The ends will drop, distorting the sides. This is known as 'hogging'.

2. Buoyancy of the ends is further reduced and hogging strains are increased.

3. With wave crests at the ends and a trough amidships the buoyancy is increased at the ends and reduced amidships. The ends tend to rise and the middle drops, a condition known as 'sagging', which caused few problems to the wooden warship.

Sir Robert Seppings
(1767–1840), Surveyor of the
Navy from 1813 to 1832.
(© National Maritime
Museum BHC3019)

A fuller understanding of the problem came with the work of Robert Seppings (1767–1840).[8] He was the son of a cattle dealer in Fakenham, Norfolk, who, through the influence of his uncle, a retired naval captain, was accepted as an apprentice by the master shipwright J Henslow, at Plymouth. His apprenticeship was completed in 1789 and he rose rapidly through the ranks of shipwright, quarterman and foreman, becoming assistant to the master shipwright at Plymouth Dock in 1797. The master shipwright was the equivalent of the managing director of a Royal Dockyard and would usually take a keen interest in the career of a young man whom he had accepted as his personal apprentice. Seppings does not seem to have had much formal mathematical teaching, but his work demonstrates a keen mind, well-trained in clear presentation.

In 1803 he received a gold medal for his work to improve the docking of ships, and the following year he became master shipwright at Chatham. In that position he was able to develop and prove a new system of ship construction, which also made possible the dramatic increase in size of the last generation of wooden warships. His work was also directed towards the use of smaller lengths of timber and reducing the need for grown timbers which were becoming difficult to obtain.

His system of ship construction grew steadily and quite quickly into a comprehensive whole. The Navy Board wrote to Seppings at Chatham on 26 February 1805 suggesting the use of Snodgrass's methods in repairs to the 74-gun ship *Kent*.[9] Seppings felt that such methods were inadequate, and proposed instead to use diagonal braces on the side in the form of Xs, probably at a shallow angle, claiming reduction in the use of

8. T Wright, 'Thomas Young and Robert Seppings. The science of ship construction in the early 19th century', joint meeting of the Royal Institution and the Society for Nautical Research, Science Museum (1981).

9. Ibid.

10. J Fincham, *A History of Naval Architecture* (1851, reprinted London 1979).

11. D K Brown, 'Speed of sailing warships' (Annex 7), 'Empires at war and peace'. Conference, Portsmouth (1988). Note: Sir R Baker made the point well in a private letter in 1981. Mathematics was introduced into design (rightly) but one of its side effects was the idea still alive that mathematics and calculation could 'get it right'.

12. R Seppings, 'A new principle of constructing ships of war', *Phil Trans*, vol 54 (1814), 285.

timber, greater strength and a straighter ship. In 1806 the Navy Board gave approval for Seppings to try his ideas on a 74-gun ship and on a frigate. The *Warspite* was a stage in the development, but the full diagonal truss system was first fitted to *Tremendous* in her repairs of 1810, and the *Albion* of 1811 was the culmination of Seppings's structural plan.

There were four elements in the final system:

a. The diagonal trussed frames which are the most conspicuous and best-known features of Seppings's construction.
b. The spaces between the bottom timbers were filled in solid and the ceiling caulked.
c. The beams were connected to the frames using continuous shelf pieces and waterways in place of knees (the French had used a similar scheme for some years).
d. Diagonal deck planking.[10]

John Barrow, Second Secretary to the Board of Admiralty, called a meeting of eminent scientists on 24 November 1811 to consider Seppings's work. They were already aware that breakage measurements taken the previous year during the undocking of *Tremendous* had shown practically no deflection. It is probable that this meeting led to two mathematical studies into Seppings's design. The first was by Thomas Young in England, the second by Charles Dupin in France. Napoleon had been informed of the discussion of 24 November within a few days and invited Dupin to comment.

Young's work largely confirmed the soundness of Seppings's views but, as Wright has shown, the mathematics used by Young was tortuous, hard to follow and not always correct. He seems to have concentrated on bending moments rather than the more relevant shearing forces. It is unlikely that this study added to the Board's understanding of Seppings and must have reinforced the shipwrights' suspicion of the value of mathematics.[11]

Seppings presented a paper to the Royal Society in 1814, as a result of which he was elected as a Fellow.[12] His paper was followed by one from Young which was seen by some as suggesting that Seppings had developed his system from earlier work by others and that the arrangement of the diagonals was not entirely correct. It is true that the idea of diagonal stiffening to prevent shear deflection had been tried before, unsuccessfully; the difference was that Seppings's arrangement worked well.

The diagonal trusses should have been arranged to take the load in compression rather than in tension, but with the short lengths involved there was little practical difference. In later developments of his system Seppings reversed the slope of his diagonals. It was suggested by his critics, and still repeated, that Seppings's construction was heavy, but this was true only when the trusses were added to an existing ship. A new ship, designed to his system, should have been stronger and lighter;

Seppings claimed a saving of 180 tons in the building of a 74-gun ship.

Seppings wrote another paper in 1815, rebutting Young's insinuations of plagiarism. This paper was not published, but much of its content was used by Barrow in an article to the *Quarterly Review* strongly defending Seppings.[13] Dupin joined in with a well-reasoned paper to the Royal Society in 1816, generally supporting Seppings and criticising Young's mathematics.[14] The English summary of this paper was prepared by Young and is misleading.[15]

Seppings's next paper was in 1817, and is of interest for its description of a trial on the old Danish 74-gun ship *Justitia* just before she was broken up.[16] Temporary diagonal members were fitted to her in dock and the breakage measured on undocking and again twenty-four hours later. The diagonals were then removed and the breakage remeasured. It was found that the stiffening reduced breakage from 2ft 3in to 1ft 2in initially, which increased only by ⅝in over twenty-four hours. Removal of the trusses increased the breakage to 2ft. In this paper, Seppings explicitly denied that his ideas were derived from others, though he acknowledged that a study of drawings of the bridge at Schaffhausen had helped.

Seppings's last paper in 1820 dealt with a modified scheme for merchant ships, in which iron straps were used for the diagonal members to increase internal stowage. This was an adaptation of the scheme which he had already introduced into frigates and which can still be seen in the *Unicorn* (currently undergoing restoration at Dundee). There seems to have been little use of this system in merchant ships, though Brunel did use it for the *Great Western*, with acknowledgement.[17]

There can be little doubt that Seppings's work was novel and based on a rational understanding of the problem. His work was continued and developed in the 1830s when Lang and Edye extended the use of iron diagonals to line-of-battle ships, enabling a vast increase in size. His other improvements will be discussed in the next chapter.

The School of Naval Architecture

As a result of the general belief in the inferiority of British design, Lord Barham, on becoming First Lord, set up a commission 'to enquire into and revise the civil affairs of the Admiralty'. This commission produced a voluminous series of reports between 1803 and 1808 in which they expressed their concern over the low standard of education of dockyard officers and their fears that this standard might fall even further.[18] Prior to 1801, the master shipwright and his assistant were each allowed to take five premium apprentices. This scheme attracted the sons of well-off parents who had already received a primary education. Working with dockyard senior officers, they received a sound training in both

13. J Barrow (unsigned), Art VII *Quarterly Review*, vol XII, No XXIV (1815), 460.

14. C Dupin, 'De la structure des vaisseaux anglais considérée dans ce dernier perfectionnement', *Phil Trans*, vol 54 (1817), 86.

15. Wright, op cit.

16. R Seppings, 'On the great strength given to ships of war by the application of diagonal braces', *Phil Trans*, vol 154 (1817), 1.

17. D Griffiths, *Brunel's Great Western*, Wellingborough (1985).

18. Third report of the Commissioners for Revising and Digesting the Civil Affairs of H M Navy, London (1808).

Left: Seppings' diagonal braced hull construction, definition of terms. *(Science Museum)*

Right: Photo of model. *(Science Museum)*

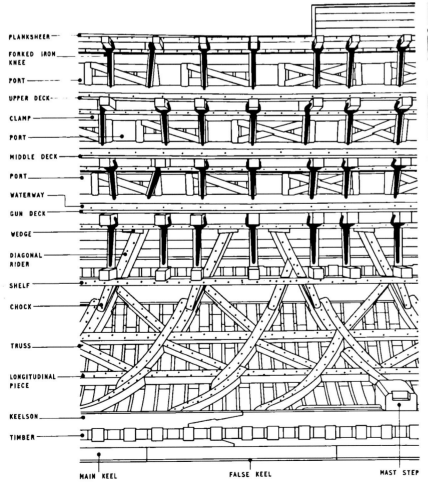

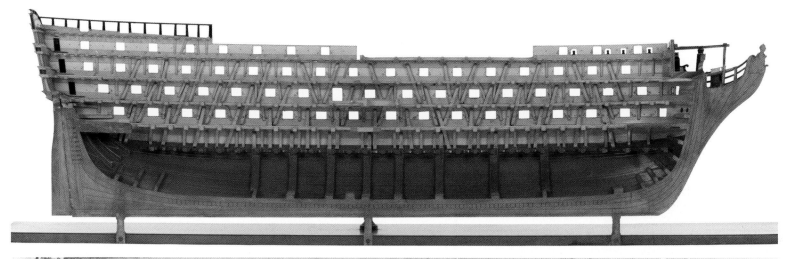

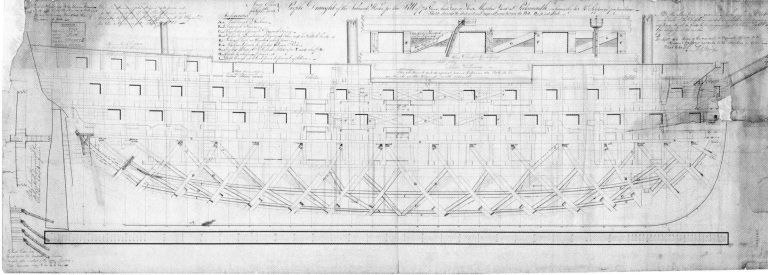

Top: A model of typical internal structure before Seppings. The heavy diagonal riders in the topsides were a clumsy, and largely unsuccessful, attempt to offset the effects of hogging. *(© National Maritime Museum L3214-001)*

Above: One of the first profile draughts to show Seppings's structural innovations, for the 74-gun *Pitt* of 1814. *(© National Maritime Museum J2722)*

the theory and practice of shipbuilding and were well placed for rapid promotion when they finished their training. This system produced many good senior officers, eg Slade (who designed the *Victory*), Seppings and many others, but there was a suspicion, probably unjustified, that their advancement owed more to corruption than merit. Though no such case was proved, the suspicion was such that premium apprentices were abolished by Lord St Vincent as part of his drive against corruption in 1801. Somewhat similar schemes for quartermen (chargehands) and foremen were abolished in 1802 and 1804.

The new apprenticeship scheme was not such as to attract bright young men or to give any prospect of producing suitable senior officers. There was no entry examination; the only qualifications required were a medical certificate and a minimum height of 4ft 8in. It was found that this class of apprentice was incapable of learning the geometrical complexity of mould loft work and they were described as a lazy and insubordinate bunch.

The Commission of Revision in their third and eighth reports made some specific recommendations on the education of shipwright apprentices and on the conduct of the school:

a. There should be two classes of apprentice, the 'ordinary' who would normally become tradesmen and the 'superior' destined for more senior posts.

b. The superior class should form a school attached to the RN College at Portsmouth which had been founded as the Naval Academy in 1773. The course would last for seven years with theoretical studies in the morning and practical shipbuilding in the afternoon. The final year was to be spent at sea.

c. Entrance to the school was to be by competitive examination conducted by the professor and three senior dockyard officers. There was to be no system of nomination or patronage and apprentices entered into the ordinary class could compete for places at the school.

d. There were to be twelve students in the first entry and, in the following years, four would be admitted, bringing the school up to a total of twenty-four, a number which it was believed would provide the required number of senior men.

e. Students would be paid £60 per annum in their first year, rising to £140 in the last two years. Of this, £8 per annum would be deducted to pay the professor.

f. Progress would be monitored by annual examinations and, on successful completion of the course, the graduates would be employed as assistants to foremen in the yards or as overseers in commercial yards until they were promoted.

g. A library was to be established containing the best books in the English and French languages on naval architecture and related subjects.

h. The professor was to give classes three evenings a week on naval architecture to anyone interested in the subject, whether they were in the service or not.

j. Two sureties in total of £800 were to be given which could be forfeit should the man leave Admiralty service within ten years of graduating.

These proposals contained much which was novel in the early nineteenth century and some might still be seen as progressive today. Almost certainly, the selection of young men for public service by competition was novel, and very much earlier than the more famous changes to the Civil Service introduced by the Northcote-Trevelyan report of 1854. It is also likely that it was the first time that a major employer had set up a formal education and training scheme aimed at producing candidates for senior posts. The use of sureties, which remained a feature of Admiralty training until 1953, was a less happy feature.

The opening of the school

The year after the commission reported, an Order in Council was published, giving effect to its recommendations.[19] Regulations were issued much as proposed by the commission, but with the sureties reduced to £500 (still an enormous sum for 1809), and with salaries reduced since the students were to be given food and accommodation free.

The professor was to be Dr James Inman, DD, MA, who had been appointed Professor of Mathematics at the RN College in 1807. Inman was a former senior wrangler of St John's College, Cambridge, and had much experience in navigation and related aspects of astronomy. His first problem was lack of suitable textbooks, as he was later to explain:[20]

A difficulty has occurred of no small magnitude in the want of books safely to be trusted to upon the theory of naval architecture. At length, two were chosen as textbooks; namely a Swedish work called *Architectura Navalis Mercatoria* by Frederick Chapman, the founder of an excellent school of naval architecture in Sweden, and an English treatise on the stability of ships by G Attwood. The former of these I translated into English, adding the notes of the French translation by Vial du Clairbois, and many of my own, together with an appendix, which translation I was able to print by the liberal assistance of the Board of Admiralty and the University of Cambridge.

This book was an excellent survey of the theory of naval architecture as it was then understood.[21] It covered the techniques of numerical integration which were neces-

sary in pre-computer days for the accurate calculation of volume and of the position of the centre of buoyancy. The theory of the metacentre and of stability were covered together with a general, but accurate, statement of the effect of metacentric height on rolling. Rather surprisingly, there was nothing on the use of the inclining experiment to determine the height of the centre of gravity, despite Chapman's own paper on the subject[22] and the use made of this technique by the French and Royal navies at the end of the previous century.

There was a discussion of the resistance of ships to forward motion but, as discussed in the previous chapter, contemporary work was of little value. Chapman did, however, draw attention to the frictional component. The strength of ships was recognised only in tables of acceptable scantlings and descriptions of suitable joints. There was no discussion of loads imposed in a seaway nor of the way in which a structure resisted such loads, as had been given by Seppings. Measurement for tonnage was explained, as was the arrangement of the sail plan for good handling.

There was also an interesting note by Inman on the economics of warship design:

A ship which in the least space carries the greatest force and has at least equal properties with others in sailing and working is to be preferred. Indeed, this is to be considered as an object on which the attention of a naval architect who has to propose constructions must especially be fixed.

Details of the school and the entry examination were published on 25 June 1810. The prospectus contained a passage which was to cause much pain and controversy in later years: 'From these the appointment of superior officers of HM Dockyards and Surveyors of the Navy shall be made'.[23] Applicants were required to produce certificates of health from two physicians or surgeons and proof from their parish that they were aged between fifteen and seventeen.

The first examining board met on Thursday, 7 November 1810, and consisted of the professor, the Commissioner of the Dockyard, and the Lieutenant Governor of the College. The subjects examined were Euclid (the first six books), arithmetic, algebra (the first four rules, up to quadratic equations), English grammar and dictation, and reading and translating French. Knowledge of French was not essential but preference was given to those candidates who had it. The first class began their studies on 1 January 1811 with lectures held in the Naval College, but the students had to live out.

The course was arduous and always blended theory with practice, but the syllabus varied from time to time. To begin with, the students had theoretical studies six mornings a week, beginning before breakfast, and spent the afternoons in the dockyard, particularly in the mould loft.[24] This schedule was found to be impractical and Monday to Wednesday were spent on theory all day

18. Third report of the Commissioners for Revising and Digesting the Civil Affairs of H M Navy, London (1808).

19. Parliamentary Papers, vol XXIV, London (1833).

20. Read, Chatfield and Creuze, *Reports on Naval Architecture*, 'Chatham committee of naval architecture', London (1842–6).

21. F H Chapman, *Architecture Navalis Mercatoria*, translated J Inman, Cambridge (1820, reprinted 1967).

22. *A Collection of Papers on Naval Architecture*, London (1800).

23. Anon, 'An explanation of the conduct of government in instituting the school of naval architecture, being an answer to the pamphlet just published', pamphlet held in the Naval Library, ref P 9.

24. Read et al, op cit.

25. Fincham, op cit.

26. J Coad, *Historic Architecture of the Royal Navy*, London (1983).

27. *Papers on Naval Architecture*, London (1827–31).

28. H S Torrens, *Men of Iron. McArthur Group Ltd*, Bristol (1984).

29. W Hackmann, *Seek and Strike*, London (1984).

while the other three days were devoted to practical work. The subjects studied included geometry and algebra, plane and spherical trigonometry and conic sections, mathematics and hydrostatics, fluxions and differential and integral calculus, strength of timber, perspective drawing, stability and construction of ships, French, and naval architecture, draughting and laying-off, both on paper and full size on the mould loft floor.

Considerable attention was paid to the practical training of the students under Fincham, then a foreman, later an outstanding master shipwright. They were required to keep a notebook in which they described and sketched the operations of laying-off and building a warship. They were required to take special note of the methods of fastening and the way in which each part of the hull was arranged. There were regular tutorials in which 'they were required to reason on these subjects, as there are always grounds of preference to use one mode over another'. Later in the course students would work in the mast house and ultimately build ships designed in the school.

Examinations were held at Christmas each year and consisted of both written papers and viva voce examinations before the professor and other officers. There is some doubt as to the extent to which students went to sea in their seventh year. Dr Inman wrote that this idea was abandoned, but Fincham mentions the participation of the students during the experimental sailing trials,[25] discussed later. On completion of the course, the students were sent to the Navy Office to learn the methods used there for draughting and designing ships and they were also sent to work in different offices of the dockyard.

The school was moved from the RN College in 1817 when a handsome new building was completed.[26] This building, which cost £18,000, still stands and is now in use by the Ship Maintenance Authority. The students lived and ate in this building. The cost of the building was the major part of the total cost of the school, which over twenty-two years came to precisely £50,578 19s 2d.

Entries to the school soon dwindled. Fourteen were accepted in the first year, of whom two died, leaving twelve graduates as originally intended. Between 1812 and 1816 other entries brought the total up to twenty-four, but thereafter numbers declined with no entries in 1817 or 1818 and only two in 1819. There was a big entry of eight in 1822, but they were the last and numbers fell until Joseph Large left in 1829. Altogether, thirty students graduated from the school, six died during or shortly after the course and five were dismissed.

The first large entry was the least successful, accounting for all five of the dismissals. It included three entrants from the ordinary class of apprentices, one of whom died young, while another, Abethell, became a well-known master shipwright. Of the thirty graduates, some twenty-four spent their whole career in Admiralty service and came to dominate the technical scene by the 1850s. Thomas Lloyd, who became engineer-in-chief of the Royal Navy, must rank in the very highest class of Victorian engineer. Isaac Watts, who as chief constructor designed some of the largest wooden ships ever built, later designed the *Warrior*, the first iron armoured battleship. Large was Watts's assistant on *Warrior* and went on to become vice president of the Institution of Naval Architects. Altogether, nine reached the rank of master shipwright or above, while most of the others reached responsible posts as assistants to the masters or became masters of wood or metal mills, draughtsmen, etc.

In 1827 Morgan, Creuze and Chatfield issued the first volume of *Papers on Naval Architecture*.[27] For four years they edited volumes dealing with all aspects of naval architecture and ship construction and with tactics, weapons, etc. Translations of foreign papers and reviews of books were also included. Morgan left the Admiralty in about 1835 and, after working for the Austrian Lloyd company in Trieste and on railways, became a partner in Acraman, Morgan & Co of Bristol, a shipbuilding and engineering company.[28]

Creuze also left the service and after a brilliant career became chief surveyor of Lloyd's Register of Shipping. Moorsom was another who left, joining the customs department. He developed new rules for measuring tonnage (which lasted until well after the Second World War) and retired as chief ship surveyor of the Board of Trade. Ritherdon held the corresponding post in the East India Company, a progressive shipowner. Boncastle became Professor of Mathematics at the University of Virginia and a pioneer in underwater acoustics.[29] The careers of these men show the dominance of graduates of the school by the middle of the century. (To emphasise this point, graduates of the First School of Naval Architecture will be indicated as 1st SNA where appropriate.)

The success of such a high proportion of graduates in widely differing fields of engineering, both within the Admiralty and in commercial undertakings, shows the value of their education. It is notable that many were

The first School of Naval Architecture in Portsmouth Dockyard. Designed by Edward Hall, the building was completed in 1817 and is still in use by the navy.

able to work in the new technologies of iron and steam engines whose use was very limited in their student days. Why, then, did the school decline, come to be seen as a failure and die in 1832?

There was a great deal of hostility to the school and its students both from the old-style dockyard officers and from naval officers. It must be remembered that Lord Barham's commission had condemned the lack of education of dockyard officers and had set up the school to replace them. The incumbents concerned cannot have welcomed these new men and hence promotion for the graduates was slow indeed. It was said, without much evidence, that the graduates were too theoretical and lacked practical skills. Abethell was the first to reach the rank of foreman (1819), and by 1833 another fifteen had reached that rank, together with four more in specialised posts of similar status.[30]

Bright young men are always in a hurry and must have found it very frustrating to work under those less well-qualified than themselves. On the other hand, in the peacetime establishment there were few senior posts and the rise into dead men's shoes is always slow.

There was even more hostility from some naval officers. Many are quoted by Sir William Harrison,[31] others can be found in the pages of the *Morning Post* and the *United Services Institute Journal*. These attacks were often on the personal background of the students ('not gentlemen'), Captain Marryat, the novelist, being particularly offensive. The seaman officer of the day seemed to believe that his experience of ships and the sea was a more important attribute for the designer than was scientific method.

Lord Melville was a frequent visitor to the school and its stalwart defender; when he resigned as First Lord in 1830 the end was inevitable. His successor took advice from the master shipwrights and from naval officers, the main opponents of the school, and in particular from the new surveyor, Captain Symonds, who wrote:

> Unlucky from the beginning, students became clever analysts, and wrote valuable papers on the theory of ships but, in spite of daily practice to be acquired in the dockyard, they wanted that experience in managing them at sea which is as essential as the test of theory and without which its deductions are so much waste paper.[32]

The school was closed in 1832; the ultimate success of its graduates is an underlying theme of this book.

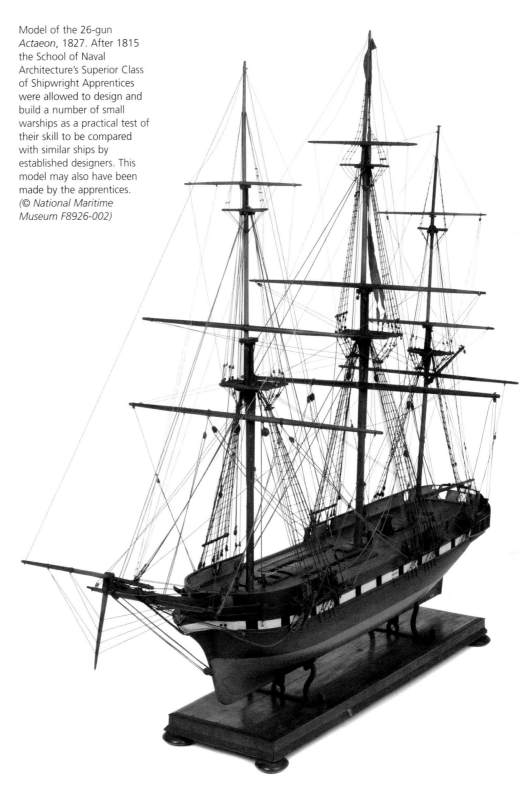

Model of the 26-gun *Actaeon*, 1827. After 1815 the School of Naval Architecture's Superior Class of Shipwright Apprentices were allowed to design and build a number of small warships as a practical test of their skill to be compared with similar ships by established designers. This model may also have been made by the apprentices. (© *National Maritime Museum F8926-002*)

30. G Dyson, 'The Development of Instruction in Naval Architecture in the Government Service in the 19th Century', MA Dissertation, University of Kent (1978); A F Creuze, 'A treatise on the theory and practice of naval architecture', Shipbuilding, *Encyclopaedia Britannica*, 7th edition, London (1853).

31. Sir W S Harrison, *Past and Present State of Naval Architecture in the Government Service*, London (1863).

32. J A Sharpe, *Memoires of Rear Admiral Sir W Symonds*, London (1858).

Three | Resources, Money and Men

Introduction: 1815

Ownership of the world's largest navy was not cheap and nineteenth-century Britain, although increasingly prosperous, was able to make only limited funds available to the Navy amid so many other demands. The Admiralty had great problems in using these limited funds to best advantage in supporting British maritime interests worldwide. Not only money was scarce; good shipbuilding timber was hard to find, sailors were not enthusiastic for naval service and the capacity of the dockyards to support the fleet was limited.

Perhaps unfortunately, the Navy was not short of ships. There was still a large number of ships built, or captured, during the wars, but most of them were smaller than those now required and many were suffering from lack of maintenance. As there were so many ships in being, there was an understandable reluctance on the part of successive governments to build new ones.

The organisation of the Admiralty had changed during the wars and would change again, most significantly in 1832. The balance between operational control and material management is never easy to find and too frequent changes were made in the forlorn hope of a perfect solution.

In the early years after the war there was no real threat to British sea power and the Navy was used for exploration, to suppress piracy and the slave trade, to aid friendly governments and as an extension of foreign policy. From the early 1830s, the increasing size and skill of the French navy made it again seem a potential threat. Resources were particularly short and by the end of that decade the Royal Navy was very hard-pressed. Small increases in the naval budget then improved matters and

a big building programme was started in the early 1840s. Few of these ships completed as sailing vessels, most being converted to screw steamers.

This background, of apparent massive superiority combined with scarce resources, must be understood before the nature and pace of technical development can be appreciated. The potential size of the wooden warship increased dramatically, an increase due almost entirely to the structural methods introduced by Seppings. There were improvements in strength and firepower of both the bow and stern, again initiated by Seppings. Gun power was increased, first by boring out older, smaller guns and, later, by re-arming with a new generation of weapons, some of which were specifically intended to fire explosive shells.

The size of the Navy

The first task of the Admiralty was to reduce the vast wartime fleet to a size appropriate to peace, a reduction most welcome to the pressed sailors, but less so to the career officers left on half-pay with little chance of employment at sea. The first reductions were made following Napoleon's surrender in 1814.[1]

Table 3.1 **Reductions in 1814**

Broken up	19 liners, 93 smaller
Decommissioned	52 line of battle
Placed in ordinary (reserve)	62 liners and 53 smaller ships together with 71 liners and 109 others not required for further service

Table 3.2 **Comparison of the Fleet in 1816 and 1820**

The Fleet in 1816

	Full commission	Harbour commission	In ordinary
Line of battle	30	3	70
Smaller	203	2	134

The Fleet in 1820

	Commission	Ordinary
First Rates	2	14
Second Rates	1	8
Third Rates	11	69
Fourth Rates	5	7
Fifth Rates	14	66
Sixth Rates	14	7
Sloops	49	57
Smaller	15	15

Howe, 120 guns, laid up in the Medway. Launched incomplete in 1815, this ship went straight into ordinary, like so much of the war-built fleet. *Howe* was not commissioned until 1835. (© National Maritime Museum PU7924)

Following the Treaty of Paris in 1815, further reductions were made with sixteen liners and seventy-five other ships being broken up and many others reduced to lower rates. There were almost as many ships fit for harbour service only. Despite these reductions, the Royal Navy was left with twice the power of the second-largest navy, still that of France, or a force roughly equivalent to the three largest navies combined – France, Russia and the USA. Table 3.2 shows the composition of the Navy in 1820.

Castlereagh gave a formal statement of government intentions in 1817: 'To keep up a navy equal to the navies of any two powers that can be brought against us', a policy which was to endure for almost a century.[2] The Admiralty's peacetime plans, set out on 8 December 1815, matched this policy. They envisaged a fleet of a hundred liners (including fourteen guard and port flagships) and 160 frigates. Of these, the older ships would be kept in commission, with the more modern laid up in ordinary.

To obtain and maintain a fleet of this size was less easy than might seem. An initial selection of 102 liners and 110 frigates was made in 1816, but in that year working hours were cut in the dockyards and shipwrights reduced by a quarter. By 1817 the Navy Board thought it would take eight years to reach these force levels, but three years later Byam Martin, the controller, still thought there were another eight or nine years of work outstanding, despite the refit of forty-three liners and fifty-four frigates.

Maintenance and repair work was and remains difficult to forecast (a familiar problem to car owners). Until the ship was docked and planking removed, the extent of the work could not be judged. Inevitably, the actual condition was often worse than that estimated from an external inspection and, of the eighteen frigates sent for refit in 1817, seven were found to be beyond repair and were broken up.

A limited programme of new building was set in hand but this too ran into difficulties. Other countries were building more ships of the bigger categories and the size of the biggest liners and frigates was increasing as well. It was hard for the Board to balance the need for numbers of ships against the requirement for bigger ships within the limits of the budget. It has been said that the work involved in the thirteen First and Second Rates building in 1830 would have sufficed for twenty Third Rates. Shipwrights' hours worked in 1830 were only two-thirds of those in 1783, due partly to a reduction in the numbers employed and partly to a shorter working week.

The Board were also conscious of the capital value of the existing fleet and had a thoroughly rational policy of avoiding changes which would hasten the obsolescence of the existing ships. Only occasionally was this reluctance to change carried to excess and increasingly the industrial might of Britain was seen as permitting the Royal Navy to let others take the initiative in change, a lead which, if successful, could very quickly be overtaken by this country. Baldwin Walker's statement quoted in the introduction was a refined version of this philosophy.

Money

Between 1820 and 1850 the gross national product increased two and a half times, in real terms, while there was some increase in the value of the pound (deflation). Much of this increase in national wealth went to support the rapidly rising population, since the per capita income increased only by some 50 per cent. There was an increase in expectation, too; the new industrial worker slowly won a bigger share of the national cake. There was not much left for the Navy.

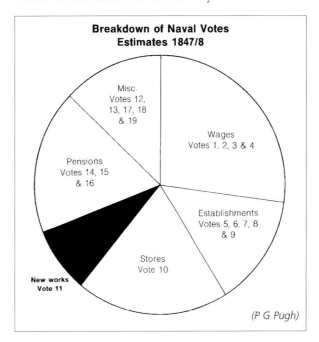

Breakdown of Naval Votes Estimates 1847/8

(P G Pugh)

1. C J Bartlett, *Great Britain and Sea Power 1815–1853*, Oxford (1967). An invaluable reference to the political, economic and strategic background.

2. Hansard, third series, XCVII, pp779–80.

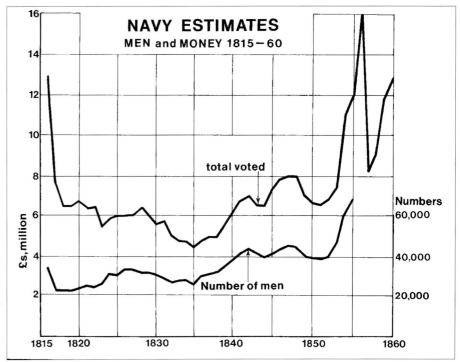

NAVY ESTIMATES
MEN and MONEY 1815–60

The total expenditure on the Navy from 1815 to 1860 is illustrated in the graph on page 27, as is the total number of men serving. The breakdown of spending within the naval budget is shown in the pie chart and Table 3.3. Shipbuilding and repair was nominally attributed to Vote 11 but this accounted only for materials and direct labour used on a specific ship. Much of Votes 6, 7, 8 and 9 and some of Vote 10 can be recognised as overheads on shipbuilding. These overheads were omitted when the direct cost of a ship was reported to Parliament and hence such costs are misleading by today's standards, though since the other expenditure was separately reported, there was nothing deceitful in this practice.

The question of overheads was raised by an MP called Seely in 1867 and the correspondence is summarised in Appendix 3. In brief, he saw that it was necessary to add to the direct cost sums representing:

a) Interest on working capital
b) Dockyard operations – buoys, cranes, dock gates, etc
c) Training, fire engines, waterworks, etc
d) Pay of professional officers, foremen, accountants, etc.[3]

It was concluded that such charges could add 40–45 per cent to the reported cost of warships in the late 1840s and was probably much the same in earlier years.

Table 3.3 **Breakdown of Expenditure by Vote 1847-8**

Vote	Heading	£ (x1000)
1	Wages of seamen and marines	1,400
2	Victualling	650
3	Admiralty Office	140
4	Pay of Admiralty officers	9
5	Scientific	80
6	Establishments at home	140
7	Establishments abroad	25
8	Wages home establishments	850
9	Wages abroad	39
10	Stores	1,510
11	New works and repairs	688
12	Medicine	29
13	Miscellaneous	81
14	Half-pay	729
15	Pensions	510
16	Civil pensions	155
17	Troop-carrying	217
18	Convicts	53
19	Post Office	611

Timber

The principal natural resource needed by the fleet was timber, a scarce and diminishing commodity. The

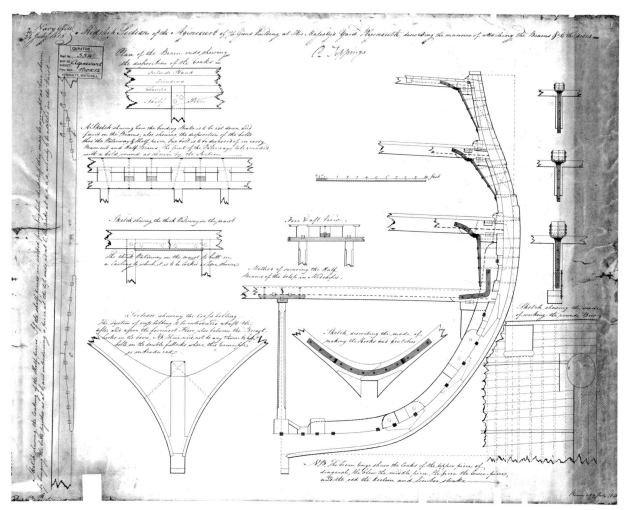

Midship section of the 74-gun *Agincourt* of 1815 showing Seppings's method of fastening deck beams with iron brackets and plates. It also demonstrates his 'small timber' system whereby frames were made up of shorter pieces that were more easily sourced. (© *National Maritime Museum J2551*)

shortage was somewhat exaggerated by Albion,[4] but it was a real problem causing some concern.

Table 3.3 Timber Consumption and Stocks

Timber Consumption

	Loads per year
Wartime	36,000
1824–30	21,600
1832	9,600

Stocks

1832	61,500
1839	41,000

The first critical shortage was of mast timbers when the supply of great trees stopped after the USA became independent. This shortage was made good by using masts built up from pieces bound together by elaborate joints and iron hoops. Iron masts were tried in 1827 in the *Phaeton*, which was given an iron main mast and bowsprit.[5] The mast was 92ft 6in high and 2ft in diam-eter, built up from cylinders 3ft 6in long, ¼in thick, connected by iron hoops, and the bowsprit was 54ft 6in x 19½in. There were a few problems: the bowsprit was carried away in an accident and there was some effect on the compass.

Iron brackets, together with the use of continuous shelves, replaced grown beam knees. Compass timbers needed for the double curvature in the tumblehome of older ships came from English oak, but before the shortage became serious there was a design change leading to straighter frames and much less tumble-home. Italian oak from Tuscany was used; this dried out more quickly and could be regarded as seasoned on arrival in Britain.

Teak was used to an increasing extent as it was very resistant to dry rot. Some came from Sierra Leone, but most from India and Burma. A number of major warships were built in India, mainly by the Wadia brothers,[6] and these usually sailed to England without guns. The empty gun deck was frequently filled with a duplicate set of frames which would be used in a ship built in a home dockyard.

3. Correspondence between the Admiralty and Mr Sealy relating to the cost of building the *Frederick William* and repairs to the *Brisk* and *Cadmus*, House of Commons (13 Aug 1867).

4. R G Albion, *Forests and Sea Power*, Harvard (1826).

5. J Bennett, 'Observations on the effect produced by an iron mast on the compass', *Papers on Naval Architecture*, London (1827).

6. R A Wadia, *The Bombay Dockyard and the Wadia Master Builders*, Bombay (1955).

Timber shortages led to the construction of ships of Indian teak, a wood offering great advantages in longevity. *Bombay*, seen here being converted to steam in 1861, was originally laid down in 1819. (© *National Maritime Museum C5331K*)

It should also be remembered that Seppings's structural improvements were largely aimed at the use of short lengths of timber which were obtained more easily than the 'great timbers' of old.

The Royal Dockyards

In peacetime virtually all major warships were built in the Royal Dockyards, which also undertook all repair and maintenance work. Dr Moriss has shown that the dockyards carried out their work economically and effectively during the late wars.[7] About 80 per cent of the fleet had been kept available for sea thanks to a policy of restricting refit work to the bare essentials. It was the need to refit a liner in some four months and a frigate in two that made the yards so unpopular with naval officers. Inevitably, many items were left undone and other items skimped in order to complete the essential jobs and get the ship back to the fleet.

Lord St Vincent believed the yards to be corrupt and inefficient but his own searching enquiries produced very few cases of either. However, his Commission of Enquiry, followed by Lord Barham's Commission of Revision, led to a relatively efficient management structure for what had become the largest manufacturing industry in the country. The dockyards were far from perfect but, by the standards of the day, they were good.

The capacity of the main yards at the end of the war (1814 figures) could be summarised in Table 3.4.

There were two main weaknesses: few of the building slips were covered, a most desirable facility since covered slips enabled the timber in the new ships to season properly, and many of the dry docks were too shallow for the new generation of bigger ships. On the other hand, the

Table 3.4 Dockyard Capacity 1814

Dockyard	Dry docks	Building slips	Number of shipwrights
Deptford	2	5	553
Woolwich	2	4	584
Chatham	4	6	783
Sheerness	2	2	267
Portsmouth	8	5	1,433
Plymouth	4	4	1,316

Industrial Revolution was already making its mark on the dockyards. Marc Brunel's steam-driven block mills at Portsmouth were the most conspicuous example, but there were many others. Much of the credit is due to Samuel Bentham, who had introduced piped water, dock caissons, steam tools and even steam dredgers.

The weaknesses were to be remedied and Bentham's policy of using new technology was to be continued as far as the limited funds permitted. The building works in the dockyards led to some very fine and advanced architecture, including the first iron-framed buildings.[8]

Roofing of the building slips began in about 1810 (No 1, Plymouth Dock). Until about 1840 the roofs were usually timber, but in 1844 two corrugated iron roofs were built at Portsmouth. Some very fine iron roofs were built at Chatham in 1847–52, which predated the better known but later train-shed roofs. Fire was a major hazard in the dockyards with vast stores of timber, rope and tar. The first 'fireproof' building was erected at Chatham in 1760. From 1843 onwards the bulk of building resources was used in the steam basins at Portsmouth and Keyham.

Naval operations and other navies

There were no great battles at sea in the years after Waterloo. The Royal Navy was used in support of foreign policy, helping friendly governments against rebels, suppressing piracy and the slave trade, and in exploration. Almost all these operations were in coastal waters and many involved actions against shore batteries and forts.

The first such operation was Lord Exmouth's (Edward Pellew) operation against the pirate stronghold of Algiers and was an overwhelming success thanks to the admiral's careful planning (see illustration in Chapter 1). For much of the 1820s and 1830s the Tagus was the principal operational base of the Navy, which supported and influenced the Portuguese government, later intervening against the Carlist rebellion in Spain. The Monroe Doctrine was intended by the USA to prevent European powers reconquering their former colonies, now independent, in South America, but was made effective only through the support of the Royal Navy.

In 1827 Admiral Codrington, with Russian and French support, destroyed a Turkish-Egyptian fleet at Navarino, which enabled the Greeks to win their independence. Steamships made their debut in a second

7. R Moriss, *The Royal Dockyards during the Revolutionary and Napoleonic Wars*, Leicester (1983).

8. J Coad, *Historic Architecture of the Royal Navy*, London (1983).

Samuel Bentham (1757–1831), as Inspector General of Naval Works from 1796, introduced many improvements into the Royal Dockyards. (© *National Maritime Museum BHC2549*)

expedition to Algiers and later, in 1831, assisted in the blockade of the Dutch coast.

By the mid-1830s the growth of other navies, particularly the French, represented a potential threat to the Royal Navy. The weakness of the Navy was a matter for concern with so many unresolved political problems. British interests conflicted with those of France in the Mediterranean, particularly over the attempted secession of Egypt from the Ottoman Empire and the French expedition to North Africa. Louis Philippe's intervention in Mexico was another source of friction.

The possible alliance of France and Russia was even more worrying, as the Russian Baltic fleet had grown from eight liners in 1827 to twenty-seven in 1837. In November 1838 the Admiralty produced a table showing the comparative strengths of the leading navies (Table 3.5).

Though these figures may not have been entirely accurate, they formed the basis for British planning. The situation was in some ways even worse than is shown by the table, since more than half of the British liners were Third Rate 74-gun ships, old, in poor condition and no

The addition of huge timber, and later iron, roofs over slipways and docks was one of the great developments of the early nineteenth century in the Royal Dockyards. Those at Woolwich are seen here at the launch of the 120-gun *Trafalgar* on 21 June 1841. *(© National Maritime Museum PW8091)*

Table 3.5 **Comparison of Leading Navies 1838**

Class	Britain			France			Russia			USA			Smaller navies					
	C	O	B	C	O	B	C	O	B	C	O	B	E	T	N	D	S	Sp
Liners																		
1 class	4	12	3	2	4	16	5	–	2	2	–	–	9	3	–	–	–	
2 class	4	13	7	5	2	11	16	2	5	–	2	8	2	6	2	5	5	1
3 class	12	33	2	3	4	2	19	1	–	–	3	1	6	6	1	5	2	
Frigates																		
1 class	1	10	–	5	8	9	4	–	–	6	9	8	7	6	4	–	1	2
2 class	1	7	2	5	7	8	–	–	–	–	–	–	–	5	–	–	–	2
3 class	7	57	8	6	7	5	20	–	–	–	2	–	–	4	14	–	7	–
Steam	5	2	5	22	6	9	8	–	–	1	–	9	1	3	14	2	–	–
Steam auxiliaries	13																	
Packets	28																	

C = in commission, O = in ordinary, B = building. Totals only for the smaller navies. E = Egypt, T = Turkey, N = Netherlands, D = Denmark, S = Sweden, Sp = Spain.

(Derived from a table in ADM 87/55, PRO)

The allied British-French-Russian squadron entering Navarino Bay on 20 October 1827. The ensuing battle – the last fleet action fought entirely under sail – saw the total rout of the Turkish-Egyptian squadron. *(© National Maritime Museum A4816)*

match for the big French and American First and Second Rates. The Navy was also very short of the big Fourth Rate frigates and it was hoped that the 74s could be used to counter enemy frigates. Some of the 74s were razéed – cut down to a single gun deck – and became very successful Fourth Rates.

Very little consideration was given to the protection of Britain's rapidly growing merchant fleet. Restrictive legislation such as the Corn Laws, Navigation Acts and tonnage rules inhibited growth until they were repealed or amended under the banner of 'free trade' in 1837. Until then the merchant fleet remained more or less constant in size at about 2½ million tons. Free trade led to a rapid change: grain imports rose from 25,000 tons in 1830 to 63,000 in 1850 and nearly 100,000 in 1860. Between 1837 and 1865 the number of sailing ships doubled, despite the much more rapid rise in the number of steamships.

Commercial shipping was a major source of Britain's wealth and the rapid growth in population made her dependent on imports of food. Defeat by starvation had become a real possibility. Contrary to the experience of

past wars, the Admiralty seems to have thought it sufficient to match enemy raiders on a one-to-one basis and little or no thought was given to convoy work.

The 1840s brought further problems in the eastern Mediterranean due to the break-up of the Turkish empire. In 1840 a British squadron intervened in Syria, seizing the heavily fortified town of St Jean d'Acre. A carefully planned four-hour bombardment enabled the town to be captured very easily. The operation was a risky one since the British fleet was undermanned and threatened by a potentially superior Franco-Russian combination.

Throughout much of the 1840s British governments feared a French invasion. It was believed, without any careful thought, that the steamship made possible a surprise landing of a large force and that such a landing could be opposed only by forts. Such fears were exacerbated in 1844 by an inflammatory pamphlet written by the Prince de Joinville, son of Louis Philippe.

Increasingly, naval operations were becoming dominated by the mobility of the steamship, whose operations appear in a later chapter.

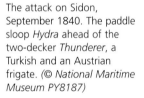

The attack on Sidon, September 1840. The paddle sloop *Hydra* ahead of the two-decker *Thunderer*, a Turkish and an Austrian frigate. *(© National Maritime Museum PY8187)*

SEPPINGS BECAME SURVEYOR in 1813, by which time the success of his system of structural design was becoming apparent. As mentioned in Chapter 1, when the *Tremendous* was docked in Malta it was found that there had been no working of the structure and that the bolts were perfectly secure.[1] By 1815 Seppings's scheme was standard practice. This is a fact all too often overlooked; for example, the 80-gun *Ganges* class of 1816 are usually described as 'copied' from the French *Canopus* (Franklin). Though the lines of the *Ganges* were indeed derived from the *Canopus*, the structure was pure Seppings,[2] making the new class far stronger.

The bow of the line-of-battle ship had long been a point of weakness as it was cut off at the cat head, level with the bottom of the upper deck gunports. Above this, there was a thin transverse bulkhead insufficient even to resist grape shot, a weakness which led to many of the casualties in *Victory* during Nelson's end-on approach at Trafalgar. The bow was not strong enough to withstand heavy seas, its weakness encouraged leaks, and these in turn led to early dry rot. From the middle of the eighteenth century the bow of frigates was carried up to the upper deck, but the full-height bow was only introduced to the battle line in 1804 when the three-decker *Namur* was cut down to two decks. It was decided that there was no point in cutting away the bow structure and she thus became the first liner with a round bow.

Ramillies, the second of Seppings's major conversions, was also left with a round bow and by 1815 the new bow shape was adopted in all new ships and in major refits (eg, *Victory*). The increased strength of the bow enabled a heavier armament to be carried forward with up to twelve guns firing ahead in the later First Rates.[3]

The stern was also a point of weakness, both in allowing the after end of the ship to work in a seaway, and because the vast array of stern windows gave no protection against raking fire from astern. There was

1. B Lavery, *The Ship of the Line*, vol 1, London (1983).
2. R A Wadia, op cit.
3. C White, *The End of the Sailing Navy*, Havant (1981).

Asia. A Seppings design of two-decker. Although her lines came from the ex-French *Canopus*, her structure was to Seppings's style and her tumblehome was reduced. She also had his unpopular circular stern, seen here in this view of the ship returning to Portsmouth with the *Albion* after the battle of Navarino. (© *National Maritime Museum PU6132*)

The round or circular stern, as seen on this model of Seppings's *Rodney* (left) offered improved defensive strength and better firing arcs on the quarters, but it was deemed ugly. Its replacement was the so-called elliptical stern, as demonstrated by this model of Symonds's *Vanguard* (right), which retained much of the structural strength of the Seppings design while giving a more traditional external appearance. (© *National Maritime Museum F7730-002 and L0364-001*)

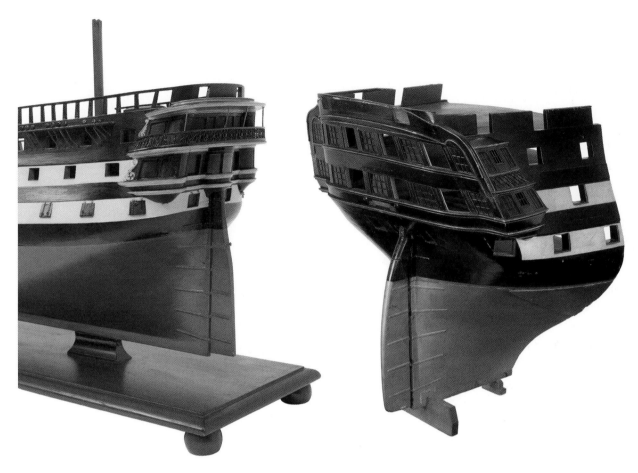

some improvement in about 1790 when galleries were abolished and the stern closed in, but with the prospect of peace the Navy insisted on the return of galleries in 1813. Seppings turned his attention to the stern in 1813, introducing vertical timbering as in the bow. The construction was almost exactly the same as that of the round bow and was called a round stern. The appearance of this stern displeased contemporary eyes and there were a few real difficulties.[4]

The old counter had given the rudder head some protection and prevented following seas from breaking onto the windows. Seppings originally provided a small projecting gallery on the centre line, partly to cover the rudder head but mainly to serve as the officers' heads. This little gallery was inadequate and inappropriately sited for a toilet and Seppings soon introduced two more galleries, one on each side, somewhat restricting the arcs of fire of the stern guns. The greater strength of Seppings's stern made it possible to mount six guns firing right astern. Inevitably, this drew opposition on the grounds that British ships did not run away, yet there were many occasions on which British squadrons, faced with a superior force, were obliged to run, and others when becalmed ships were attacked from the almost undefended stern by oar-propelled gun boats. The importance of all-round fire increased as steamships began to carry guns and could attack regardless of the direction of the wind.

However, the round stern was unpopular and was soon superseded by the elliptical stern whose design

was claimed by three master shipwrights, Roberts, Lang and Blake.[5]

In 1816 the Admiralty introduced a new rating system in which, for the first time, carronades were included in the number of guns which justified a rate. This had the consequence that most of the famous 74s were now rated as 72-, 76- or 78-gun ships. The new class of 80-gun Third Rates became 84-gun Second Rates.

In the first years of peace, new shipbuilding was confined to ships started or at least designed during the war. Particulars of the building programme are given in Appendix 4, but the sequence is not easy to follow. Ships were left on the slip as long as possible, to season and to keep them dry, and they were launched only when the slip was needed for another ship or the vessel was required for service. The line of battle programme while Seppings was Surveyor can be seen in Table 4.1.

Table 4.1 **Seppings's Programme**

Ordered	Rate	Number of ships	
1816–25	2	9	*Ganges*, etc
1819–27	2	3	*Indus*, *Hindostan* and *Calcutta*
1819–25	1	6	*Caledonia*, etc
1827	2	3	*Rodney*, etc

Of these, four were built in Bombay, starting with the *Ganges*, which brought a duplicate set of frames to

4. J Fincham, *A History of Naval Architecture* (1851, reprinted Scholar Press, London 1979).

5. Ibid.

6. Ibid.

7. Lavery, op cit.

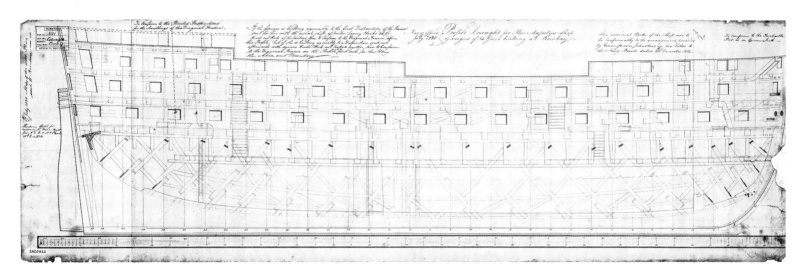

The profile draught of *Ganges* launched in Bombay in 1821. Seppings's construction shows clearly. *(© National Maritime Museum J2337)*

England, probably used for *Indus* (of dissimilar lines). *Vengeance*'s frames were brought in the *Asia*, *Hindostan*'s in *Repulse* and *Goliath*'s in *Calcutta*. This programme was initiated under Jamsetjee Wadia and continued after his death in 1821 by his son, Nowrojee Wadia.

Calcutta is usually described as a new design by Seppings,[6] but Wadia lists her as of the *Ganges* class. It is probable that any changes were small, since *Ganges* herself had all the features of the Seppings scheme, including diagonal deck planking. *Ganges* had a long life, being broken up only in 1929 when a well-known photograph was taken showing her diagonal braces very clearly.

The 90-gun two-deckers of the *Rodney* class were probably the only liners for which Seppings was entirely responsible, including the form. Only *Rodney* herself saw prolonged service as a sailing ship, in the Syrian campaign of 1840 and in the Black Sea in 1854. *Rodney* was matched against *Canopus*, *Albion*, *Vanguard* and others in the sailing trials of 1845. She proved fastest in head seas but was a midfield runner under other conditions, though it was noted that she rolled less than the other ships and hence was a better gun platform. It is sometimes claimed that Seppings's ships were heavy, and hence sluggish sailers, but these trials, the only clear evidence, do not support the charge. Seppings's frigate *Castor* consistently outpaced rivals in trials during 1835 and 1837.[7]

Experimental sailing

Even during the wars, a few experimental ships had been built, including the Third Rate *Plantagenet* by Rule in 1801, but in the main, experiment was confined to smaller vessels. The belief that British ship design was inferior led to several more ambitious series of trials from 1821 onwards. It must be to Seppings's great credit that he, the Surveyor, was willing to compete against a variety of challengers and he was also a strong supporter of the School of Naval Architecture, even though his own son failed the entry examination.

The first experimental craft from the school was the 18-gun sloop *Rose* designed by Inman, under protest, since he maintained that her specified armament was too heavy for the size of the vessel. Seppings designed the

Official model of *Rodney* as Seppings finalised the design in 1827. The ship was lengthened and given engines in 1859 and was to become the last wooden battleship in commission, not being paid off until 1870. *(© National Maritime Museum F7730-001)*

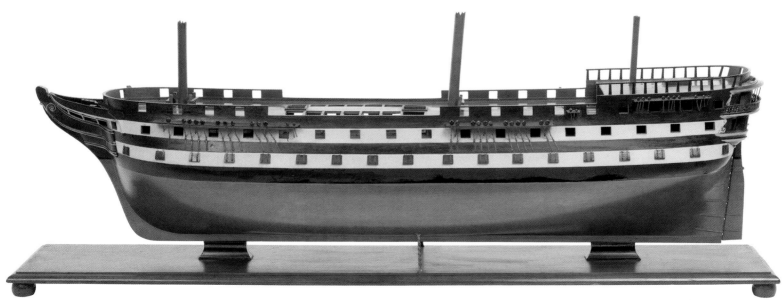

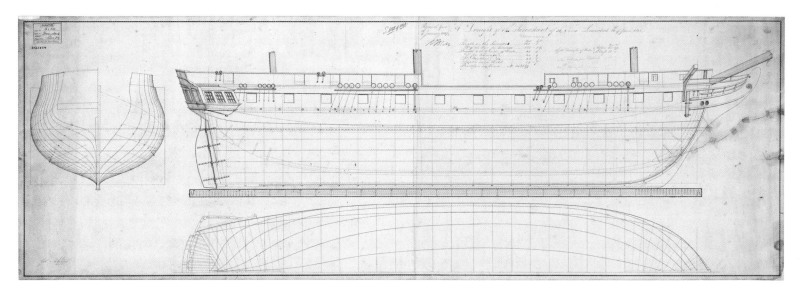

The sheer draught of *Inconstant*, designed by Captain John Hayes. Unlike Symonds, he was no gentleman-amateur, having trained as a shipwright in his young days. After the sailing trials of 1837, the official report says, 'Inconstant will always take the lead in any weather', though Seppings's *Castor* joined later and was even more successful. (© National Maritime Museum J5775)

Martin to the same requirement. *Rose* performed well under sail and was said to be a good sea-boat and, after a favourable report from Captain Clowes,[8] the Board ordered four repeats. They were not built, as the Board decided that the school should design a sloop with the dimensions that they thought appropriate to the armament. The difference between the new vessel, *Orestes*, and *Rose* does not seem enough to have any great effect on performance.

Table 4.2 **The School Sloops**

Ship	Length	Breadth (gun deck)	Depth (extreme)	Tonnage
Rose	104ft 2½in	29ft 6in	13ft 4in	397
Orestes	109ft 11in	30ft 6in	17ft 5¾in	459

Seppings designed the *Pylades* and Captain Hayes the *Champion* with similar dimensions; all were 18-gun corvettes. During competitive trials in 1824-5 all three did well, their relative performance varying with loading, trim and sailing conditions. After the early trials *Pylades* had a deeper keel and both she and the *Orestes* had their masts moved.[9] In consequence, these two, which had been a little inferior to *Champion*, became superior. All three were thought to be better than the other ships which they sailed against, but these other ships had not had the same experience of competitive sailing, nor had they had the same chance to modify rig and trim. *Orestes* was thought good enough for three similar ships to be built to her design.

Fincham points out the flaw in this and later, similar trials:

> But nothing was accomplished by these trials towards supplying data for the naval architect: for all the improvements in the sailing qualities of the ships and in their motions in a sea, which were made after the first trial, were the effects of alterations quite irrespective of the form. The experiments showed what might be gained in the performance of a vessel by changing her trim and

by changing the position of the centre of effort of her sails, but beyond that, the facts of the experiment do not lead us.[10]

There were several more sets of competitive trials and Fincham's strictures apply to them all. The next series of trials involved three 28-gun ships and four 18-gun corvettes by different designers.

Perhaps the most interesting aspect of these trials was the difference in performance between *Acorn* and *Satellite*, identical ships. *Satellite* was consistently good in light and moderate winds, while *Acorn*, which was generally poor, came in first in heavy weather. There were three series of trials, ships being altered between each. *Columbine* had a small advantage in moderate winds, but was inferior in heavy weather, particularly to *Acorn* and *Satellite*.[11]

Competitive trials continued for another twenty years or so and, while one must agree with Fincham that little was learnt of direct value, the effort put into such competitions demonstrates the will of successive Boards to improve the fleet. The trials also provide negative evidence since, while they did not demonstrate any clear superiority, they showed that no one designer produced ships which were significantly slower.

Anglo-French sailing trials 1832[12]

There was one other series of trials which is worth further study, even though subject to the same difficulties of interpretation. In 1832 a series of trials were held in the Downs between a British squadron under Sir Pulteney Malcolm and a French squadron under Admiral Ducrest. In the following year the French appointed a commission to enquire into the 'inferiority' of their ships in sailing and the frequency of their sustaining damage.

The French commission made a very careful study of the proportion and forms of the ships of both navies. Though they identified a tendency for British ships to have greater beam, less length and greater height of ports, there were several cases in which this tendency was

8. D K Brown, 'Speed of sailing warships', 'Empires at peace and war' conference, Portsmouth (1988).

9. Fincham, op cit.

10. A F Creuze, 'On the experimental cruise of HM Corvettes *Champion* and *Pylades*', *Papers on Naval Architecture*, vol 1 (1827).

11. Fincham, op cit.

12. J Bennet, 'Observations on the dimensions and properties of ships of various classes in the British Navy with an application of the subject to ships of the late experimental squadron under Rear Admiral Sir Thomas Hardy', *Papers on Naval Architecture*, vol 11 (1828).

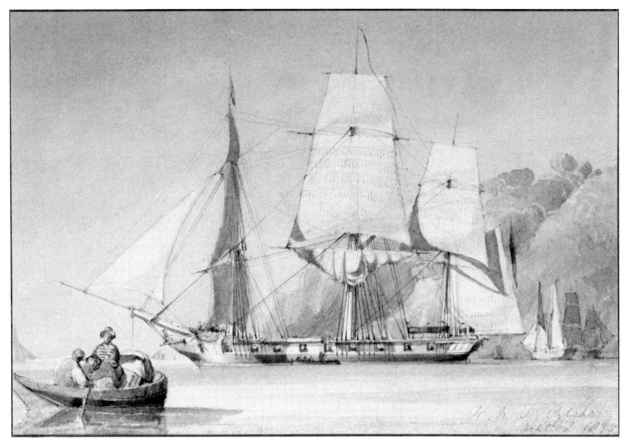

Pylades, designed by Seppings (left), and *Champion* (below) by Hayes were two 18-gun corvettes built to similar requirements that sailed against one another in trials carried out in 1824-5. (© *National Maritime Museum PW6105 and PW6107*)

reversed. Royal Navy ships were also thought to have a smaller midships section, less displacement and a higher centre of buoyancy. These differences were examined, class by class, without any clear conclusion being drawn.

It was seen that the sailing qualities of French designs were improved when captured and put into service with the Royal Navy. For example, HMS *Donegal*, captured in 1798, was given a lighter armament, lower masts, less ballast and a deeper false keel, with an overall improvement in performance.

The French commission then considered some problems which were thought to arise in service and noted that the following propositions were widely accepted:[13]

a. Their ships hogged early because of excess weight at the ends. The commission thought that even if this had been a problem in the older ships, the current ones were stronger and the effect of hogging could be ignored.

b. The shape of the waterplane varied rapidly with draught, ie as stores were consumed.

c. The copper sheathing was too thin and badly applied. Ducrest and his captain believed that this was the major problem in 1832. (The rate at which the copper sheathing eroded was also of concern to the British Admiralty who, in 1827, asked Sir Humphry Davy to investigate. He tried protecting the copper of the frigate *Samarang* by attaching lumps of zinc at intervals to stop the electrolytic action. This reduced the loss of copper but destroyed its anti-fouling properties and the trial was abandoned.)

d. The sails were badly cut, of poor material and not well positioned.

The rig and masting of the two navies differed considerably, with much taller masts in the French ships. This gave increased sail area, particularly high up, which helped in light breezes, but meant that less sail could be carried in strong winds because of the heel produced. Once again, the myth of French superiority under sail is weakened.

Gunnery

During the 1820s there were a number of proposals for a uniform armament of 32pdrs, with shorter, lighter guns on the higher decks to minimise top weight. The writings of Paixhans are the best known and were read and studied in Britain: for example, the lengthy review in *Papers on Naval Architecture* from which the following passage is adapted.

Paixhans examined three alternative structures for his future fleet:

1. Continuation of the present mix of liners and frigates but with a uniform calibre of 36pdr shot-firing guns.
2. As above but armed with shell-firing guns.
3. Replacement of the whole sailing fleet by small steamers with shell-firing guns.

The object of solid shot was not so much to penetrate the side of a wooden ship, as any such holes would be

The experimental sailings of 1844. *Mutine* (Fincham) is in the foreground, with behind (left to right) *Daring* (White), *Espiegle* (Chatham Committee), *Osprey* (Blake), *Waterwitch* (White) and *Pantaloon* (Symonds). *Flying Fish* (Symonds) and the old *Cruizer*, which provided the performance benchmark, are not shown. *Espiegle* was usually fastest. (© *National Maritime Museum PW8103*)

small and would close up to some extent due to the elasticity of the wood, but to rend and tear the timbers, throwing off a cloud of splinters. However, such an armament would do little to reduce British supremacy.

Shells were well-known and in 1810 Napoleon had proposed their use at sea. The problems were seen as the range of the shell and the recoil of the gun. The safety of the largest ship could be endangered by a smaller one, and expenditure of money and men would no longer purchase its immunity from smaller ships. There would no longer be a need for a large force of experienced seamen.

Steamships were independent of wind, had a shallow draught, were easy to turn and could fight end on. Paixhans was right in many of his views, but ahead of his time. The engines of the day were so heavy that few guns could be carried, fuzes were highly unreliable, and the chance of a hit at long range was so remote that many guns were needed. Above all, Paixhans forgot that Britain's lead over France was then greater in industry than in seamen, and his plan would have increased rather than destroyed, British power at sea.

A similar scheme to Paixhans' uniform calibre proposal was put forward by Colonel Monro RA in 1825. Due to lack of resources, progress in implementing such schemes was slow until 1830 when some eight hundred 24pdrs designed by Congreve and about the same number by Blomefield were bored out to take 32pdr shot (6.35in). Some shorter 24- and 18pdrs were also converted at about the same time. These conversions added greatly to the firepower of the battlefleet and were possible only because of the improved casting and testing methods introduced by Blomefield.[14]

Sir Robert Seppings's great career was brought to a premature end in 1832 when he was replaced by Symonds, as one of the major changes brought about by the new First Lord, Sir James Graham. His true merit was spelt out by the House of Commons Finance Committee in 1819.[15]

Your Committee deem it their particular duty to notice Mr Seppings, one of the Surveyors of the Navy, to whose abilities and exertions this country is mainly indebted for many of its most valuable improvements in naval architecture; … They are fully convinced that the result of them will be to effectuate, in the construction of ships of war, a great saving to the public, and to secure a proportionate economy of human life, arising from the superior durability and greater power of resistance to the elements, and to the casualties incidental to nautical life, which the modern system of keeping our fleet at sea, at all seasons and in all weather, has rendered of the utmost importance. These services, although they have nothing of that brilliancy which forcibly excites public admiration, will continue to confer a lasting benefit on the British nation, long after that period when the beneficial effect of victories, however splendid, shall have passed away.

The committee was right: Seppings's scheme of structural design, modified a little, was to endure as long as the wooden ship.

Sir William Symonds

Symonds was one of many naval officers who, as a result of service in the late wars, had become convinced of the inferiority of British design. He was one of the few who believed that they could improve the breed.

As captain of the port in Malta in 1819, he designed a very successful racing yacht, the *Nancy Dawson*. In the next few years he designed several other yachts, mainly for aristocratic customers, which drew the attention of the First Lord, Melville, to his work. As a result, Symonds was asked to design the 18-gun sloop *Columbine*, which competed successfully in the 1828 sailing trials. A brigantine, the *Pantaloon*, added to his reputation, and in August 1831 the Duke of Clarence (later William IV) and Sir James Graham invited him to design the frigate *Vernon*.

Symonds characterised his design features as 'great beam and extraordinary sharpness'.[16] In fact, this meant a high rise of floor with the turn of bilge and maximum beam above the waterline. The beam was greater than in previous ships, increasing stability (perhaps too much) and reducing the need for ballast. The great hydrody-

13. Fincham, op cit.

14. Ibid.

15. H M Baker, *The Crisis in Naval Armament* (National Maritime Museum Monograph 56), London (1983).

16. D K Brown, 'The structural improvements in wooden ships initiated by Sir Robert Seppings', *The Naval Architect* (May 1979).

Sir William Symonds, Surveyor of the Navy 1832–47. (© *National Maritime Museum PZ8837*)

namicist R E Froude later said that the Symondite form differed from its predecessors in:

a. Greater beam.
b. More beam some way out of the water.
c. No ballast, heavy bottom construction, floors close together.

He also said that they were 'jerky, uneasy rollers'.[17] Symonds was concerned only with the shape of the hulls and with the sail plan. The structure was left to others. Oliver Lang, the master shipwright at Woolwich, who built the *Vernon*, followed Seppings's scheme but added a deep false keel as a protection against grounding and sited the magazine amidships to improve the supply to the guns.

Vernon was a 50-gun frigate with the dimensions of an 80-gun liner, with gunports 9–10ft above the water-line and spaced 7ft 6in apart. Her spacious berthing areas, combined with the stability to carry much sail in moderate winds, made her popular with her officers and crew. She was built of a mixture of English and Italian oak but she was planked too early and rot set in quickly.

In setting out the dimensions of the *Vernon*, Symonds had been allowed to build a much bigger ship than had previously been considered for a 50-gun frigate. In a sailing ship, size tends to mean speed, and big ships are always well-liked. However, size is expensive and, at £62,115, not many such ships could be afforded in comparison with *Raleigh*, a Fourth Rate costing about £45,000, or *Leda*, a Fifth Rate at £30,000.

Captain William Symonds was appointed Surveyor in 1832 in place of Seppings, the first non-professional officer to hold that post. Since the appointment coincided with Graham's closure of the School of Naval Architecture, there was dismay among graduates of that school and the other progressive designers in the service (eg, Fincham, Lang).

The controversy was bitter on both sides and was long enduring. The author remembers being taught at Liverpool in the late 1940s of the evils of the Symondite form! A poem in praise of the *Vernon* concludes:

Thus ends my log, a glass of grog
to Symonds their projector.
Bred in the school of common sense
and not of architecture, …

Vernon. Symonds and Lang designed this big frigate in 1831. She was generally regarded as successful though her first captain, Cockburn, was very critical of her performance to windward. (© *National Maritime Museum PY0849*)

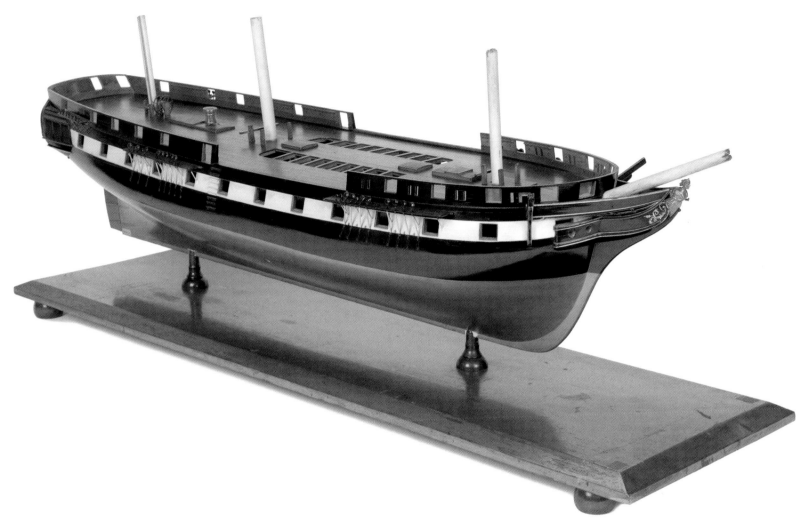

Pique. Symonds' first design as Surveyor; she was a reduced version of *Vernon*. (© National Maritime Museum F8830-002)

The verse clearly brings out the contempt felt by Symonds and his supporters for the science of naval architecture and, indeed, for any technical development. In time, this was to prove his undoing. Graham defended his choice against those who would have preferred a master shipwright in the debate on the Navy Estimates in June 1834 by saying, 'It may as well be said that a civil engineer should be a stonemason'. If nothing else, this remark shows Graham's total ignorance of the skills of a master shipwright and, perhaps, that Telford, the great civil engineer, had indeed begun as a stonemason. Fincham and Lang certainly had the education, ability and presence to make a fine surveyor while Roberts and Blake, of whom little is known, at least showed a capacity for original thought.

Symonds did have some creditable achievements; with *Vernon* he had broken away from the old establishment rules and won the freedom to design ships of the size to match their role. He soon introduced a standardised system of masts and spars which enabled a spare spar to be used, in different positions, on a wide variety of ships. This was not an original scheme; Chatfield (SNA) had proposed it in *Papers on Naval Architecture* some years before, but Symonds deserves credit for forcing it through. Symonds also abolished 'job and task' pay (a form of piecework) in the dockyards, substi-

tuting a day rate. He claimed a 16 per cent saving as a result, but arguments continue to this day on the most effective pay scheme for a repair industry. The Steam Factory at Woolwich, built at his instruction, was another achievement.

As surveyor, his first major design was the 36-gun frigate *Pique*, a diminutive of the *Vernon*. He had appointed John Edye, a foreman shipwright, as his first assistant and it was Edye who was responsible for weight and structure. *Pique* ran aground off Labrador on 22 September 1835, causing serious damage. Her captain, Mends, in his autobiography[18] credits Symonds with *Pique*'s survival, but this must rest with Edye's adaptation of Seppings's solid bottom structure. A number of derivatives of *Vernon* and the smaller *Pique* were built and others started. Later ships of these classes were modified by Symonds's successors and, in many cases, completed as screw steamers.

Symonds's first line-of-battle ship was the *Vanguard* (80 guns), laid down in May 1833. She had an extreme rise of floor and, when launched, was the broadest ship ever built in England. In tonnage she was little less than the three-decker *Neptune*, which may have prompted the Surveyor to argue in 1836 for displacement rather than tonnage to be used to characterise warships. He claimed that the new tonnage rules, in which the engine

17. J A Sharpe, *Memoirs of Rear Admiral Sir William Symonds*, London (1858).
18. B S Mends, *Life of Sir William Robert Mends*, London (1899).

room volume was deducted from the tonnage of the steamer, made this measurement particularly inappropriate. (It does not seem that engine room tonnage was deducted in warships.)

Vanguard and her ten sisters had all the virtues and faults of Symondite ships. They were fast in moderate winds but rolled quickly and heavily, making them poor gun platforms. *Queen* was ordered as a 120-gun First Rate in 1827, but was totally redesigned by Symonds and Edye before she was laid down in 1833. Edye extended Seppings's frigate style, using iron diagonals in liners as well, saving in both weight and space. The topsides of *Queen* and Symonds's later ships were fastened with copper bolts rather than iron, a desirable but expensive solution. *Queen* was given an elliptical stern.

Queen carried 110 guns and was criticised for being under-armed. Her metacentric height was 7.19ft which must have caused rapid, jerky rollings. However, she was spacious and hence well-liked. She was usually in commission as a sailing ship, until 1858 when she was lengthened and cut down to two decks on conversion to a steamship. She was broken up in 1871.

Symonds's last notable sailing ship was the 90-gun *Albion*. Her tonnage was even greater than that of the

Queen which led to even stronger but, perhaps, ill-informed criticism of lack of gun power. She was entirely fastened with copper or mixed metal bolts, adding further to her cost.

Contemporary views of Symonds were strongly expressed both for and against. In general, seamen officers were strong supporters, while naval architects were hostile. Captains are normally proud of their ships and their views must be treated with caution, a view which works both ways, since captains of earlier ships did not always subscribe to the legends of Symondite superiority.

An important critic of Symonds from the earliest days was Cockburn. He hoisted his flag in *Vernon* in January 1833 and by March was writing to Graham in very critical terms over the sailing of the *Vernon*.[19] He complained of her pitching, and the damage caused resulting in leaks. 'I firmly believe that in smooth water and a good breeze, she will beat anything that swims upon the sea, particularly to windward, but the moment she is opposed to a sea ahead she becomes more than can be believed … and I can compare her to nothing but a child's rocking horse moving up and down without advancing a step'. These memories cannot have

Queen (Symonds). Painting of a royal visit to the fleet flagship at Portsmouth on 1 March 1842. (© National Maritime Museum BHC0629)

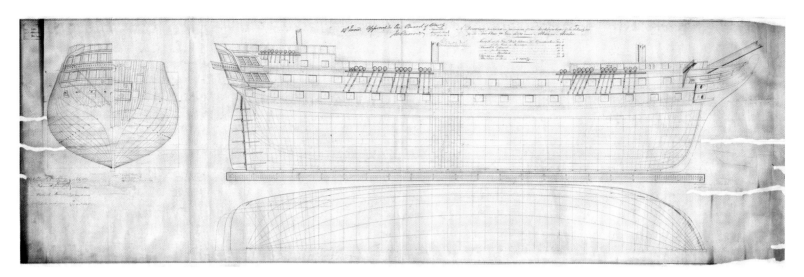

Admiralty draught for the *Albion* class showing the typical Symonds midship section. (*© National Maritime Museum J1672*)

improved their relations when Cockburn became Senior Naval Lord in the 1840s.

There was a very interesting set of sailing trials in 1845 involving *Trafalgar* (Rule), *Queen*, *Albion*, *Vanguard* and *Superb* (Symonds), *Rodney* (Seppings), *St Vincent* (Surveyor) and *Canopus* (French design). Like all such trials, conclusions are hard to draw. *Vanguard* and *Superb* were re-coppered during the lengthy trials programme, turning the latter ship from one of the slowest ships in the squadron into one of the fastest. On the other hand, *Canopus* lost most of her copper and, with it, her speed.[20]

Speed depended on the strength and direction of the wind and sea. In moderate winds the stiffness of *Queen* and *Albion* gave them an advantage in carrying sail, while in head seas *Rodney* and *Trafalgar* did best. The older *St Vincent* and *Canopus* were certainly not disgraced, showing that any improvement since the war was small.

On 27 October measurements of roll angle were attempted using pendulums. A simple pendulum will give a very inaccurate measure of roll angle if its point of support is moving (try it!), but the angles below were recorded; maximum out to out, and the order of the ships is probably correct.

Table 4.3 **Roll Angles, 1845 Trials**

Ship	Roll (degrees, out to out)
Albion	31
Rodney	16
Superb	19
Canopus	21

Captain Moresby of the *Canopus* noted, correctly, that it was not the *Albion*'s roll angle which was notable but the rapidity of rolling, which would increase the apparent angle shown by the pendulum. On another occasion, Captain Corry (*Superb*) rolled about three times while *Canopus* rolled twice. It was this rapid roll, and the lateral accelerations associated with it, which made Symonds's ships such poor gun platforms.

Creuze told the select committee of 1848 that this rapid rolling caused the rigging to wear out quickly and also led to working of the hull.[21] While Creuze had no love for Symonds, there seems to have been some truth in his complaint of wear.

Symonds claimed for his designs:

She would carry more deadweight; would be staunch under canvas when pressed by the wind; would roll less, be capable of more velocity and would offer more resistance to leeway. She would admit of greater depth of hold; would shift her cargo less and would require less ballast.[22]

It was Symonds's lack of numeracy which caused his failure as a designer. As Morgan had noted earlier, increased rise of floor helped to reduce leeway in a sailing ship, while more beam and less ballast was also a move in the right direction. Because he was incapable of making the necessary calculations and would not take advice from those who could, Symonds overdid both aspects; in design, enough is enough.

His hostility to new technology, particularly the screw and iron hulls, lost him the confidence of the Board. From 1841 his work was subjected to ever more embarrassing scrutiny by professional men. His reluctance to resign was matched by the Board's reluctance to dismiss a man who still had much support in the fleet. Only late in 1847 did he finally accept the inevitable and go.

Because of the failure of the threat from France to materialise, Symonds's reactionary approach did little direct harm. His opposition to all scientific and technical progress caused a very long-lasting suspicion between naval architects and naval officers which must have done immense harm over the years which followed. Had he been born a century earlier, perhaps his talents might have been considered valuable.

The Chatham Committee

The first challenge to Symonds came when the Board of Admiralty directed three of the graduates of the School of Naval Architecture to meet at Chatham and prepare a

19. J Pack, *The Man who Burnt the White House, Admiral Sir James Cockburn 1772–1853*, Emsworth (1987).

20. Fincham, op cit.

21. Parliamentary Papers 1847–8, vol 21, Part I.

22. Sharpe, op cit.

series of designs, including a ship of each of the major categories, to be 'accompanied by an explicit statement of the methods used in preparing them'. The chosen designers were Read, Chatfield and Creuze (known as the Chatham Committee), and their reports are among the earliest papers on the nature of the ship design process to be published.[23] Scott Russell, a man not over given to praising his contemporaries, was to say of their work in 1858, 'These gentlemen, however, produced a treatise on naval architecture which would do great credit to the authors'.

Creative design involves inspiration as well as hard work; it will usually involve false starts, blind alleys and closed loops. Such a process is hard to describe even today and is all too likely to sound mechanistic when written down. The Chatham Committee describe a simple process, but from some passages, which will be quoted, they clearly understood the essentials of the design process.[24]

It is likely, too, that the methods they described were, with one exception, little different from those used by Edye. The exception was the vital one in that they wrote down and published the methods they used. Publication is a fundamental rule of scientific method and shows clearly that they had moved away from the attitudes of the old craft guilds that retained the 'mystery' of their learning for their own members. It must be mentioned that Edye published a number of useful papers, though these consisted of data rather than methods.

The committee's first design was a 36-gun, Fifth Rate frigate, the *Thetis*.[25] This was followed in 1844 by the 80-gun *Cressy*.[26] The armament was to comply with the scale of February 1839 and the masts and yards were to be from Symonds's scale of September 1838.

The outline of their approach to design is distilled from the two reports. The first step was to select suitable dimensions by comparison with previous ships of good report. They said 'naval architecture is a science of analysis and comparisons'. Their aim was a:

ship which shall have sufficient displacement with a moderate draft of water and an adequate height of ports above the water; sufficient and convenient stowage; ample accommodation for officers and crew; good quar-

The ships which took part in the 1845 sailing trials assembling at Spithead on 23 June. From left, they are *Albion*, *Queen*, *Superb*, *Rodney*, *Trafalgar*, *Canopus*, *St Vincent* and *Vanguard*. (© *National Maritime Museum PU7791*)

Thetis. The Chatham Committee's first design. *(© National Maritime Museum PU5808)*

ters at the guns; enough stability to render the lee guns effective when the ship is under a press of sail in moderate weather, the capability of lying well up to the wind; and of working well to windward against a head sea; easiness of working in heavy weather and quickness in all her evolutions; and all combined with a rate of sailing at least equal to all ships of her class.

They saw that some of these attributes were functions of the form and proportions of the hull alone while others depended on the sail plan as well. The comparisons made were inevitably with recent ships, ie Symonds's designs, though they chose proportions which were longer and narrower. They aimed for a form with vertical sides at the waterline to minimise changes of displacement as the ship moved in a seaway. Port height was a little less in *Thetis* than in *Pique* but adequate based on experience at sea.

The displacement of the hull at launch was obtained from previous ships, this being equal to the weight of the bare hull. The weight of the new hull was then estimated in proportion to the change in the dimensions. Direct calculation of hull weight was seen as impossible, a rather surprising conclusion. The calculations are tiresome but simple and the three graduates should have had little difficulty in obtaining a good estimate in a week or two's work.

Very detailed tables were prepared listing the weights of guns, carriages and ammunition; of spars, rigging and sails; of provisions and all other stores. Some of the

more interesting tables are given in Appendix 5. The naval architect would add the appropriate total weights from these tables to the weight of the hull to obtain the load displacement.

The hull form was a compromise with more rise of floor than in wartime ships but much less than in the Symondites. As discussed in reference 8, the forms used in all sailing warships were very different from those hydrodynamically desirable and it is most unlikely that any practical changes would affect resistance or speed. The form had to be excessively bluff in order to support the weight of guns at each end and had to be kept short due to lack of strength in the timber joints. Their designs were intended to be economic:

> We apprehend that it is the object of our labours, as it is the business of science, to endeavour to produce the best effects with given means.

Thetis was sailed in competition with *America*, a razée (50-gun frigate, ex-74), and with *Superb*, a Symonds 80-gun ship, during March 1847 and with other ships later in the year. As usual, there were no clear conclusions, though *Thetis* won at least her share of races.

Committee of Reference

In December 1841, the Board invited the master shipwrights of the major dockyards to assemble in committee to consider improvements in the construc-

23. S Read, H Chatfield and A F Creuze, *Reports on Naval Construction*, London (1842–8).
24. Ibid.
25. R Scott Russell, 'Remarks on a paper by E J Reed, "On the modifications which ships of the Royal Navy have undergone during the present century"', Society of Arts (15 December 1858, reprinted in *Mechanics' Magazine*, 1859).
26. Lavery, op cit.

Nankin. One of the last of the big sailing frigates, launched in 1850. *(Maber)*

tion of ships. Their meetings were critical of the designs of Symonds and Edye, including their strength. In view of the long life of many of these ships, including their use as steamships, this last charge was probably not justified.

In the light of this criticism, a more formal Committee of Reference was set up under Captain Lord John Hay in 1846, supported by Dr Inman and two master shipwrights, Fincham and Abethell (1st SNA). All designs from the Surveyor were to be referred to this committee for comment and alteration if necessary. In fact, the committee altered all ships whose construction was not too far advanced, the beam being reduced and the rise of floor made less extreme. A large number of ships were involved, but in most cases they were further altered before completion to accept steam engines.

In 1848 Captain Baldwin Walker was appointed Surveyor with new terms of reference making him responsible for the overall material state of the Navy, but specifically precluding him from personal involvement in design. Design was the responsibility of his assistant surveyors, initially John Edye and Isaac Watts (1st SNA). Edye retired soon after, leaving Watts as the only assistant and in sole charge of design as the Navy moved firmly into the new technologies.

A Committee of Science was appointed to review designs from the new assistant surveyors. There were only two members, Fincham and Read (1st SNA), and they seem to have met only rarely, if at all, and not to have criticised Watts's work in any way. Graduates of the school had at last reached the top of their profession and could demonstrate the value of their approach to naval architecture.

THERE WERE MANY PROPOSALS in the early eighteenth century to use the novel Newcomen engine for ship propulsion, but none was practical as the engine was too heavy. From about 1780 onwards, the steam engine had advanced to a stage at which it could – just – be fitted into a ship, and inventors such as the Marquis de Jouffroy d'Abbans in France, Rumsey and Fitch in the USA and Miller in Scotland all built prototype steamships.

By the turn of the century, Fulton in the USA and Symington in Britain had built steamships which could perform useful work. In 1807 Fulton's *Clermont* entered service on the Hudson River and in 1812 Bell's *Comet* began commercial operations on the Clyde; these were followed by many others on sheltered waters.[1] Once the Napoleonic wars were over, commercial developments on short sea routes were rapid, with steamships operating between Glasgow and Belfast, across the English Channel, and on rivers such as the Clyde and Thames.

The Admiralty is often accused of being slow in accepting the steamship. However, Archimedes' principle is inexorable: weight must equal buoyancy, and if heavy and bulky machinery is put into a ship there will be little to spare for guns and not much room for the crew. Fuel consumption was very heavy, limiting early steamships to short voyages.

The first serious attempt to build a steam warship came in the early 1790s when the Earl of Stanhope proposed a vessel to be driven by feathering paddles (not wheels) or, as he called them, duck feet. The earl was encouraged by the Admiralty but his ship, the *Kent*, was built at his own expense.[2] *Kent* was built on the Thames by Marmaduke Stalkartt (an early member of the Society for the Improvement of Naval Architecture) in 1793 and had a flat bottom with straight, flared sides.

There were six 'vibrators' on each side – paddles pivoted near the top, swinging fore and aft, feathered on the return stroke. The engine was built by Walker at Rotherhithe at a cost of £4,498 with two vertical cylinders (6ft x 3ft 3in, 5ft x 2ft). This engine, probably atmospheric, was a failure and, though there is brief mention of the trials of the *Kent Ambi-Navigator*,[3] it seems that the paddles were only worked by hand – foreshadowing Napier's hand-operated paddle wheels which he tried in *Galatea* in 1829. By 1797 she had lost her engines and was used as a privateer with fourteen 12pdr guns. A proposal for a steam warship by Bell in 1800 was rejected.

Fulton began work in the USA on a much more ambitious fighting ship in 1813. His plans for a large catamaran were approved by Congress in 1814. His ship, the *Demologos*, was laid down in June 1814 and launched that October, but completion was delayed by Fulton's death and trials only started in June 1815. She had a single cylinder engine in one hull and a copper boiler in the other. Accounts vary but her speed on trial was probably between 3 and 5 knots. Her intended armament was thirty 32pdrs firing red-hot shot heated in the boilers, but she only received twenty-four guns. She probably never went to sea again and was used as a receiving ship at Brooklyn until she was broken up in 1829.[4]

Table 5.1 *Demologos*

Dimensions	156ft x 56ft x 11ft draught
Displacement	c2,475 tons
Engine	1 cylinder, 48in bore, 5ft stroke
Paddle wheel	16ft diameter, 14ft wide
Sails	Though designed without, she was fitted with a light lateen rig

Fulton's novel configuration had overcome some of the problems inherent in a paddle warship; the paddle wheel was between the hulls and protected by them, with sides 4ft 10in thick, and there was no obstruction to the mounting of guns on the broadside. Patrick Miller's steam catamaran tried on the Clyde in 1787 showed

1. E C Smith, *A Short History of Naval and Marine Engineering*, Cambridge (1937); R Armstrong, *Powered Ships: the Beginnings*, London (1975); K T Rowland, *Steam at Sea*, Newton Abbot (1970); P M Rippon, *Evolution of Engineering in the Royal Navy*, vol I, Tunbridge Wells (1988).

2. E C Cuff, 'Naval Inventions of Charles, third Earl Stanhope, 1753–1816', *Mariner's Mirror*, vol 66 (1942).

3. *Collection of Papers on Naval Architecture* (1800).

4. J P Baxter, *Introduction of the Ironclad Warship*, Harvard (1933, reprint Archon 1968).

Kent. An early (1793) and unsuccessful attempt to design a steam warship by the Earl of Stanhope. (*Society for Nautical Research*)

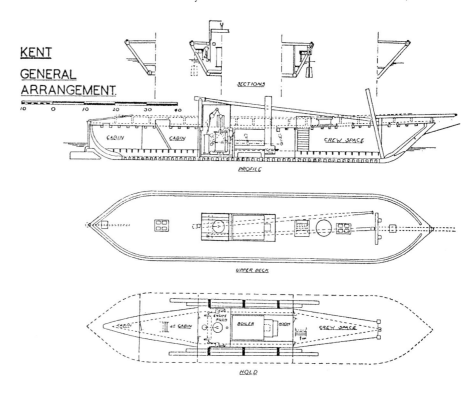

5. G C Mackrow, 'Twin Ship Propulsion', *Trans INA*, vol 20 (1879).

6. Smith, op cit; C Lloyd, *Mr Barrow of the Admiralty*, London (1970). Note: this reference says that *Congo*'s engine went to Plymouth, a less likely but not impossible story. No confirmation of either report has been found. Lloyd also says that Sir Joseph Banks was instrumental in persuading the Admiralty to fit a steam engine.

King George IV embarking for Dublin on 12 August 1821 in the packet *Lightning* (not the warship of the same name). After many renamings (see text), she entered Admiralty service as *Monkey*, though still as a packet. (© *National Maritime Museum BHC0619*)

some of these advantages. On the other hand, the catamaran form poses its own problems, since the flow between the hulls is confused and it is not a good site for a paddle wheel: the well known cross-Channel paddle catamarans, *Castalia* and *Calais-Douvres*, failed largely for this reason as late as 1879.[5] The catamaran is a very stiff form, and in a seaway would have suffered from severe accelerations at the deck edge, making the working of guns difficult and accurate gunnery impossible. All these problems could be solved, or at least ameliorated, as could the structural problems of a catamaran, and it is a little surprising that this configuration was not developed.

During the great wars the Admiralty was too busy to think about steamships but was quick to move when peace returned. In 1815 an expedition was planned to the Congo river and John Barrow, the Second Secretary, persuaded the Board to adopt a suggestion of John Rennie, the famous civil engineer, then building the breakwater in Plymouth Sound, and it was decided to build a steamship for the expedition. Boulton and Watt offered, for £1,700, an engine already being built for another ship on the Tyne. It was a beam engine of 20NHP and weighed 30 tons. As was usual in those days, the package from the engine builder included two 'engine men' to run it.

The *Congo* was built in Deptford Dockyard and was launched on 11 November 1816. It was seen at once that she was much overweight and that at a draught of 8ft 6in, the side paddle wheels were too deeply

immersed to work properly. Rear Admiral Sir Home Popham was put in charge of the trials. He was a most progressive officer who had sponsored the introduction into naval service of Congreve's rockets and Fulton's 'torpedo'. Popham and the engineer, Murdoch, were both worried about *Congo*'s weight and stability, the former writing, 'the ship is very crank and I do not, by a more intimate acquaintance, improve my opinion of her'.

For the first trial Popham is said to have ordered ballast removed to give a draught of 4ft at which 3 knots was achieved at 18rpm. Since a change in draught of 4ft 6in would have required the removal of at least 100 tons (three times the weight of the engines), it will be realised that the accounts are, to say the least, inconsistent. A second trial on 22 June 1816, with James Watt present, confirmed that she would be unseaworthy at such a light draught. Her engines were removed and *Congo* became a sailing ship – schooner – the engine being used to run a pump at Chatham.[6]

General Bentham had introduced a number of steam engines into the Royal Dockyards and by 1816 these included two dredgers, non-self-propelled craft but with engines to work their buckets. Despite the early failures, the Admiralty's interest in steam persisted. In 1816 Marc Brunel, who had designed the steam-powered block-making machinery for Portsmouth, and later introduced steam machinery in Chatham Dockyard, suggested further trials on steamships. The First Lord, Lord Melville, who had supported the *Congo* trials, wrote an encouraging reply, suggesting that in the first instance Brunel should concentrate on the use of steamships to tow sailing vessels out of harbour against contrary winds. In view of the problems of steam warships and in the light of previous failures, Melville's approach seems quite sensible for 1816, though often derided by later writers.

The steamer *Regent*, which had been built for service on the Thames, was hired at a cost of £52 10s per week in the winter of 1816 and used at Portsmouth for towing trials.[7] This *Regent* was probably built by Count Pope at Rotherhithe in 1816 and was of 112 tons with a Maudslay engine of 24NHP. The currents in the entrance to Portsmouth are strong and it seems that *Regent* was not powerful enough.[8] There were problems over the insurance and the hire charges were disputed by

the Admiralty. Beamish says that Brunel was 'dismayed'.[9]

A more successful trial was carried out in 1819 when a steamer called *Eclipse* was hired.[10] She left London at 0730hrs on 4 July 1819 towing the 74-gun ship *Hastings* and reached Margate at 1330hrs. The Admiralty would also have been aware of the successful trial by the East India Company in August 1816. They used the steamer *Majestic* of 90 tons and 24NHP to tow the ship *Hope* from Deptford to Woolwich at 3 knots against the wind. *Majestic* had made the first steam crossing of the Channel earlier that year, carrying 200 passengers.

The next step came from the Post Office, whose mail packets were built under Admiralty supervision. They ordered two steamers, *Lightning* and *Meteor*, from William Elias Evans of Rotherhithe, which entered

7. R Beamish, *Memoirs of Sir Marc I Brunel*, London (1862).
8. J Fincham, *A History of Naval Architecture* (1851, reprinted Scholar Press, London 1979).
9. Beamish, op cit.
10. G A Osbon, unpublished notes now owned by the World Ship Society. *Eclipse* may have been the ship built by Brent at Rotherhithe for the General Steam Navigation Company. She was completed in 1820 but may have been used for trials before acceptance. Brent's ship was 88 tons (bm), 104ft x 16ft 9in and had a Boulton and Watt engine of 60–70NHP, giving her a speed of 12 knots.

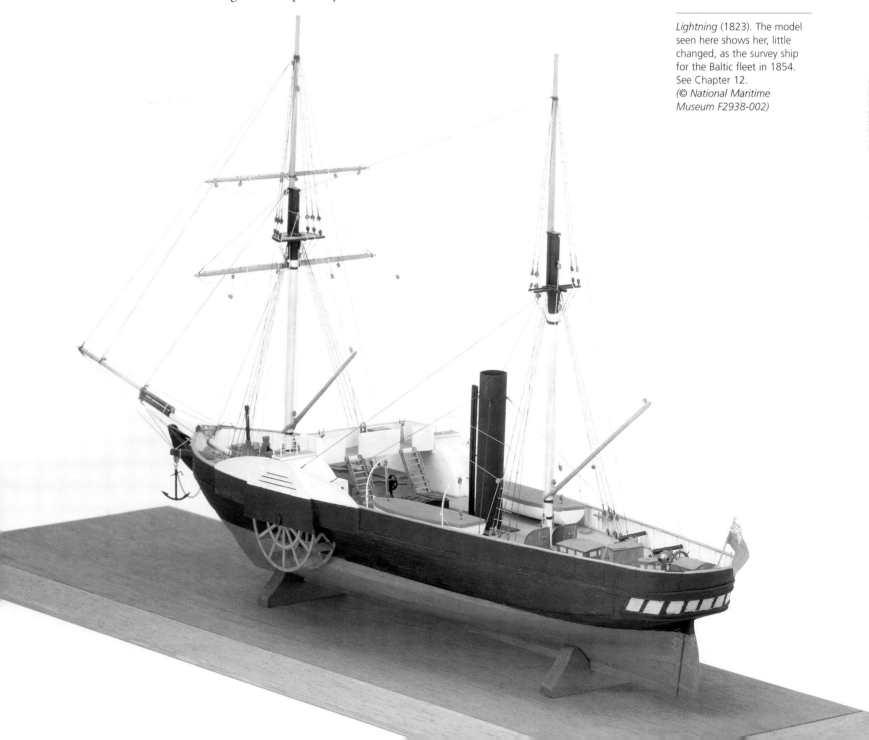

Lightning (1823). The model seen here shows her, little changed, as the survey ship for the Baltic fleet in 1854. See Chapter 12.
(© National Maritime Museum F2938-002)

A 'motion drawing' of the side-lever engine of the *Lightning* (1823). The side-lever is the rocking arm, in black, at the bottom of the drawing. (© *National Maritime Museum L2542-002*)

lever, with 35½in bore and 42in stroke costing £5,050. Steam at 4lb/sq in drove a pair of wheels 14ft in diameter. Fuel consumption was about 10cwt/hr.

The *Comet* was used as a yard craft on the Thames until 1831, apart from escorting the Royal Yacht in 1827. Later (1842) she was employed as a survey vessel and in 1854 became a tug at Portsmouth, finally being broken up in 1868. She was not listed as HMS until 1831 but, after all, *Comet* was built and served as a harbour tug. A light armament was usually carried and some of those carried were as follows: two 6pdr; two 18pdr; four 9pdr.

By 1837 it was said that she 'laboured in a heavy sea in consequence of her being deeper in the water than was intended at first by her constructor'.[11] Her draught was 8ft 9in forward, 9ft 0in aft.

Two slightly larger steamers of Lang's design were built in 1823, *Lightning* and *Meteor*. *Lightning* accompanied the expedition to Algiers in 1824, perhaps the first operational voyage of a Royal Navy steamship and, towards the end of a long life, was used as a survey vessel in the Baltic fleet in 1854.

Developments overseas

There were a number of other steamships whose design or operations affected the attitude of the Royal Navy towards steamships in these early years. In May/June 1819 there was the first Atlantic crossing by a steamship, the *Savannah*, though since she used her engines for a mere eighty-five hours of the voyage of twenty-seven and a half days, her significance may not have been apparent.

In 1821, Lord Cochrane ordered a warship, the *Rising Star*, from Brent of Rotherhithe for use in support of Chilean independence. She had a two-cylinder Maudslay engine operating a paddle shaft through bell cranks. The wheels were contained within a watertight casing in the hold, open at the bottom and, with steam at 2–3lb/sq in, she reached 5–6 knots on the Thames. She arrived too late for the war but Cochrane's activities were always of public interest and her performance was noticed favourably.[12]

During 1824–5 the steamer *Diana* (60NHP) of the East India Company proved invaluable as a transport during the First Burmese War, working on the fast-flowing waters of the Irrawaddy. The officers of RN ships in company were much impressed. In August 1825 the steamship *Enterprize* left England for India under the command of an RN lieutenant, Johnston, reaching Calcutta on 7 December.[13] Her voyage was troubled and, because of heavy fuel consumption, considerable use was made of sail (sixty-four days under steam, out of 113), but she was seen as a success and was purchased by the East India Company. Her voyage may well be compared with the pioneer aircraft flights of almost exactly a century later, of no direct value but of immense potential.

In July 1824 Captain Frank Hastings RN persuaded

service at Holyhead in May 1821. By the end of the year both ships had made over 140 crossings of the Irish Sea with an average passage time of seven and a half hours (best six hours, worst sixteen hours). This was a faster and more reliable service than could be maintained by a sailing ship.

Lightning had two cabins, one with six berths for ladies and one for fourteen men. On 12 August 1821, King George IV was due to sail to Ireland, but because there was no wind that day, he transferred to the *Lightning* (Captain Skinner) for the voyage. To mark the first royal steamship voyage, the ship was renamed *Royal Sovereign King George IV*, soon shortened to *Royal Sovereign* and then to *Sovereign*. In 1837 the Post Office packets were taken over by the Admiralty and her name was changed again, to *Monkey*. These renamings and confusion with a later naval steamship, also called *Lightning*, have led to incorrect statements that she was the first steamship built for the Admiralty.

Later in 1821 the Admiralty hired the *Tartar* of 180 tons for a few voyages across the Irish Sea, but by then their own plans were well advanced for a steamship to act as a tug and tender. The design was put in the hands of Oliver Lang, the master shipwright of Woolwich Dockyard, the Surveyor, Seppings, maintaining a keen interest in the project. The steamship was laid down at Deptford on 21 November 1821 and launched as the *Comet* on 23 May the following year.

Comet was 115ft long, with a knee bow and a square stern, very similar to the contemporary brig sloops. A single, very tall funnel stood amidships with a waste steampipe well abaft it and she was rigged as a two-masted schooner. Her paddles worked in circular boxes, without sponsons. The engine was a two-cylinder, side

11. PRO Adm 95/87.

12. Smith, op cit.

13. Smith, op cit; Rowland, op cit.

14. D Dakins, 'Lord Cochrane's Greek Steam Fleet', *Mariner's Mirror*, vol 39 (1953).

the Greeks, who were fighting to free their country from Turkish rule, to buy two, later three, steam warships. The dubious financial arrangements are described by Dakins but eventually the first ship was ordered from Brent with engines by Galloway – whose son was in Egyptian pay![14] The ship was named *Perseverance*, renamed *Karteria* on arrival in Greece, and ran trials on 18 May 1826 which were moderately successful.

By then two other steamers, *Enterprize* and *Irresistible*, were nearing completion and Lord Cochrane, who was to command the squadron, left for Greece. *Perseverance* left Deptford on 26 May 1826, unarmed to comply with the law. Her four 68pdrs had been sent via the USA, where they were temporarily mislaid, to join her in Greece. *Enterprize* left the Thames in April 1827, breaking down three times in the Channel and finally bursting a boiler, arriving in Plymouth under tow. She was repaired and arrived in Greece in September to be renamed *Epicheiresis*. Her equally unsatisfactory sister, *Hermes*, only arrived in September 1828.

By this time *Karteria*, under the command of Hastings, had established a legendary reputation as a fighting ship. As in all good legends, it is likely that her performance was exaggerated. During 1827 she claimed to have captured or destroyed some twenty-four small Turkish vessels, carried out a few bombardments and acted as a transport. Hastings was a great believer in red-hot shot and had a special furnace for heating them. The

claim that she fired 18,000 rounds – twelve per gun per day – must be seen as 'legendary'. Hastings used her paddles to turn her at rest, perhaps with one wheel disconnected, using each gun in turn against the victim. *Karteria*'s machinery was never very satisfactory; she, too, burst a boiler before arrival, the 'two 42NHP' cylinders were inadequate for her 400 tons (RN practice was 3.7–4 tons per NHP) and the paddles were heavy with insufficient immersion. Under sail, she was slow but satisfactory.

During the Missolonghi campaign, Hastings was mortally wounded in the attack on Fort Anatolico,

The pioneering steamship *Enterprize* arriving off Calcutta on 7 December 1827, 113 days out from Britain. (*© National Maritime Museum PU6662*)

Diana (left foreground). Purchased by the East India Company for the war in Burma in 1824, she was probably the first steamship to go into action. (*© National Maritime Museum D3594*)

Karteria. Built in England, her exploits in the Greek War of Independence in 1827, commanded by Captain Hastings, helped to convince the RN of the value of steam fighting ships. (© *National Maritime Museum PW8052*)

dying on 1 June 1828. Under other captains, *Karteria* and her sisters achieved very little. *Karteria* was blown up in 1831 during the Greek civil war.

The Greek War of Independence had been followed with great interest and sympathy in England, and the Mediterranean fleet had closely observed the events of the war. *Karteria* had performed well in front of a critical and well-informed naval audience, many of whom had now become convinced of the value of steamships.

Another notable event was the first crossing of the Atlantic by a steam warship, the Dutch *Curacoa*. She was built at Dover in 1826 and later purchased by the Dutch, making three round-trips to Dutch Guyana between 1827 and 1829, taking about a month on each voyage.

Progress in the Royal Navy

The next group of six ships was started in 1824 to Lang's design, still loosely derived from the sailing brig sloops. They were conceived as auxiliaries with two brass 6pdrs, but were brought onto the Navy List in 1828 with a lieutenant in command. Their armament was later much increased; *Alban*, when lengthened in 1839, received a 32pdr/56cwt pivot and two 32pdr/25cwt, making her a powerful fighting ship.

Originally, they were rigged as two-masted schooners but *Alban*, at least, was re-rigged as a brigantine. For long voyages under sail, the lower six paddle boards (or floats) on each side were unbolted and removed so that they would not drag in the water. This was a hazardous job in any conditions, but one almost impossible to carry out in bad weather. In consequence, a ship caught suddenly in bad weather or on a lee shore could be in difficulty, unable to use steam.

Coal consumption was heavy and they could only carry enough for four days' steaming in their bunkers, together with about 4 tons on deck. When *Alban* crossed from Barbados to Falmouth in July 1834 she took fifty-one days, of which only seven were under steam. Another similar ship was laid down in 1827, after which there was a pause in the construction of steam warships.

This lull was probably due to lack of money rather than lack of interest; the graph in Chapter 3 shows how small was the Navy Vote at that time. The Post Office were building steam packets steadily, and probably with

Alban (1824). Typical of Lang's early paddle steamer designs based on brig sloops.

Admiralty encouragement. The story, widely repeated, that Lord Melville wrote to the Colonial Office in 1827 discouraging the use of steamships for a mail service to Corfu and Malta seems to be a later fabrication.[15] It is inherently improbable, since Lord Melville had already ordered a considerable number of steamers for the Royal Navy, and because the Post Office, with or without Admiralty blessing, had a large and growing fleet of steamers.

Table 5.2 Post Office Packets

Year	Number	Total built	Year	Number	Total built
1821	5	5	1832	–	29
1822	1	6	1833	1	30
1823	2	8	1834	1	31
1824	3	11	1837	3	34
1825	3	14	1838	2	36
1826	4	18	1840	2	38
1827	6	24	1844	1	39
1828	–	24	1845	2	41
1829	1	25	1846	1	42
1830	–	25	1847	4	46
1831	4	29	1848	2	48

From G A Osbon, unpublished notes

There was also support from other quarters. Joseph Hume told the House of Commons on 21 February 1825, 'The discovery of steam navigation has altered the nature of maritime warfare in narrow seas altogether,' and there were pamphlets published on steam warships by Rear Admiral J Ross and Captain William Bowles. It is also true that there was some opposition and even more dislike of the steamship, but such opposition must not be exaggerated since the steamship programme made steady progress.

As a gesture towards economy, the Board decided in 1826 to purchase two existing steamers, *George IV* and *Duke of York*, for the Corfu–Malta service, but funds only became available in 1830. Renamed *Hermes* and *Messenger*, they proved a false economy, being discarded after a brief service career. The Corfu service was opened by *Meteor* sailing from Falmouth on 5 February 1830. Sailing ships had taken three months for the round trip, but the steamers were able to cut the time to about one month. The Admiralty continued to operate the mail service until 1837, when it was passed to the Peninsular & Oriental Steam Navigation Company (P&O).

Inspired by Paixhans' writings, and perhaps aware of developments across the Channel, the French had begun to consider steam warships in 1824, but they only completed the first effective one, *Sphinx*, in 1829.

The machinery weighed 831kg/NHP and burnt about 6kg/NHP/hr. French industry was unable to

Table 5.3 *Sphinx*

Tonnage	777
Dimensions	152.2ft x 25.9ft x 10.9ft
Guns	11 (small)
Sail area	8,964sq ft
Machinery	160NHP by Forrester, Liverpool
Speed	7 knots approx

15. P W Brock and B Greenhill, *Steam and Sail*, Newton Abbot (1973).

Ariel. The Post Office packet *Arrow* of 1822, acquired by the RN in 1837 and renamed. (© *National Maritime Museum BHC3204*)

provide suitable machinery and her engines were built in England. She and other early French ships were lightly armed, seen as very vulnerable, and mainly of use for towing sailing ships in a calm.[16] She and six similar ships accompanied the expedition to Algiers in 1830.

The Tory government resigned in November 1830 and Lord Melville was replaced by Sir James Graham. The new Board continued to build small numbers of steamers, generally similar to earlier ships. It is likely that the first two, *Flamer* and *Firebrand*, ordered in January 1831, were planned under the previous administration. Though to Lang's familiar design, they were built by commercial yards in Limehouse. *Flamer* was wrecked off West Africa in 1850, one of the only losses of early steamships.

Firebrand was used by the Board to tour the Royal Dockyards in 1835 and in 1842 became the Admiralty Yacht. As such, she was lengthened, given two funnels and three masts and was renamed *Black Eagle* in honour of the Prussian royal family who frequently cruised in her. *Firebrand* was re-engined (machinery ex-*Columbia*) in 1832, retaining her set of Morgan's feathering wheels. In 1843 she received the first set of Penn oscillating engines, which occupied the same space and weight as the original engines but with double the nominal power. At the same time, her simple flue boilers were replaced by tubular boilers with 2,250 brass tubes of 2in diameter, ⅛in wall thickness and 5ft 1in long. Later still, in 1856 she was used to try J Wethered's superheater, in which part of the steam was heated to 500–600°F before being mixed with wet steam.

Dee, laid down as a sailing ship in 1828, was the largest of the group and, at £27,000, the most expensive. In later years she was able to carry two long 32pdrs, as well as two shorter guns of that calibre. One of her captains reported that she 'was very slow and steers very wild, being trimmed by the stern. Using after coals first improves her. She rolls very deep and always uneasy. Cannot carry quarter boats in a moderate beam wind'.[17]

The Science Museum has a very fine model of her Maudslay engines, shown here. Contemporary usage was that one cylinder was an engine; two-cylinder machinery was called 'engines' (plural). Like all the early steamships, she had side lever engines, virtually the classic beam engine with the beam split longitudinally and the two half-beams dropped down beside the cylinders. The piston worked the split beams through levers at the side; hence 'side lever' engine. Two-cylinder machinery was necessary, since a single piston might stop at dead centre and be impossible to start.

Dee's 200NHP engines had cylinders of 54in diameter and 5ft stroke and, with steam supplied from tubular boilers at 3½lb/sq in, developed 272ihp. These engines turned wheels 20ft in diameter at 18rpm, giving a speed of 8 knots.

The transitional ships

The next group of ships (Table 5.4) were much more warlike in intent, and the Board decided to build four competitive designs from the surveyor (Seppings) and three master shipwrights.

Fincham's comments on these four ships may be applied to all the early steam warships:

> It is no disparagement of the talents of their respective constructors to say that these vessels showed in their imperfections which were almost necessary to a time when the conditions of excellence in steam vessels were only in the course of development; at the same time it is fair and just to say that they were all useful vessels, and they have been durable and permanent in their usefulness.[18]

Otway says that *Rhadamanthus*, and possibly *Medea*, reflect credit on their designers. In general, they were 'sylph-like' ships, beautiful to look at, with sharp bows and fine in calm weather.[19] *Rhadamanthus* was in a class of her own and well worth imitating. In view of Otway's flattering remarks, it is a little surprising that *Rhadamanthus* was the first to be reduced to second-line duties.

In 1831 the French army moved into Belgium to protect it from the Dutch, who had refused to withdraw from Antwerp. The Royal Navy blockaded the Dutch ports in support of the French operation during 1832, using three liners and twelve other ships, including the steamers *Rhadamanthus* and *Dee*. In one month alone, the force detained commerce worth £1 million. A truce was agreed in May 1833, and peace was signed in June.

16. Genie Maritime Bicentenary book, Paris.

17. PRO Adm 95/87.

18. Fincham, op cit.

19. R Otway, *An Elementary Treatise on Steam*, London (1834).

20. Smith, op cit.

21 W H Henderson, Parliamentary Papers, 1847.

The side lever engines of *Dee* (1832). Note the 'Gothic' framework, introduced by Marc Brunel. This Science Museum model was probably made by Henry Maudslay. *(Science Museum)*

Table 5.4 **The Transitional Ships**

Ship	Designer	Yard	Laid down	Tonnage	NHP
Rhadamanthus	Roberts	Devonport	1831	813	220
Medea	Lang	Woolwich	1832	835	220
Salamander	Seaton	Sheerness	1831	813	220
Phoenix	Seppings	Chatham	1831	802	260

The two steamers had been particularly useful in the narrow channels of the Dutch estuaries with their fast tidal currents.

Steamers were called on again during the unrest in the south of Ireland in 1831. Here, too, the ability of a steamship to arrive at a prearranged time, regardless of wind or tide, made them invaluable.

Rhadamanthus was the first British steamship, naval or commercial, to cross the Atlantic. She left Plymouth on 21 April 1833 and steamed across the Bay of Biscay. Her engines were stopped, the lower paddle boards were removed and she sailed the rest of the way to Madeira where she took on another 320 tons of coal.[20] Sailing again on 30 April, she reached Barbados on 17 May, having covered the 2,500 miles at an average speed of 6.1 knots. Steam was used intermittently, boards being removed when conditions were favourable for sailing. Her log makes frequent mention of extra rum being issued to engineers, stokers and trimmers in recognition of their hard work.

Captain W H Henderson was very pleased with her: 'An excellent sea-boat, and a very serviceable vessel', though he thought *Salamander* was not very strong.[21] Otway thought *Rhadamanthus* was 'as sharp in the bows as the bill of a snipe'. She remained in service as an armed transport until 1864.

Medea, too, went to the West Indies, setting a notable record of reliability. From February 1834 until October 1837 no repairs were carried out, other than by her own staff. Towing was still a major task for steamships, and

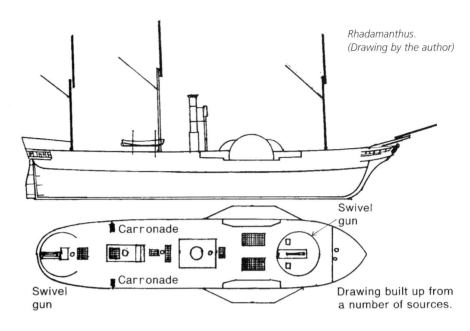

Rhadamanthus.
(Drawing by the author)

Swivel gun

Carronade

Carronade

Swivel gun

Drawing built up from a number of sources.

Rhadamanthus. The first British steamship to cross the Atlantic, though much of the voyage was under sail. *(© National Maritime Museum L2456-003)*

Firefly, an early steamer of 1832, enjoyed a long life and is seen here in action during the Crimean War on 8 August 1855. (© *National Maritime Museum neg 8089*)

22. PRO 95/88.

23. O Lang, *Improvements in Naval Architecture for which I have been Responsible.*

Medea showed her ability while in the Mediterranean in January 1835. The fleet was becalmed ten miles off Malta and *Medea* towed five liners into harbour, one after the other. Some steamship officers saw this as a menial task, while others rejoiced in the consistent power of steam.

Four more steamers were built in 1833–4 (*Falcon, Blazer, Tartarus* and *Vulcan*). Also in 1834, *Hermes* was started, the first steamship designed by the new Surveyor, Symonds. She was never a very satisfactory vessel, as Symonds persisted in his high rise of floor, making the installation of machinery very difficult. In 1840 it was said of her by her captain, Blount, that she was 'a good sea-boat and behaves well under canvas but needs engines of additional power'.[22] That year she was docked at Chatham and lengthened by 20ft. Lang says he lengthened the bow to bring it up, there being too much after-body.[23] Her old engines were removed and given to *Spitfire*, while *Hermes* received a set of Maudslay Siamese engines which, though of the same NHP as the earlier engines, were much more powerful. They drove 19ft wheels at 19rpm giving a speed of 8.5 knots. After lengthening, she was hard to steer, the paddles being too far aft. *Hermes* was originally a brig, but as with most of the early steamers she was given a mizzen later.

Her original armament was a token pair of 9pdrs but by 1842 she carried two 8in and four 32pdrs/25cwt. In 1862 the 8in were replaced by 40pdr Armstrong breech loaders (BL). Despite her faults, *Hermes* formed the basis

for several later classes. During 1835–8 three ships were built to the original design and four more followed in 1839–40. Four longer ships of the *Hydra* class were approved in 1837. Though often described as derived from the lengthened *Hermes*, their design predates this alteration. All these vessels were relatively cheap.

Table 5.5 **Cost of Steamships**

Volcano	£25,000
Tartarus	£11,618 hull only, £20,324 ready for sea
Acheron	£7,445 machinery and paddles only

When Graham left the Admiralty, he told his successor, Lord Auckland, to lay down six *Medea*s and four *Gladiator*s (eleven laid down in 1831–4). Auckland, in turn, warned his successor, Earl de Grey, that there would be a great demand for steamers in the event of war, but there were still problems to be overcome. Some were underpowered, in others the engines left little space for guns and crew, the machinery was lacking in uniformity and was expensive to maintain and repair. Auckland decided that steamship building should continue at a slow pace while commercial developments were studied.

There were also seven steamers built or purchased for use on the Canadian lakes. While not significant in the history of design, they added further to the Navy's experience in steam operation.

State of the art

By 1837, nearly thirty steamships had been built for the Royal Navy, together with a number of others purchased for minor duties.

Table 5.6 **Steamship Building to 1837**

Date	Cumulative total	Date	Cumulative total
1822	1	1830	11
1823	2	1831	14
1824	3	1832	19
1825	4	1833	20
1826	5	1834	25
1827	8	1835	27
1828	8	1836	28
1829	9	1837	29

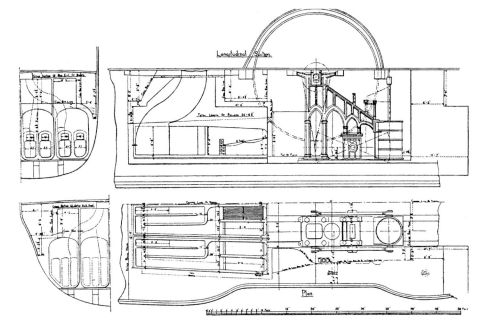

Machinery of *Hecla* and *Hecate* showing the relative positions of paddle shaft, engine and boilers.

Initially, they were built as auxiliaries, tugs, despatch vessels, survey vessels, etc, but from the first they carried a light armament and became involved in police operations. By 1828 the first vessels appeared in the Navy List as HM Steam Vessels. Their value was increasingly appreciated by commanders-in-chief; for example, in 1833 Admiral Malcolm, Mediterranean fleet, wrote that a large steamer 'is more useful to him than another 74'.

Because of their utility, steamships were generally kept in commission at a time when a large part of the fleet was laid up in ordinary.

With money for warship-building so scarce and fears that rapidly changing technology would quickly render current ships out of date, the modest building programme appears quite rational. There were, of course, many more steam merchant ships, though the ratio of steam to sail seems about the same as in the Royal Navy.

In 1840, the sailing ship was still predominant, with 28,138 ships of 3,215,731 tons in commercial service manned by 261,194 sailors. Of the commercial steamships in 1830, less than eighty were over 200 tons

Hecate aground in 1861. An unusual view of the deck of an early paddle warship. (© *National Maritime Museum PX9919*)

and only seventy had engines of more than 100NHP. The largest was the *Shannon* of 513 tons and 230NHP, built in 1826.

Table 5.7 **Steamship Usage**

Date	In ordinary	In commission
1828	3	4
1829	3	4
1830	5	3
1831	2	8
1832	1	13
1833	–	19
1834	1	17
1835	3	20
1836	5	18
1837	2	22
1838	7	21 + 30 mail packets

Note: numbers do not agree precisely with the previous table due to inclusion of different auxiliaries.

Not much attention was paid to the protection of the growing steam trade, but some thought was given to the use of commercial steamships as auxiliary cruisers. Byam Martin, Comptroller, wrote to Lord Melville in 1830 that 'with such means [merchant ships] within reach, it was, perhaps, prudent and economical not to incur great expense in forming an expensive establishment of such vessels, while the machinery and its application are subject to continual experiment with the view to improvement'.[24]

Table 5.8 **Commercial Steamships**

	Merchant ships		Royal Navy	
Date	Number steam	Tonnage	Number steam	Tonnage
1830	315	23,444	7	2,796
1835	538	60,520	14	7,381
1840	824	95,807	45	19,796
Average tonnage		116		428

The only countries, other than Britain, that built substantial numbers of steam warships during this period were France and the USA. France listed mail packets as warships from the earliest days and hence her numbers were impressive, though it would seem that individual ships were significantly inferior to those of the RN. The US Navy successfully operated the *Seagull* against pirates in the West Indies in the early 1820s.

The arrangement of all these early steamships was generally similar, even though they grew in size from *Comet*'s 238 tons and 115ft length to *Medea*'s 835 tons

and 179ft. The arrangement of *Porcupine*, shown here, was generally typical, though it was uncommon to put the two boilers at each end of the machinery. All had the hull painted black and the funnel was usually black, too.

The machinery took up the middle third of the vessel with a crew of about sixty men berthed forward and the three officers aft. This is sometimes referred to, scurrilously, as the 'democratic' system, half the ship for the men and half for the officers! They were strongly built ships with a double layer of planking each between 4in and 7in thick. Iron diagonal riders were used extensively to maintain their form and, in consequence, they lasted well with an average life of over thirty years, two ships achieving their half century. In view of the weight and heavy vibration of early steam engines, this long life was a great tribute to their designers, particularly Oliver Lang, and to their builders. The armament was carried in the open on the upper deck, which facilitated frequent changes. A well-documented example is that of *Hermes*, which was fairly typical.

Table 5.9 *Hermes* **Armament Changes**

1842	Two 9pdr
1843	One 8in, two 32pdr
Late 1840s	Two 8in, two 32pdr carronades
1856	Two 8in, four 32pdr/25cwt
1862	Two 40pdr RBL (rifled breech loader), four 32pdr/25cwt

Since they were often used for intervention in coastal waters during the wars and insurrections of the period, these steamers often carried landing parties. From about 1830 they carried large boats, capable of holding a hundred men, upside down over their paddle boxes; this scheme was probably devised by Captain Smith, though there are other claimants. The earliest ships had semi-circular paddle boxes, but quite soon substantial sponsons were added, which were used to contain the galley, meat and provision stores and the heads.

Most were originally given two masts and rigged as brigs, but a mizzen was added later and this rig was standardised in 1843. The length of the machinery made it difficult to find strong support for two masts in suitable places to give a balanced sail plan, and hence the mizzen was added to improve handling under sail. It has been suggested that a three-masted rig would cause less drag under steam than would two taller masts. Most captains were happy with the handling of their ship; *Blazer* claimed 6.4 knots on the wind and 7.6 knots before the wind.[25]

The heavy fuel consumption made sails essential for long voyages. The figures in Table 5.10 give some idea of what could be expected.

In home waters coal cost about five shillings a ton, but overseas, transport costs could quadruple that figure, and coal was only available at all in a limited number of places. Captains were anxious not to be short of fuel when it was needed and for this reason, as well as parsi-

24. Letter to Lord Melville, 1830. *Letters and papers of the Admiral of the Fleet Sir Thomas Byan Martin*, Navy Records Society, London (1901).
25. PRO Adm 95/87.
26. PRO Adm 92/7.

Porcupine lower deck plan. (Drawing by the author)

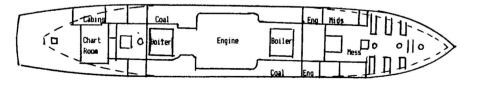

HER MAJESTY'S STEAM SHIP, PHŒNIX.   *Plate 28*

4 points from the Wind

5 ½ points from the Wind

Head to the Wind

Before the Wind

Sailing a paddle warship (*Phoenix*). Note that the topmasts are lowered when steaming into the wind. (© *National Maritime Museum PW8057*)

mony, they used sail quite often, though they were not in this era reluctant to steam when needed. Table 5.11 shows how *Black Eagle* used her engines in the 1840s; in the light of her special duties, however, these figures may not be typical.

Machinery and its coal were both heavy and bulky. In *Porcupine*, 37 per cent of the length and in

Table 5.10 **Typical Coal Consumption**[26]

Ship	Phoenix	Rhadamanthus	Firefly	Tartarus
Bushels/hr	20–22	20–22	17	13
Tons of coal for 10 days	188	188	110	122

Note: A bushel was actually a measure of volume and seems to have corresponded to about 1 cwt (112lb).

Table 5.11 **Black Eagle – Engine Usage**[27]

Year	Miles steamed	Coal burnt (tons)	Miles per ton	Days under repair
1843	2,104	334	6.3	5
1844	5,402	629	8.6	–
1845	6,852	826	8.3	24
1846	2,898	430	6.7	78
1847	3,537	558	6.3	68

Table 5.12 **Weights of *Medea*'s Machinery and Fuel**[28]

	Tons
Engines	165
Boilers	35
Water in boilers	45
Coal	320
Total	565

Rhadamanthus 42 per cent were devoted to power. Table 5.12 gives a weight breakdown for *Medea*'s 220NHP Maudslay engine.

The side lever engines were easily maintained, reliable but very inefficient. Steam was supplied at 3–5lb/sq in to force the piston down and was exhausted from the cylinder before it could expand, wasting much of its thermal energy.

The boilers were rectangular iron boxes full of sea water with a furnace at one or both ends. Rectangular flues, 18in wide, led the hot gases through the boiler to the funnel, which was tall to give a good draught. In 1842 *Driver* had three boilers, each 26ft long, 9ft wide and 12ft 6in high. Together, they weighed 40 tons and contained 50 tons of water. Each boiler had three furnaces, 7ft 8in long, 2ft 6in wide with 18in flues, 5in apart. From the furnace to the top of the funnel was 70ft.

Driver's boilers were of wrought iron but some ships had copper boilers, on what seemed good economic grounds. *Volcano*'s copper boilers cost £5,000, but were expected to last nine years and still be worth £3,000 as scrap. Iron boilers would have cost £1,500 and only lasted three years before they were so corroded that they would have to be replaced and there was no scrap value. Copper boilers were not used extensively as several suffered from unexpectedly early corrosion; the metallurgy of copper-based alloys is complex and small impurities could have led to these early failures. During the late 1840s the rising price of copper made its use uneconomic.

Routine maintenance tasks were demanding and unpleasant. After 144 hours' steaming, the flues had to be cleaned of a thick deposit of soot. The salinity of the brine in the boiler had to be checked frequently, usually

Black Eagle, so named because of her frequent use as a yacht by Queen Victoria's Prussian relatives. (© *National Maritime Museum PY8662)*

by measuring its boiling point. If over 215°F (102°C) there would be serious danger of incrustation. Every two hours the boiler would be blown down – the bottom layer of water, being the most salty, was discharged into the sea. This was a somewhat hazardous procedure until John Kingston, of Woolwich Dockyard, devised in 1837 a valve which bears his name to this day. He also invented a special safety spanner which could not be taken off the blow-down cock when it was open.

The boiler was usually topped up using the discharge from the air pump with gravity feed from a tank on the upper deck. Sometimes there was an annular tank around the base of the funnel to give some preheat to the feed water. Smith gives some fascinating insights into the operation of this early machinery.[29]

As early as 1837 an attempt was made to use a condenser (Hall's) but it did not work well 'owing to the engineer having misunderstood it'.[30] In fact, the poor engineer may not have been to blame; it was at least another thirty years before condensers became a normal equipment and even in the First World War 'condenseritis' was a prime cause of trouble. Leaking joints and blocked pipes were all too common.

The ship was driven by paddle wheels some 20ft in diameter and 6ft wide, with about twenty boards or floats, each 2ft 10in deep, spaced round the circumference. The efficiency varied considerably with the immersion and in later vessels it was possible to draw the boards in towards the centre when running at deep draught or even further in, clear of the water, for sailing. In about 1860 Howard Douglas gave the following guideline for the dimensions of paddle wheels based on contemporary practice:

– Dip, the immersion of the paddle, should equal the depth of the board, ie the upper edge of the bottom board should be awash.
– Diameter should be four and a half times the stroke of the piston; the inner edge of the board should move at the speed of the ship.
– The length of the board should be one-third of the diameter.[31]

At best, the paddle wheel was inefficient compared with the screw propeller, a major loss of power occurring as each blade slapped the water as it entered. The cycloidal wheel was an early attempt to reduce these impact losses; invented by Field in 1833 it was rediscovered in 1835 by Elijah Galloway. Each float was split into several narrow strips set stepwise in advance of each other towards the rim, along a cycloidal curve. Brunel used such wheels in the *Great Western*, as did a few warships. In 1839 *Alecto* had her cycloidal wheels replaced by a common one because the floats kept falling off.[32]

The feathering wheel was a more elaborate and, overall, a more successful scheme. It was first patented by Galloway in 1829, but little used until William Morgan (1st SNA) purchased the patent in 1830 and improved

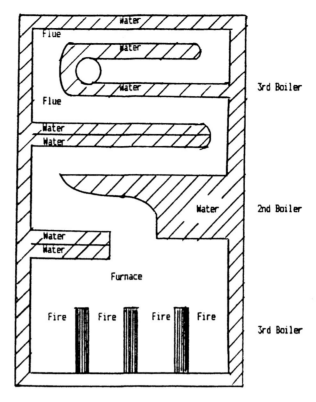

Interior of a square boiler. *(Drawing by the author)*

on it. Each float turned on a central spindle under the action of a linkage connecting it to a crank incorporated within the wheel. A pair of feathering wheels were fitted to the *Confiance* in 1831 and she was then tried against her sister, the *Echo*. It was claimed that the Morgan wheel gave an increase in speed of 28 per cent in calm water and 55 per cent in rough seas.[33] Increases of this order are not physically possible due to improvements in the action of the wheel and, if the figures are correct, there must have been some other cause. The feathering wheel was used only occasionally on warships since it was thought that its complicated linkage would be vulnerable to battle damage and the simpler, though less efficient ,'common' wheel was preferred.

Since the nineteenth-century Admiralty did not have today's passion for 'policy' documents, it is only possible to deduce their attitude to steamships from their actions: a slow but steady building programme and an

27. Select Committee 1848.
28. Smith, op cit.
29. Smith, op cit.
30. PRO Adm 95/88.
31. H Douglas, *Naval Gunnery*, London (1855).
32. PRO Adm 95/87.
33. G L Overton, *Marine Engineering, History and Development*, Science Museum, London (1935).

Interior view of a cylindrical boiler. *(Drawing by the author)*

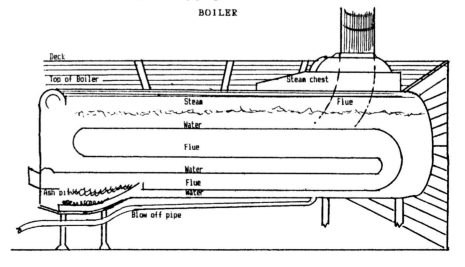

Morgan's feathering paddle wheel, similar to that fitted to *Confiance* in 1831. It was an improvement on Galloway's earlier design, having more floats, using central pivots for the floats and having more cross bracing, important because only the side nearest the ship was driven. This drawing was for the *Gulnare*, built in Britain in 1834, the Sardinian Navy's first steamer. *(© National Maritime Museum PZ5068)*

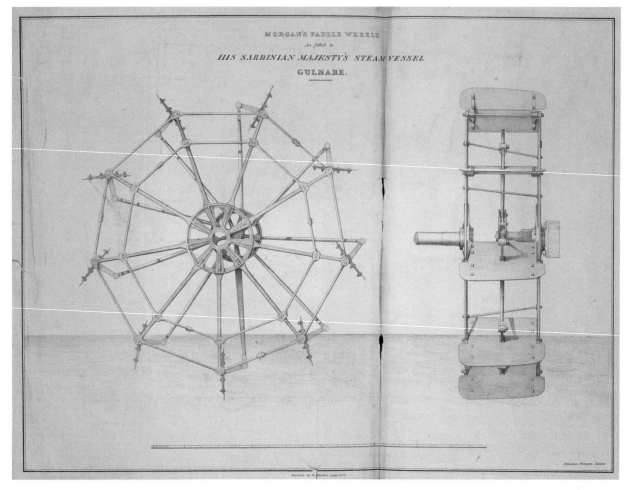

Maudslay twin-cylinder oscillating engines, in which the cylinders pivoted on trunnions at the base, allowing the pistons to act directly on the crankshaft and producing a compact arrangement. Originally introduced about 1827, the system fell from favour until revived in an improved form by Penn in 1838. *(© National Maritime Museum L0360-001)*

active encouragement of new technology. Admirals at sea were keen to have more steamships and it is clear that many of the prejudiced statements so often quoted were either fabricated or the utterances of officers who had not been to sea since the end of the Napoleonic war.

There was a small but growing number of real enthusiasts. Cooper Key and William Hall, both future admirals, studied steam propulsion. In 1834 Commander Otway published *An Elementary Treatise on Steam*, mainly for the benefit of seamen officers who wanted to understand the new power which drove their ships.[34] Indeed, he made it clear that it was as much the duty of the officer to understand his engine as to understand his guns. Captain James Ross also wrote a book on steam in 1834, amongst others, and there must have been many more who read their books.

The engineer and his assistant were rated as warrant officers, a rank of considerable status, and avoiding the risk of social conflict in the wardroom.[35] Overall, there are strong indications that stories of prejudice against steam and engineers in this period are much exaggerated.

There was a strange incident off Portugal which seemed to show the engineers in a bad light. Sir Charles Napier was commanding the fleet of the Liberal side in the Portuguese civil war and intended to use his steamers to tow the sailing ships into action against the Miguelist faction off St Vincent. It is believed that his engineers refused to fight and went on strike. A different story was given to the Select Committee of 1847 by C Wye Williams, of the Dublin Steam Packet Company, a progressive shipowner.[36] He said that Napier's steamships were chartered from his company and the contract forbade the use of the ships in battle and hence the engineers were merely fulfilling their obligations in refusing battle! This story, too, has been denied, but in various versions it contributed to some suspicion of engineers.

It is interesting to see to what an extent steam warship building was concentrated on the Thames (see Table 5.13).

Table 5.13 **Early Steamship Building**

Shipbuilder	Number	Engine builder	Number
Deptford Dy	4	Maudslay	9
Woolwich Dy	11	Boulton & Watt	10
Sheerness Dy	3	Butterly	3
Thames-		Seaward & Capel	3
Commercial	2	Scott, Sinclair	2
Chatham Dy	4	Morgan	1
Pembroke Dy	1	Miller & Randle	1
Devonport Dy	1		
Portsmouth Dy	1		

(See map of Thames yards in Chapter 12)

There was a good deal of lobbying in Parliament to get a bigger share of this work for the Clyde and though many allegations were made of corruption, none was proved. The Admiralty defence was that these yards were the best, particularly on the engine side.[37]

The Board recognised the need to maintain and support the growing fleet of steamships. In May 1835 Mr Ewart was appointed chief engineer and inspector of machinery, with a salary equal to that of a master shipwright. The following year, the Steam Factory at Woolwich was opened to refit the engines and boilers of the steam fleet. There was soon plenty of work for the factory; a typical weekly report (1846) shows twelve ships in hand for work such as fitting machinery to new construction, new boilers, repairs to flues, etc. There were also eight ships laid up and three more awaiting sale.[38] In store there were seven sets of reconstructed engines, removed from their original ships, and nine new engines, together with five sets of boilers. 'Garages' were not popular, then as now, and Otway commented that many ships went in with a defect, expecting to be out in forty-eight hours, but only leaving after a six-month rebuild. Woolwich was to nurture a number of outstanding engineers and generally seems to have been a most effective facility. The Admiralty was well placed to take the next step forward in the development of the steam warship.

A cycloidal paddle wheel, invented by Field in 1835 and reinvented by Galloway in 1837. This model is similar to that used by Maudslay for the SS *Great Britain*. (Science Museum)

34. Ibid.

35. N A M Rodger, *The Wooden World*, London (1986).

36. Select Committee 1847, evidence by J Edye.

37. R A Buchanan and H W Doughty, 'The choice of steam engine manufacturer by the British Admiralty 1822–1852', *Mariner's Mirror*, London; A Gordon, *Marine Steam Engines of the Royal Navy*, Glasgow (1843).

38. PRO 7 Jul 1846. Weekly report from the steam factory.

Six | Paddle Fighting Ships

IT IS CONVENIENT TO CONSIDER the ships already described as belonging to an experimental age and the *Gorgon* as opening a new era. In fact, the distinction was less clear-cut, with another thirteen small paddlers generally similar to the earlier ships being built by 1845.

Gorgon was conceived by Symonds towards the end of 1836 as a slightly enlarged *Medea* with machinery of 220NHP and 200 tons of coal. As usual, the engine builder was given a space and a budget weight and left to do his best. Seaward and Capel were able to offer engines of 350NHP with coal in proportion (380 tons) in the same weight and space limits. This offer was accepted, making *Gorgon* a much more powerful vessel and, with a heavy armament, the first true fighting steamship.[1]

The builder's model of the engines in the Science Museum shows how they worked.[2] There were two cylinders (64in diameter x 5ft 6in stroke) with the piston rods guided by a parallel linkage, the other end of which drove the air pump. The pistons drove the crankshaft through a short connecting rod. Eight wrought iron columns (7in diameter) replaced the heavy cast iron framing of the side lever engine, and these in turn were carried on two foundation plates each weighing 10 tons. It was claimed that the Seaward and Capel engine was 60 tons lighter than the corresponding side lever engine.

There was a basic problem with this layout of engine. The limited height between its base and the crankshaft forced the use of a short connecting rod or a short cylinder. The former causes an uneven torque, leading to excessive wear and heavy vibration, while the latter solution implies a short crank with heavy loading on the crankpin, and hence rapid wear on the pin and bearing.

Gorgon at a mooring and drying her sails. The high freeboard shown in this and other pictures seems to disprove allegations that she was seriously overweight. *(© National Maritime Museum A1551)*

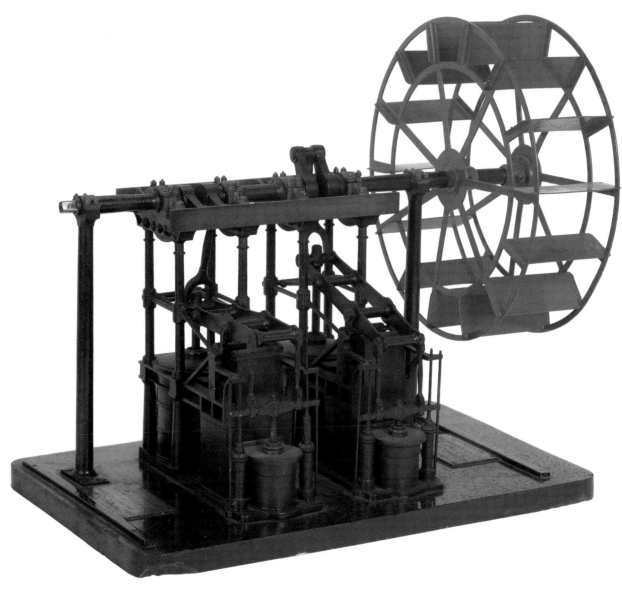

Gorgon's engines. Built by Seaward and Capel, they were the first vertical, direct acting marine engines and were more powerful for the same weight and space than earlier designs. (© *National Maritime Museum L2404-002*)

Steam at 5lb/sq in was supplied by four tubular boilers with a total of twelve grates in two stokeholds. The bunkers were arranged outboard of the engines and boilers, holding 400 tons of coal and giving 4ft of protection, and an endurance of sixteen days at 7¾ knots. On trial, the mean speed was 9.8 knots with 800ihp, using one ton of best Welsh coal per hour.

The complete machinery cost £21,073 and drove common wheels 27ft in diameter at 18rpm. Later, cycloidal wheels were fitted. There were forty-eight teak floats, each 7ft wide.

The total weight was 32 tons greater than that of *Medea*'s machinery. It is often alleged that the *Gorgon*'s machinery was overweight, leading to increased draught, and that this was the reason why main deck guns were not fitted. An extra 32 tons would cause a 3in increase in draught, though the extra coal might have caused a further 18in sinkage. However, the weight of coal, at least, was predictable and should have been allowed for. The armament of *Gorgon* and her half sister, *Cyclops*, will be discussed later.

Gorgon had teak frames, originally cut in Bombay for the frigate *Tigris* built at Plymouth, but dismantled before launch. The frames were stored until it was decided that they would do for *Gorgon*. Her beams were of oak. The displacement was 1,610 tons at a mean draught of 16ft 8in giving a freeboard to the main deck of 6ft 4in. Her wide beam and sharp rise of floor

Table 6.1 *Gorgon* – Machinery Weights[3]

Item	Tons	Cwt
2 cylinders, cover slides, jackets, pistons	29	14
2 condensers, air pump, buckets, hot wells, foot and head valves	27	11
2 upper main frames	16	14
3 shafts	15	2
2 wheels	20	5
Cycloidal fitting	3	16
Miscellaneous	35	–
4 boilers, chimney, fire box	64	19
Coal boxes	14	18
Water in boilers	48	–
Total	277	1

1. J A Sharpe, *Memoirs of Rear Admiral Sir William Symonds*, London (1858).
2. Science Museum, Inv 1891–123.
3. PRO Adm 95/87.

Cyclops. Described as a frigate despite the lack of main deck guns; there were sixteen gunports on the main deck but they were never armed. *(© National Maritime Museum X0628)*

was typical of a Symonds design. She cost £54,306.

Table 6.2 compares *Gorgon*, *Cyclops* and Brunel's *Great Western*. The resemblance is no coincidence: Brunel acknowledged the help of Edye in the structural design of his ship.[4]

Gorgon was a handsome ship with a single funnel abaft the paddle boxes, rigged as a brig. Her first captain,

4. D Griffiths, *Brunel's Great Western*, Wellingborough (1985).
5. PRO Adm 95/87.
6. Select Committee to inquire into the practicability of providing, by means of the commercial steam marine of the country, a reserve steam navy, 1849 (in future referenced as '1849 Committee').
7. PRO Adm 12/417.

Table 6.2 **Big Paddlers of the 1830s**

Ship	Gorgon	Great Western	Cyclops
Laid down	Jul 1835	28 Jul 1836	Aug 1838
Tonnage	1,111	1,340	1,195
Displacement	1,610	2,372	
Length, gun deck	178ft 0in	212ft 0in	190ft 3m
Breadth	37ft 6in	35ft 4in	37ft 6in
Draught	23ft	23ft 6in	23ft
NHP	320	450	320
ihp		750	
Boilers	4 flue	4 flue	4 flue
Steam pressure (lb/sq in)	5	5	5
Coal (tons)	380	380	420

Henderson, said of her, 'I consider the vessel powerful, easy and a first rate sea-boat and when not too deep, of more than average speed under steam. While under plain sail in smooth water I found her very handy, staying quickly, holding a good course and fast'.[5] Henderson amplified these remarks to the 1849 Select Committee.[6] 'She was a very powerful, strong vessel. She could carry 1,600 troops with six field guns and their limbers. … Her speed under steam was 9½–10 knots under favourable conditions. Against a headwind she was 2–3 knots slower under full rig than with topmasts housed'. Henderson was then questioned on his last point (Q): 'In a strong double-reefed topsail breeze, head to wind, spars aloft, what difference would it make to her velocity if you were to strike (topmasts)?' The wind described would have been Beaufort force 7, speed 23 knots, as then defined. His reply was 'three knots'. It was also found that cleaning the copper sheathing to remove fouling would increase speed by 1½ knots.[7]

Gorgon took part in the Syrian campaign of 1840, including the bombardment of Acre, and, with her sisters, winning the praise of Admiral Stopford: 'the steamships have been eminently useful in constantly moving along a great extent of coast with troops and arms and taking part in the attacks on different forts'. *Gorgon* later went to South American waters where, on 10 May 1844, she ran aground and was nearly lost. Her young first lieutenant, Cooper Key, already an advocate of steamships, played a prominent part in the salvage, adding to his reputation and bringing him another step nearer to his final post of First Sea Lord.[8]

In the meantime, on 22 June 1836 the Surveyor had ordered timbers to be cut for a sister ship to be called *Cyclops* and in November it was decided to fit bigger engines and copper boilers, and soon afterwards it was decided to lengthen her by 12ft 3in.[9]

Cyclops was rated as a frigate on completion, a surprising description. Frigates were defined as ship-rigged vessels, with the principal battery on the main deck with a complete upper deck over the guns. *Cyclops*, like *Gorgon*, mounted her few guns on the open upper deck and was rigged as a brig. Symonds's biographer, Sharpe, lists the design armament in Table 6.3 for the two ships.[10]

Table 6.3 **Design Armament**

	Upper deck	Main deck
Gorgon	Six 32pdrs	Ten 32pdrs
Cyclops	Two 98pdrs, four 48pdrs	Sixteen 32pdrs

The builder's model of the *Gorgon* in the Science Museum reserve collection shows twelve main deck ports which, allowing for the bow guns to have alternate firing positions, supports Sharpe's figures.[11] On the other hand, John Edye, in evidence to the 1847 Select Committee, says that these two ships were never designed to carry guns in the 'tween deck.[12] They did have ringbolts and ports in the main deck and the upper deck guns could be lowered to protect their crews in river operations, an idea suggested by Sir Thomas Hardy. The lower half-ports on the main deck were 'chinced' – lightly caulked. This story does not explain why they had many more ports on the main deck than guns on the upper deck; *Gorgon* did

8. P H Colomb, *Memoirs of Admiral Sir Ashley Cooper Key*, London (1898).
9. Note: John Edye told the 1847 Committee (12) that the lengthening was *not* carried out. William Edye, master shipwright of Devonport, then said she was lengthened by 12ft.
10. Sharpe, op cit.
11. Science Museum, Inv 1920–334.
12. Select Committee on Estimates, 1847–48. Parliamentary Papers, vol XXI, part 1 (in future referenced as '1847 Committee').

Spiteful, a *Driver* class paddle sloop. *(© National Maritime Museum N05434)*

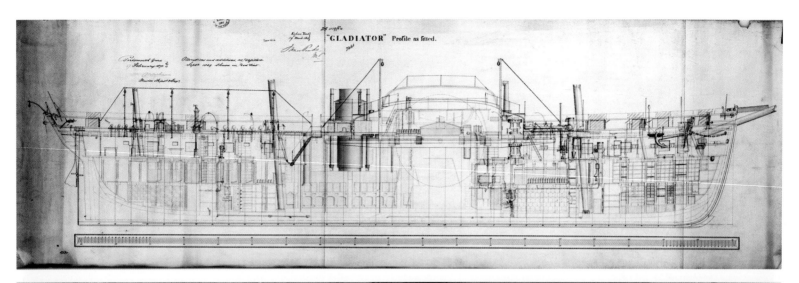

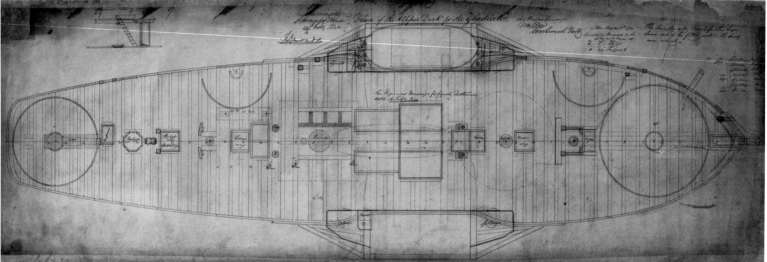

Top: *Gladiator*. Second-class paddle frigate of the *Firebrand* class, profile as fitted, 1844. (© *National Maritime Museum DR3000626*)

Above: *Gladiator*. Upper deck draught, 1844, showing paddle box boats and racers for pivot guns. The draught lists the armament as two 8in 112cwt on the pivots fore and aft, four 8in 55cwt on the broadside and two 24pdr carronades. (© *National Maritime Museum DR7580*)

not lower her guns for the Parana River operations.

Contemporary writers said that the main deck guns could not be carried because the ships floated deeper than designed, but in view of the machinery weights given earlier any such loss of freeboard would have been small. The many artists' impressions of these two ships all suggest a higher freeboard than most paddlers of the day. There seems little doubt that they were designed for a main deck armament, but the reason it was not carried is obscure. It may be that shortage of deck space for the gun crews was a problem, though in the light of their troop-carrying capacity that, too, seems unlikely.

By the 1840s many senior officers had become enthusiastic supporters of the steam warship and some rather exaggerated claims were made for their effectiveness. It was claimed that a ship like the *Gorgon* could defeat a 74-gun liner and even Henderson claimed that his ship could 'annoy' a line-of-battle ship. Steamers could not carry many guns because of the obstruction presented by the paddle box, and hence were given the largest guns available and these were mounted to give 10–12 degrees elevation for maximum range. Henderson believed that a single steamer could disable a *St Vincent* while two steamers could sink the liner.[13]

Captain Chads, formerly of the *Excellent* gunnery school and himself a considerable innovator, had little patience with such arguments. 'Even in a calm and without the heavy pivots [guns with which the liners were also fitted] the liner could use her boats to keep turning and so keep the steamer at least 3,000 yards away … with a dead calm, knowing the distance and with every advantage that it is possible to give her she would not strike a line-of-battle ship above 8–9 per cent at 3,000 yards.'[14] Chads' own firing trials suggest that even that was a very generous estimate.

In 1847 firing trials were carried out by the *Excellent*, moored in the quiet upper waters of Portsmouth harbour, against the old 74, *Leviathan*, and also against canvas screens fitted to poles at ranges of up to 3,000yds. Firing at 1,500 and 2,000yds range was from a 'lump', a fixed battery on shore, but the 3,000yd firings were from *Excellent*. All firings took place under the most favourable conditions – weather fine and clear, wind light, water smooth, the ship having but slight motion at any time. The range was known precisely and both firing ship and target were stationary. The figures in table 6.4 show what the highly trained gun crews could do in these ideal conditions.[15]

Firings with shells were even more inaccurate, by

about a quarter, due, it was believed, to the powder moving about within the casing and by the projection of the fuse which also meant that the centre of gravity of the shell was not at the centre of the sphere. Firing from a moving ship in a seaway would reduce the accuracy considerably, particularly at long range. For example, modern tests (*c*1980) with a destroyer gun showed that accuracy diminished with vertical motion of the gun from 46 per cent in a calm to 15 per cent with a velocity at the gun of 6ft/sec.

There is one particular problem associated with firing from a rolling ship, known as 'cross level correction', which was not solved until the Second World War. If a gun at an angle of elevation is pointed forward and the ship rolls, the combined angles of roll and elevation will move the line of sight off the target. For this reason, the chance of hitting at long range from the bow chaser of a relatively small ship was low.

Gorgon and *Cyclops* were prototypes for considerable numbers of first-class sloops and second class frigates, respectively (see Table 6.5).

In both categories, the trends were similar, with reduced rise of floor, increased beam and continually increasing power – up to 500NHP in the later sloops and 560NHP in *Dragon*. The earlier ships were

Table 6.4 **Accuracy of Gunfire**

Gun and projectile	Weight of gun (cwt)	Weight of charge (lb)	% hits at a range of (yds)			
			1,500	2,000	2,500	3,000
68 solid	91	15				
68 solid	87	14			25	11–12
56 solid	87	14				
32 solid	56	10	75	45		
10in hollow	85	12				
8in hollow	65	10			22	8–9
32 solid	50	8				
32 solid	45	7				

Table 6.5 *Gorgon* Derivatives

Sloops *Gorgon derivatives*		Frigates *Cyclops derivatives*	
Stromboli	2	*Firebrand*	3
Driver	8	*Sampson*	1
Devastation	1	*Centaur*	2
Thunderbolt	2		
Sphynx	1		
Bulldog	4		
Total	18	Total	6

Dragon. A second-class paddle frigate derived from *Cyclops* via the *Firebrand* class. (© National Maritime Museum PW8109)

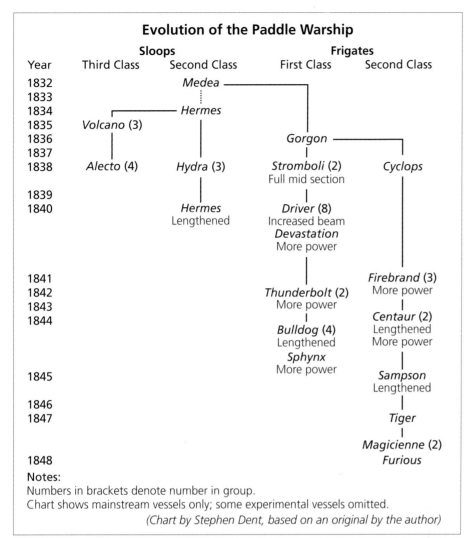

Evolution of the Paddle Warship

| | Sloops | | Frigates | |
Year	Third Class	Second Class	First Class	Second Class
1832		*Medea*		
1833				
1834		*Hermes*		
1835	*Volcano* (3)			
1836			*Gorgon*	
1837				
1838	*Alecto* (4)	*Hydra* (3)	*Stromboli* (2) Full mid section	*Cyclops*
1839				
1840		*Hermes* Lengthened	*Driver* (8) Increased beam *Devastation* More power	
1841				*Firebrand* (3) More power
1842		*Thunderbolt* (2) More power		
1843				
1844		*Bulldog* (4) Lengthened *Sphynx* More power		*Centaur* (2) Lengthened More power
1845				*Sampson* Lengthened
1846				
1847				*Tiger*
				Magicienne (2)
1848				*Furious*

Notes:
Numbers in brackets denote number in group.
Chart shows mainstream vessels only; some experimental vessels omitted.

(Chart by Stephen Dent, based on an original by the author)

completed as brigs and later converted to barques, while *Sphynx* and later ships were built with three masts.

The armament was altered over the years and varied from ship to ship but the *Devastation* and *Dragon* (Table 6.6) were typical.

Table 6.6 **Armament of *Devastation* and *Dragon***

Devastation (Sloop)

1842	Two 42pdr/84cwt, two 68pdr/64cwt, two 42pdr/22cwt
1856	One 68pdr/9cwt, one 10in/84cwt, four 32pdr/42cwt
1862	One 10in/84cwt, one 110pdr/82cwt, RBL, four 32pdr/42cwt

Dragon (Frigate)

1845	Two 10in/84cwt, four 68pdr/64cwt
1856	Two 68pdr/95cwt, four 10in/84cwt
1862	Two 110pdr/82cwt RBL

All these ships were dockyard built and though Pembroke, always seen as primarily a new construction yard, took the greatest number, orders were given to all the home yards. Machinery contracts were even more widely distributed with ten companies involved, no one company being particularly favoured.

There was one other first-class sloop, *Basilisk*, built for comparison with the screw sloop *Niger* and discussed with that ship.

A few more *Hermes* derivatives (see chart, left) were built as second- and third-class sloops. There were also some experimental vessels built to test new ideas in machinery, layout or new materials. In 1843 *Trident* was

Vesuvius in action with Russian forces, 1 September 1855. A sister of *Stromboli* and closely derived from *Gorgon*. (© National Maritime Museum PW5680)

the first iron fighting ship to be ordered for the Royal Navy, as described in the next chapter. *Argus* (Fincham), *Buzzard* (Edye) and *Barracouta* were less radical.

Janus was designed by the Earl of Dundonald (Cochrane) and was double-ended, with boilers of his own design and an American rotary engine, which was a failure. These sloop variants serve to show still further the Board's desire to innovate during the 1840s. There were another six second-class frigates, most of which carried all their armament on the upper deck.

The development of the First Rate paddle frigate was much more complicated and difficult to follow. The first was *Penelope*. John Edye was keen to increase the

Table 6.7 **Programme of Paddle Warship Building**

Year laid down	1837	'38	'39	'40	'41	'42	'43	'44	'45	'46
Sloops	1	2		4	5		2		2	3
Frigates			1		2		1		2	1

Shipbuilders		Engine Builders	
Second-class frigates			
Pembroke	5	Seaward & Capel	3
Portsmouth	3	Miller & Ravenhill	3
Woolwich	2	Fairbairn	2
Devonport	1	Rennie	1
Chatham	1	Boulton & Watt	1
		Penn	2
Sloops			
Pembroke	5	Seaward & Capel	1
Portsmouth	4	Napier	3
Sheerness	4	Fairbairn	1
Woolwich	4	Scott, Sinclair	6
Chatham	3	Miller & Ravenhill	2
		Maudslay	2
		Boulton & Watt	1
		Penn	2
		Rigby	1
		Fawcett	1

Table 6.8 **Weights of *Penelope*'s Machinery**

	Tons	Cwt
Engines with Hall's condensers	242	10
Boilers	110	4
Water in boilers	42	0
Coal boxes	21	5
Miscellaneous	55	5
Total above	522	14
Total[17]	544	15
Coal	500	
Power plant	1,044	15

Bulldog, name-ship of a class of first-class paddle sloops. (© National Maritime Museum PW0932)

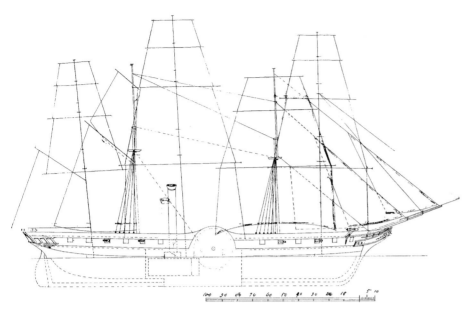

Above: *Penelope*. This drawing shows the original intention to install paddle machinery without lengthening the ship. *(Drawing by the author)*

Right: Maudslay's 'Siamese' engines for the *Devastation*. *(Science Museum)*

Below: *Ardent,* a third-class paddle sloop of 1841. *(© National Maritime Museum PY0908)*

number of paddle warships in the RN and suggested that some of the older sailing frigates be converted. The *Penelope* was chosen as a prototype and taken in hand at Chatham in 1843. A drawing in the National Maritime Museum shows that the original intention was merely to drop engines into the existing hull, but it was soon appreciated that an increase in length was needed. This increase not only gave the additional space needed for engines and coal, but also gave buoyancy to carry the weight of Seaward's 650NHP engines, based on the *Gorgon* design.[16]

The additional length of 65ft would provide some 1,200 tons of buoyancy from which the weight of the extra structure has to be subtracted.[17] *Penelope* completed with draughts of 19ft 3in forward and 20ft 3½in aft. The bulwarks were raised, which somewhat improved her appearance, but the freeboard was still too low.[18]

Penelope (1828). The only sailing frigate converted (1843) to paddle propulsion. (© *National Maritime Museum PY0922*)

Jones, her first captain, wrote in September 1843 that 'landing six carronades would only reduce her draught by one inch (20 tons). The speed was satisfactory; after two days' steaming, the rpm increased from 12 to 14'.[19] He thought it better to retain the full armament and accept that the main deck ports were too close to the waterline, though he was willing to reduce the number of grape and case shot carried, the number of field guns, etc.

Penelope's original armament as a steamship was:

| Main deck | Eight 68pdr/65cwt, two 68pdr/36cwt |
| Spar deck | Two 42pdr/84cwt, ten 42pdr/23cwt |

As with all ships of the period, there were numerous changes and the number of guns was reduced later, though the size of individual pieces increased.[20]

Her Seaward and Capel two-cylinder engines worked

16. PRO Adm 95/88, letter from Woolwich of 30 Sep 1843.

17. 1847 Committee.

18. Science Museum, Inv 1920–334.

19. PRO Adm 95/88, letter from Woolwich of 30 Sep 1843.

20. 1847 Committee.

Retribution (centre, with prominent row of gunports) at the bombardment of Odessa (see Chapter 12). Designed by the Surveyor in 1844, this was the first class of paddle frigate to carry a main deck armament. (© *National Maritime Museum B6872*)

Terrible as completed with four funnels. The largest paddle warship ever built for the RN. *(© National Maritime Museum PU6189)*

Sidon was heavily armed with a full main deck battery of sixteen heavy guns and six more on the upper deck. *Sidon* was modified by Sir Charles Napier from Fincham's *Odin* with considerably increased depth. *(© National Maritime Museum A2469)*

at 8lb/sq in and were unusual in that Hall's surface condensers were used, probably unsuccessfully. She was a barque and had iron standing rigging. Captain Jones reported that, 'In a heavy sea and a strong gale she steamed to windward without much pitching or straining and appeared dry, she answered [her helm] on all points, but under sail alone was leewardly'.[21] A few days later he wrote direct to Edye, claiming that under steam she could do what she liked with a line-of-battle ship, and under sail, with wheels disconnected, could keep company with the fleet. The wing furnaces were not a source of danger and the wire rigging worked well. The height of the ports above the water had always been at least 4ft.

Edye was pleased with *Penelope* and advocated further conversions. There were some thirty similar ships of which fifteen were in good condition and four could be converted each year. He suggested smaller engines of 500NHP, so that the length of the machinery spaces could be reduced by 12ft 8in, so improving living spaces and reducing weight by 245 tons, and hence draught by 14in to 18ft 6in, giving 6ft freeboard to the gunports. Four hundred tons of coal would last twenty-one days at an annual cost only three-quarters that of *Terrible*.

It was claimed that the cost of conversion would be £3,000 to £5,000 less than for *Penelope* (hull £25,447, machinery £34,042 = £59,489) or about 40 per cent of a new ship. Seaward quoted £24,650 for a single set of 500NHP machinery but would give 5 per cent off a second and third set if three sets were ordered (plus £1,656 if only one set of spares was ordered). Edye's weight estimates are listed in Table 6.9:[22]

In March 1842 Edye's new design, which became *Retribution*, was approved. Both the name and concept of the ship were altered before she completed as a brig with a very flat floor. She seems to have been a satisfactory ship, particularly after being re-engined and rigged as a barque in 1849. The main deck guns were probably not mounted until 1850.

Later, in July 1842, Lang was invited to prepare a design for a much bigger frigate of 1,640 tons (1,850 as completed) and with 800NHP. *Terrible* was an exceptionally strong ship; the main frames were so close that

Table 6.9 **Paddle Frigate Conversion**

	(Weights in tons)		
Item	*As sail*	*As converted*	*Penelope*
NHP	–	400–500	675
Coal	32	500	500
Masts, rig, sails	85	25	25
Anchor and cables	49	51	51
Boats and stores	48	32	50
Water	100	70	70
Provisions	59	52	65
Crew	40	37	40
Ballast	117	10	10
Equipment	550	1,227	1,341
Guns, powder and shot	143	102	131
Hull	795	1,220	1,293
Displacement	1,468	2,549	2,766
Draught mean	19ft 2in	18ft 9in	19ft 8in

they were watertight before the planking was added. As built, she had four double-ended tubular boilers, each with six furnaces and its own funnel. These provided too much steam and two boilers with their funnels were removed in about 1850.

Her original armament was:

Main deck   Four 56pdr/98cwt, four 68pdr/95cwt, three 12pdr/6cwt

Upper deck   Four 56pdr/98cwt, four 68pdr/95cwt

21. Ibid.
22. Ibid.

Sidon. Admiralty drawing of twin-cylinder direct acting engines by Seaward & Capel, dated 1850. (© *National Maritime Museum DR7945*)

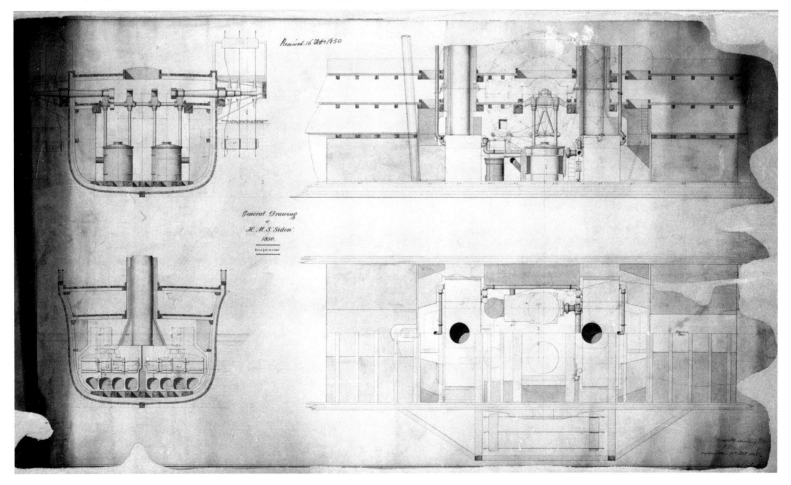

Above: *Caradoc*. Symonds' entry in the 1846 design competition for a Holyhead–Kingston packet service. One of the least successful on the run, she is seen here in later life as a dispatch vessel during the Crimean War. (© *National Maritime Museum PU9008*)

and like other ships of her day, was frequently altered.

Halsted gives an interesting picture of her usage of steam.[23] In 1846–8 she covered 15,371 miles at a mean speed of 6.83 knots, of which only 6,277 miles were under sail alone. Between March and October 1846, while in the Mediterranean, she completed 5,725 miles at 9.07 knots, burning coal at the rate of 4.35 miles/ton.

She remained in service well into the 1860s and was a well-liked ship, not least for her impressive appearance. With a displacement of 3,189 tons and a length of 226ft 2in, she was the largest paddle warship completed – if we ignore the converted US Navy paddle aircraft carriers of the Second World War, *Sable* and *Wolverine*!

Odin was a smaller ship, by Fincham, as were her derivatives, *Sidon* (by Captain Sir C Napier), and

Valorous. Second-class frigate of the *Magicienne* class. She was hit on one wheel off Sevastopol and was able to continue in action. She remained in service until 1891, the last paddle frigate in the Navy. (© *National Maritime Museum neg 6845*)

Leopard (Fincham). They were heavily armed with ten to fourteen guns on the main deck (32pdrs or 8in) and six big guns (68pdrs or 10in) on the upper.

There was an interesting design competition for mail packets on the Holyhead to Kingston run which led to some very fast paddlers. The ships and their designers were:

Caradoc	Symonds	*Llewellen*	Miller & Ravenhill
Banshee	Lang	*St Columba*	Laird

They all had 350NHP engines though ihp does not seem to have been measured. *Banshee* was the fastest on trial at 16.13 knots, made the fastest crossing both in 1848 and 1849, and had the shortest average crossing time. *Llewellen* was never far behind but the other two were much slower; twenty to forty minutes in a four-hour crossing.

The big first-class frigates were all dockyard built, four at Deptford and two at Chatham. The engine builders were Seaward & Capel (three), Maudslay (two) and Fairbairn (one). By far the largest number of the later small paddlers were also dockyard ships, though a few experimental vessels were built in commercial yards.

When the building of paddle fighting ships came to an end in 1852, there were a number of designs in hand, one at least for a very large ship:

2,540 tons (bm), length 260ft, 1,000NHP
Upper deck   Two 68pdr/113cwt, sixteen 68pdr/95cwt
Main deck   Eighteen 68pdr/95cwt

There were no serious proposals for a paddle line-of-battle ship. Presumably, fear of damage to the paddles dissuaded the Board from any such plan. A catamaran was well within the capability of the age (eg, Miller's multihulls), but by that time the screw was offering a more practical solution.

The risk of damage to the wheels was greatly exaggerated, as shown by the following account by Sulivan on the fighting in the Parana River in 1846.

There was one remarkable case there to show what a steam vessel could stand. The French steam boat *Fulton* (600–700 tons) went up to cover her chief, who was suffering dreadfully, and anchored between him and the batteries. The boom not being cut, she was detained there for, I think, three hours. They put 56 heavy round shot into her paddle wheels and sponsons; they destroyed every part of the wheel nearest the side, both the wheel and the paddle beam, so that the shaft had only a mass of broken iron to heave round; and yet, when the chains were cut, she was the first that went through with her remaining wheel, and she afterwards came down and repassed the batteries, to tow up some other vessel with her own wheel. Though three round shot went in among her engines they did not do any damage.[24]

The *Valorous* was hit on her wheel during the Crimean War, again with little effect. In fact, reducing the effective width of a paddle wheel by a half has little effect on propulsive efficiency. There was a risk of a wheel being jammed, but in most ships it was

23. E P Halsted, *Steam Fleet of the Navy*, London (1850).
24. H N Sulivan, *Life and Letters of Admiral Sir B J Sulivan*, London (1896).

Opposite: *Tiger*. Designed by Edye as a *Sphynx* class sloop. In 1847 her depth was increased by 6in and she was reclassed as a second-class frigate but with a main deck battery which, in 1852, was ten 32pdrs. She finally departed from the Symondite form having a very flat floor. She ran aground near Odessa in May 1854 and was destroyed. (© *National Maritime Museum F7747-001*)

The attack on Obligado, 1845. In this battle the French paddler *Fulton* had one wheel destroyed but remained in action. She can be seen to the far right approaching the line of blockships that supported a boom across the river. *(Courtesy of Beverley R. Robinson Collection, US Naval Academy Museum)*

a fairly simple matter to disconnect one wheel.[25]

It is even more surprising that no attempt was made to design a paddle ram. With separately driven wheels such a ship could have had exceptional manoeuvrability, and iron reinforcement to the bow would have given the necessary strength. Considering the general lack of success of rams in the American civil war and elsewhere, it may be as well that resources were not squandered on such schemes.[26]

Paddle fighting ships had only a brief period of active service and none fought in major battles. Once superseded by the screw steamer, they were seen as obsolescent and of little fighting value. However, the later ships carried a heavy armament and were little inferior in speed

to the early screw ships. Above all, the paddle steamers taught the new generation of naval officers to recognise the value of reliable mobility independent of wind.

---

25. W E Smith. His manuscript work book records the following stability particulars for *Valorous* in 1875.

Condition	Displacement (tons)	Draught mean (ft in)	GM (ft)
Arctic, deep	2,373	18 2½	2.47
Deep	2,243	16 5	2.16
Light	1,851	14 2½	1.16

26. W Laird Clowes, 'The ram in action and in accident', *Journal of the United Service Institution*, March 1894.

Iron Ships | *Seven*

T HE RAPID GROWTH of the iron industry in the mid-eighteenth century led to a demand for improved transport, satisfied by the growing canal network. It was soon recognised that the strength of iron in relation to its weight made it a very suitable material for building barges. A Birmingham newspaper reported on 28 July 1787:[1]

> A few days ago a boat built of English iron, the *Trial*, by J Wilkinson of Bradley Forge, came up our canal to this town, loaded with 22 tons 15cwt of its own metal. It is of nearly equal dimensions with other boats employed on the canal being 70ft long, 6ft 8½in wide, the thickness of plates of which it is made is about ⁷⁄₁₆in and it is put together with rivets like a fire engine boiler but stem and stern posts are wood and the gunwale line the same. The beams are of elm plank and the weight is about 8 tons. She will carry, in deep water, upwards of 32 tons and draws 8in or 9in when light.

The advantage of iron in constructing a barge which could carry four times its own weight is clear. A much later and smaller but similar barge can be seen at the Blists Hill Victorian Town, Ironbridge.

Quite a number of these barges had been built by the end of the Napoleonic war and worked well, though they generated considerable prejudice and ill-informed comment.[2] Stories were already current of distinguished reactionaries who were reported to have said that iron vessels were impossible since iron does not float. Similar legends of nineteenth-century admirals appear to be unfounded. Prejudice sometimes went further and allegations of sabotage were quite common; for example, the *Tipton*, built by Jevons in Liverpool in 1815, was said to have been sunk soon after entering service.

The next step, an iron seagoing ship, raised many new problems not found in canal navigation which would prove hard to solve. The first such attempt came in 1820

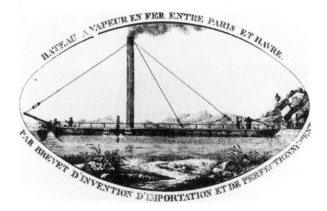

when Aaron Manby, the owner of the Horsely Forge, Tipton, joined with Captain (later Admiral Sir Charles) Napier to build a ship for service between London and Paris.[3] This ship, the *Aaron Manby*, was built in sections and assembled in the Surrey Commercial Docks, London, during 1821. She took on a cargo of linseed and iron castings and, under Napier's command, steamed from London to Le Havre and on up the Seine to Paris. Thus she became the first seagoing iron ship and for thirty years the only ship to sail from London to Paris direct.[4]

Table 7.1 *Aaron Manby*

Tonnage (bm)	116
Dimensions	106ft 9in x 17ft 2in x 3ft 6in
Depth	7ft 2in

The paddle wheels had feathering floats worked by eccentrics on the shaft.[5]

The career of the *Aaron Manby* was one of mixed fortune, as French navigation laws forbade direct voyages from London to Paris. As a result, a similar ship, constructed in sections at Horsely, had to be assembled at Charenton where Charles Manby, Aaron's son, had established an iron works. Because of these problems, the Manbys sold their shipping interests in 1830, Napier losing much of his investment, and in consequence becoming a bitter opponent of iron ships.[6] Up to the sale in 1830, the *Aaron Manby* had required no maintenance or repairs to her hull, despite frequent groundings in the Seine. It is known that she remained in service until about 1880, though by then she had been converted to screw propulsion.

Manby built a number of other iron ships at Horsely, including one which crossed the Irish Sea in 1825 to work on the River Shannon. Other builders followed this example, of whom the most notable was John Laird of Birkenhead. His first iron ship was the *Savannah* (1833), followed by the *Garry Owen* for the Shannon service in 1834.[7] At the suggestion of her owner, C W Williamson, this ship was the first to have iron watertight bulkheads. Due to the working of the planking, it was not possible to incorporate effective watertight bulkheads in wooden ships.

The Admiralty had been using an increasing amount of iron, mainly as beam knees, brackets and for Seppings's diagonal trusses, and even with this limited amount of iron had found its effect on the magnetic compass to be a serious problem (see also Chapter 3, *Phaeton*). The effect on the compass of an iron ship was

1. J Grantham, *Iron Shipbuilding*, London (1858).
2. W H Bailey, 'The first iron boat and its inventor, John Wilkinson', Manchester Association of Engineers (9 Oct 1886). Note: Bailey quotes the following anecdote: 'Will that swim?' said an indignant local blacksmith as he threw a horse shoe with some violence into his water trough, on being told that John Wilkinson was making an iron boat. This must be the earliest version of the legendary admirals who are said to have objected that iron does not float.
3. C Manby, letter of 11 Feb 1842 quoted in Grantham, op cit.
4. D Lobley, *Ships Through the Ages*, London (1972).
5. Marine engineering catalogue, Science Museum, Inv 1891–132.
6. *Life and Letters of Sir Charles Napier*, Naval Records Society.
7. S Dupuy de Lôme, *Mémoire sur la Construction des Bâtiments en Fer*, Paris (1844).

Aaron Manby. The only known illustration of the first iron, seagoing ship. It may not be very accurate as contemporary reports say that her paddles were well aft. (*Science Museum*)

much greater, and such ships were incapable of operating out of sight of land.[8]

Many contemporary writers and most more recent ones have failed to understand the significance of compass deviation and have unfairly accused the Admiralty of being tardy in accepting iron ships. In particular, John Laird made many unsuccessful attempts to persuade the Board to purchase iron warships. It was, however, the Admiralty which made the only effective efforts to obtain a solution. In 1835 Captain B J Johnson was ordered to carry out experiments with Laird's iron paddle steamer, *Garry Owen*, in order to improve understanding of the problem and if possible to find a solution. Johnson did not find the answer but he was the first to identify the two components of ship magnetism, induced and permanent. Two years later the Board directed the Astronomer Royal, Sir George Airy (an Admiralty employee), to study Johnson's work and improve on it.[9]

In 1837 the Admiralty chartered the *Rainbow* for trials by Airy at Deptford, in which he attempted to correct the compass for the effect of the ship's magnetism by arranging permanent magnets and masses of unmagnetised iron round it. This first attempt seems to have been partially successful, but in 1838 Airy corrected the compass of the iron sailing ship *Ironsides* of 200 tons. This ship was built by Jackson, Gordon & Co and her three voyages from Liverpool to the USA and back carrying cotton were the first ocean passages of an iron ship and demonstrated the success of Airy's work.

His method required a lengthy series of measurements while the ship was 'swung', that is, turned to known bearings while the compass was corrected at each. Charlwood was to say that the process demanded no great skill, but meticulous care, and until experience was gained mistakes were not unusual.[10] It was probably not until the work of the Liverpool Compass Committee in 1855, backed by the Admiralty, that the correction of compasses became truly reliable in merchant ships.

There were alternative approaches, such as that of Captain Sparkes, who allowed for deviation by producing a compass card with unequal divisions. While this method was valid, it was hopelessly difficult to use such a compass for multiple bearings. An even more impractical approach used a table of corrections to be added – or was it subtracted? – from the reading of the compass card.

By the time that Airy published his work in 1839,[11] the railway boom had passed its peak and there was an abundance of expertise in the supply of iron and means of using it. Reaction to Airy's paper, one of the most influential papers ever written on marine transport, was rapid. The Admiralty's response was cautious, but positive, in ordering the iron cross-Channel packet *Dover* from Laird's in February 1839. Brunel made a bigger step in changing the design of the *Great Britain* from wood to iron construction, but it was the Honourable East India Company which ordered the first iron warship, the *Nemesis*, early in 1835. She was laid down in August that year in Laird's yard at Birkenhead, carried out trials

8. C H Collier, 'Compass deviation and the INA', *The Naval Architect* (Nov 1976); see also the references given in the article.

9. Ibid.

10. 1847 Committee.

11. G B Airy, 'Account of experiments in iron built ships', *Phil Trans*, vol 13 (1839), 167.

Nemesis. A contemporary engraving of the world's first iron warship. (© *National Maritime Museum PU6707*)

in December and was completed in January 1840.[12]

The *Nemesis* was Laird's twenty-eighth iron steamship and was a typical small paddler but, as the first iron fighting ship, she may be seen as one of the most revolutionary ships ever built.

Table 7.2 HEICoS *Nemesis*

Tonnage	660 (bm)
Dimensions	184ft (oa) x 29ft x 6ft (max)
Depth	11ft
Machinery	120NHP (Forrester, Vauxhall Foundry, Liverpool), 2 cylinders, 44in x 48in, 2 boilers
Paddle wheels	17ft 6in diameter, 16 floats each 6ft 9in x 144in
Masts	Foremast 50ft (deck to head), 15in diameter, topmast 24ft x 10in Main mast 50ft 6in x 15in, topmast 33ft x 10in
Armament	Two 32pdr, four (later five) 6pdr, 1 rocket launcher
Complement	Design 46, actual 60–90

Note: The draught quoted is with twelve days' coal and water and with provision for four months, together with three years' general stores. For river work she could be lightened to a draught of 5ft.

Her first and most obvious advantage was her shallow draught, which compared most favourably with the 13ft or so typical of small RN paddle sloops.[13] Some of this advantage was due to the weight-saving due to the iron hull and some to the choice of a nearly flat-bottomed hull (instead of Symonds's peg top) combined with a parallel-sided section for the engine and boiler room.

There were six watertight bulkheads, the first to be fitted to a warship. Originally, there were only small hand pumps in each compartment, and major flooding had to be drained from one compartment to the next through stopcocks, until the water reached the pump in the engine room. After her accidental grounding off St Ives, this complicated and dangerous arrangement was replaced by a system of suction pipes to each compartment. A partial bulkhead with an arched opening was sited between the boiler and engine rooms to provide transverse strength without impeding access.

She had two masts, each with a topmast and a sliding gunter rig. To improve her sailing qualities, *Nemesis* was given two drop keels, each 7ft long, which could be extended 5ft below the flat bottom. These keels were stowed in iron trunks 12in wide extending to the deck, and were worked by a small windlass through an endless chain. The trunks ended on a bulkhead which they helped to support, an example of Laird's attention to detail. When the keels were lowered, a corresponding 5ft extension piece was lowered from the rudder. The ship's officers reported that the keels were most valuable in going to windward and in keeping the ship steady.

She was originally armed with a 32pdr at each end, but two 6pdrs at each side were added early in her career and a fifth such gun later. Later still, a rocket launcher was fitted on the bridge between the paddle boxes.

Nemesis' compass was corrected on the principles set out by Airy, but unlike the company's other ships, including *Phlegethon* (Laird's number 27, completed after *Nemesis*), the work was not done by Airy himself and in consequence her compass was never very accurate. When crossing the Indian Ocean it was found that the compass read true when she was heading north or south, but there were large errors when heading east or west. It was probably her defective compass which caused her to run aground on The Stones, off St Ives, during her maiden voyage. She hit a sharp rock at about 8½ knots, which pushed in the forefoot some 3in and caused an 8in split. Seven feet further aft, the keel was dented but not pierced. The main damage was at the turn of bilge by the forward bulkhead, where the shell was forced against the bulkhead, which then penetrated the flats, the lower boundary of the bulkhead also being broken.

12. W D Bernard and W H Hall, *The Nemesis in China*, London (1846); see also *Warship* 8.

13. 13. David Lyon & Rif Winfield, *The Sail & Steam Navy List: All the Ships of the Royal Navy 1815-1889*, London (2004).

Phlegethon, the HEICo's second iron warship at the head of a line attacking the Dunoo Stockade in January 1852 during the Second Burma War. (© *National Maritime Museum PW4891*)

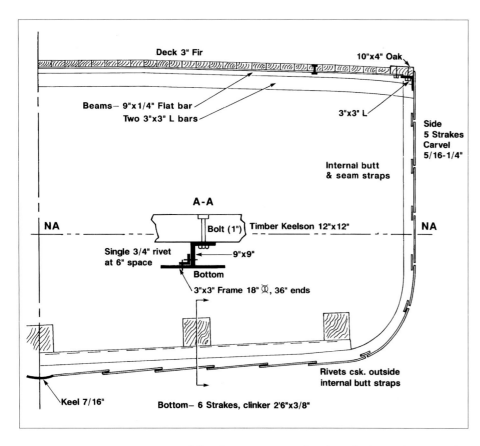

Deck 3" Fir

10"x4" Oak

Beams— 9"x1/4" Flat bar
Two 3"x3" L bars

3"x3" L

Side
5 Strakes
Carvel
5/16-1/4"

Internal butt
& seam straps

A - A

NA

Bolt (1")

Timber Keelson 12"x12"

NA

Single 3/4" rivet
at 6" space

9"x9"

Bottom

3"x3" Frame 18" ⌀, 36" ends

Rivets csk. outside
internal butt straps

Keel 7/16"

Bottom— 6 Strakes, clinker 2'6"x3/8"

Nemesis. Structural section.
(Drawing by the author)

The damage was confined to the immediate area hit by the rock, since the rivets did not give. *Nemesis* borrowed a powerful pump in Penzance and was able to continue to Portsmouth where she was taken in hand in the dockyard for repairs. A shoe was riveted over the damaged forefoot and two plates were replaced. Altogether 3cwt of new materials was used and this, together with labour costs, brought a bill of £30. Mr Laird said that with the right equipment, as installed at Birkenhead, the job could have been done for £20, but since Portsmouth had not repaired an iron ship before, the cost seems reasonable.

Laird wrote to the Admiralty in March 1840 suggesting that they took the opportunity to carry out a full survey of an iron ship while *Nemesis* was in dock. This task was given to Augustin Creuze, one of the outstanding graduates of the first school, who later published his report in the *Journal of the United Services Institution*.[14] It was the first of many favourable reports which their Lordships were to receive on the *Nemesis*.

The accompanying drawing of the midships section (see also Appendix 6) has been reconstructed from Creuze's account and is incomplete in some aspects; for example, the vertical keel is not described (there may not have been one). The first point to note is that the iron structure forms an open bowl with a top of wood planking. An iron deck would have added very considerably to her strength. Other than that, her structure was well thought out and used the biggest plates available, about 8ft x 2ft 6in. If she followed Laird's normal practice she would have had a keel of Low Moor iron at £21 per ton and Coalbrookdale iron elsewhere at £15 per

ton. With labour costs added, this would have led to an overall hull cost of about £40 per ton.[15]

Nemesis was built almost entirely of iron, except for the deck of 3in fir, the gunwale of oak, 4in x 10in, and four 10in square beams supporting the bitts and forward gun. The great beams supporting the paddle boxes were of oak, 12in square, and wood was also used for the knee of the stem, rudder, paddle boxes and cabin bulkheads. Creuze concluded his report by discussing the advantages of iron ships. Iron was cheaper and available in unlimited quantities in Britain, and iron was also more durable. Less convincingly, he argued in favour of a system of diagonal framing.

Nemesis cleared Portsmouth on 28 March 1840, ostensibly for Odessa, a cover story for her true destination of China. She sailed with a crew of sixty, increased to ninety when her 6pdrs were mounted, and crossed the Bay of Biscay at a steady 7–8 knots, burning 11 tons of coal per day. After crossing the equator, Captain Hall tried disconnecting one paddle wheel, running under sail and the lee wheel. This procedure worked well, the ship making 6–7 knots at 12–15rpm with little or no leeway. A trial with both cylinders worked from one boiler was less successful since the steam supply was insufficient. Nearing South Africa, the rudder extension fell off and a new one was made and fitted. Lee boards were also made and tried, reducing the leeway under sail alone by about a half (presumably in addition to the drop keels).

This careful experimentation was typical of the master, William Hutchens Hall, who had entered the Navy in 1811 and had been made up to master in 1823. He undertook a training course in the use of steam engines and as a result was lent to the East India Company to command the *Nemesis*. His achievements in this ship were so outstanding that the Admiralty obtained an Order in Council to enable him to be made a lieutenant on 8 January 1841. Later, he was allowed to count his time in *Nemesis* for seniority in the RN and was promoted to commander in 1843, becoming a captain the following year.

Hall later invented a patent anchor and also introduced the use of iron bilge tanks, as a result being elected as Fellow of the Royal Society in 1847. He retired as Rear Admiral with a KCB in 1869 and died nine years later. There are many accounts of prejudice against officers who rose from the lower deck, and against steam, and it is pleasant to show that such prejudice was not universal. His knowledge of steam machinery came at just the right time and his unique ship drew attention to him. His career shows that in 1840 merit could be rewarded, and that experience in new technology was valuable.

The most exciting and technically interesting part of the voyage came soon after leaving Cape Town. On 16 July near Algoa Bay the barometer started to fall, eventually dropping to 28in; a strong wind from the northnorthwest freshened to full gale and the sea was 'high and heavy'. This area is still regarded as particularly dangerous since the ocean swell turns to steeper waves as it enters shallow water. The paddle boards had been removed and the *Nemesis* was under sail alone when at 0300hrs on the 17th a tremendous sea struck the port quarter and she broached. The starboard wheel broke and a crack started on both sides of the ship at the corner of the square opening for the beam supporting the aft end of the paddle boxes. These cracks extended through all the plates below the sheer strake and partly into that plate. Initially, the cracks were about 2ft 6in long and the plates were bulged; sketches of the damage suggest the initial failure was in compression.

The first concern was for the broken paddle wheel. The damaged section was hooked up with a boat anchor and brought on board. The prior removal of the floats had weakened the wheel and it was also thought that it should have an additional ring of stiffening. (This was fitted in later ships.)

On the 18th the wind moderated and the ship was able to make 4 knots on the port wheel alone. Three days later the starboard wheel was repaired just as the wind freshened once again. Some planks were put around the stern to keep the sea out and the after 32pdr was dismounted and lowered into a coal bunker. The cracks, now 3½ft long, were patched on the 22nd with an iron plate outside, bolted through to planks inside the hull.

In the new storm the cracks extended a further 18in in five hours. Wooden cross braces were put inside, between the frames, to prevent the broken plates from overriding each other, and the frames at each side of the cracks were joined with long bolts to take the tensile loads. These repairs held out until the *Nemesis* reached the shelter of Delgoa Bay, where further repairs were made. The cracks were now 7ft long each side out of a total depth of 11ft. The long timbers required for the repairs were obtained by threat of force from a local slave trader.[16]

From these timbers, three wooden stringers, each 23ft long, were cut and fitted inside the frames each side. The spaces between the hull and the stringer were filled with short pieces of wood. The cracked plates were removed and new ones riveted in place.

The design of these early iron ships was often criticised for the lack of an iron deck, since this would have changed the ship from the nature of a trough to that of a tube, a much stronger shape. In fact, *Nemesis*'s overall strength was adequate, though inefficient, as shown both by a modern conventional strength calculation (Appendix 6) and by the fact that she survived a severe storm with cracks extending 7ft down each side; a large proportion of her 11ft depth. The cracks initiated at a badly designed structural detail, which produced a local high stress at the corner of the square hole where the 12in beams for the paddle boxes passed through the hull.

The *Nemesis* then wandered slowly and rather vaguely across the Indian Ocean, still plagued by her erratic compass and with her speed much reduced by heavy fouling on her bottom, protected only by red lead. Reports from P&O liners a few years later showed that barnacles up to 9in long could grow in a single voyage out to India.

Recently, Barrett has shown that a lesser growth over eighteen months on the unprotected bottom of the aircraft carrier *Illustrious* increased her resistance by about 80 per cent.[17] Fouling was one problem which was not solved during the history of the iron ship and it remains an expensive nuisance today (Appendix 7).

Once arrived in China, the *Nemesis* experienced the normal exciting life of a gun boat during the first China war. She was the first ship past the Bogue forts, she surveyed the Canton River and took part in actions against Amoy, Ningpo and Woosung. The book by her captain, Hall, gives a fascinating picture of Imperial Britain at work; both good and bad aspects.

Only one of these actions was of technical significance, that of the bombardment of Whampoa in February 1841:

> *Nemesis* was struck several times but fortunately only one man was wounded. One of the large shots passed completely through the outer casing of the steam chest and was very near to penetrating the steam chest itself. Besides receiving several shots in the hull she had her spars and rigging a good deal cut up. ...

Hall and his engineer, Pedder, kept the ship running and frequently in action until 1843, when the commission was over and she returned to Bombay to refit. She required much less maintenance than did the wooden ships on similar duties and fears that her own gunfire would loosen the rivets or that she would rust away were unjustified. On docking at Bombay it was reported:

> The *Nemesis* has for some time past been in our docks, and I have carefully examined her. She displays in no small degree the advantages of iron. Her bottom bears the marks of having repeatedly been ashore; the plates are deeply indented in several places, one or two of them to the extent of several inches. She had evidently been in contact with sharp rocks, and one part of her keel plate is bent sharply up, in such a way that I could not believe that cold iron could have been; indeed, unless the iron had been extremely good [it was probably 'best' Low Moor], I am sure it would not have withstood it without injury. Her bottom is not nearly so much corroded as I expected to have found it and she is as tight as a bottle.[18]

The first commission of the *Nemesis* has been described in some detail since it was the first operational use of an iron warship and illustrated many of the advantages and problems of such ships in the 1840s. Hall's report to the Admiralty when he returned on 22 November 1843 was enthusiastic and was said by the senior naval member, Admiral Sir George Cockburn, to have been the main factor, together with Creuze's earlier report and that

14. A F B Creuze, 'On the *Nemesis*', *Journal of the United Services Institute* (May 1840).

15. Dupuy de Lôme, op cit.

16. Airy, op cit.

17. M G Barrett, 'HMS *Illustrious* – effect of no anti-fouling', *The Naval Architect* (Mar 1985).

18. Airy, op cit.

from Bombay, in deciding to order several iron frigates.[19] Hall said that he much preferred a well-built iron ship to a wooden vessel; *Nemesis* had been in action on many occasions and had been hit up to fourteen times in one engagement. These hits had not caused any serious problems and were easily repaired. The effect of splinters was about the same or not as much as in a wooden hull.

Considering that *Nemesis* had suffered continually on her first voyage from fouling and from compass errors, and that she suffered a near catastrophic structural failure, her other merits – mainly shallow draught and ease of maintenance – must have seemed overwhelming. She was fortunate that most of her actions were fought in the warm, fresh waters of the Chinese rivers where neither fouling nor compass errors were serious and the iron plates were warm enough to avoid brittle failures. During the vessel's first commission there had been many other developments in iron ships which will now be described.

Iron ships 1840–3

The *Dover* was built entirely to Laird's design, but from the time of her completion a careful record was kept of her maintenance and repair costs in comparison with

the wooden packet *Widgeon*, on similar service (see illustration on page 109). By 1848, when the results were reported to Parliament, there was a small difference in favour of the iron ship. The hull of the Dover cost £4,816, slightly more than *Widgeon* at £4,257. Total bills for the hull averaged £58 per annum for the first eight years of the iron ship, whereas the first eight years of *Widgeon* averaged £131 (£124 pa over eleven years). Symonds was not enthusiastic, but was not openly hostile, writing in 1840 to Edye that he could not comment on iron ships until more experience had been obtained on their durability. [20]

In October 1839 the Surveyor was asked to investigate the building of three small iron gun boats with a shallow draught ranging from 4ft 6in to 6ft, for use on the Niger. These three ships, *Albert*, *Soudan* and *Wilberforce*, were ordered from Laird's early in 1840, launched within a month or two, and commissioned in October that year. These two-masted, topsail schooners were the first iron fighting ships in the Royal Navy, *Albert* and *Wilberforce* having three 12pdrs and four lpdrs while the smaller *Soudan* had a single 12pdr howitzer. None of them lasted long in service; *Soudan* was wrecked in 1844 and the other two sold in 1844–5.

The next iron ship was the *Mohawk*, also designed for overseas service, and ordered from Fairbairn in June

The three ships of the Niger expedition in 1841, *Albert* in the centre with *Wilberforce* ahead and *Soudan* astern. *Albert* was a shallow draught, river gun boat ordered from Laird's in 1840, the first iron fighting ship for the RN. *(© National Maritime Museum PY0907)*

1841. She was constructed in sections which were shipped across the Atlantic and reassembled in Kingston, Ontario; perhaps the first of many ships sent overseas in sections. This sectional construction must have been valuable when in 1846 she was lengthened 25ft. *Mohawk* carried one small gun and served first on Lake Ontario and then on Lake Huron until 1852. Two small tenders, *Rocket* (Fairbairn) and *Ruby* (Acraman, Morgan (1st SNA)), were ordered in September 1841, possibly for exploration work, though they were always used as dockyard tenders. Both were unsatisfactory, with many complaints of rusting and leaks. *Rocket* was broken up in 1850 and *Ruby* blown apart in gunnery trials in 1846.

Pressure was being put on the Board to mount a more adventurous iron shipbuilding programme. Brunel's *Great Britain* was taking shape at Bristol and attracting much public interest. Laird had been submitting proposals for iron ships ever since 1836 – at which date the compass problem was still unsolved. Eventually, Laird began the construction of Ship No 42 at his own expense, which he clearly hoped to sell to the Royal Navy. Any such hopes were dashed by a letter in January 1842 in which the Board rejected the ship after an inspection by J Large (1st SNA, a very progressive man and later assistant to Watts in the design of *Warrior*) who

described her as 'unfit for service'. She was launched in April 1842 as the Mexican steam frigate *Guadalupe*.[21]

Table 7.3 *Guadalupe*

Displacement	878 tons (with 10 days' coal)
Tonnage	788 (bm)
Dimensions	187ft (deck) x 30ft x 9ft
Depth	16ft
Machinery	180NHP Forrester 2-cylinder 52in x 5ft stroke
Paddle wheels	21ft diameter 22rpm = 9 knots
Armament	Two 68pdr pivot (bow and stern) Two 24pdr added on arrival in Mexico Two 24pdr added later

While the *Guadalupe* was still building, the young and brilliant French naval constructor, Dupuy de Lôme, arrived in Britain to prepare a report on iron ship-building. This report, written in 1842–3 and published in Paris in 1844, is a fascinating account of the design and building of iron ships in the heroic age and has much of interest on the social side too.[22] (See also Appendix 8.)

Dupuy de Lôme's report falls into two parts, the first dealing with the advantages and problems of the iron

Guadalupe. Laird's private venture iron frigate, sold to Mexico. Note that this ship is often called *Guadeloupe* in English sources, but the above is the correct form. *(© National Maritime Museum A2480)*

19. 1847 Committee, evidence by Admiral Cockburn.

20. 1847 Committee, evidence by Symonds.

21. D K Brown, 'The paddle frigate *Guadeloupe*', *Warship* 11 (1979).

22. Dupuy de Lôme, op cit.

ship and the second covering the shipyard practices used by various builders, together with a more detailed description of individual ships. He rightly saw that the virtue of the iron hull was that it was effectively a single piece of material. The riveted joints along the seams of the plates prevented the slipping which, between caulked planks, would allow hogging to take place and also allow water to penetrate and cause rot. Because the hull was made entirely of one piece, there was no need for the complication of Seppings's diagonal trusses. Overall, an iron hull was lighter by some 25 per cent of the laden displacement, more spacious inside and, perhaps best of all, watertight. Additional advantages which a British reporter might have noted were that iron hulls were cheaper and that the materials needed, iron ore and coke, were readily available in Britain (Appendix 9).

Dupuy de Lôme emphasised the value of transverse bulkheads to contain flooding, instancing the grounding of the *Garry Owen* in the Shannon estuary on 6 June 1839 as well as that of the *Nemesis*, already discussed. He thought that corrosion would be no problem provided that a little care was taken in painting (145 years later one might still say the same).

There is an interesting discussion on production costs and the reason for variations between one ship and another and between two builders. Unlike today, the ship with heavier plating cost more per ton than lighter-built vessels, since the work in cutting, bending and drilling the heavier plate was greater. Dupuy de Lôme included many detailed drawings with his report, some of which, dealing with shipyard machinery, are reproduced by Corlett.[23] These machines were simple and effective, including shears and punches, rolls and drills,

but most were hand-worked. It is no wonder that it was expensive to work the thicker scantlings. Some of the machines shown were portable and could be moved round the slipway and, perhaps, lifted on board.

Laird's price averaged about £40 per ton, which was fairly similar to that of London and Bristol shipbuilders. Glasgow was cheaper at about £33 per ton, partly due to lower labour costs but partly to more extensive use of the cheaper grades of iron (Appendix 8).

The overall cost of £40 per ton breaks down into £12 for material and £28 for direct labour, overheads, wastage and profit. Dupuy de Lôme quotes about 24 tons of scrap out of a steel weight of 830 tons for the *Great Britain*.

Plates were about 7ft 6in x 1ft 9in and were arranged using a half block model. The joints between plates could be lapped or strapped. A good yard could build at the rate of 100 tons in 100 days using eighty men.

Guadalupe was thought by Dupuy de Lôme to be the strongest ship built at that time. She had 121 frames, each made up of an angle with a reverse bar making a Z shape, spaced 16in apart in the engine room, then 18in, increasing to 20in fore and aft. Her bottom plates were ⅝in reducing to ½in at the waterline and ⅜in above. Despite this most enthusiastic report, the French navy rejected Laird's proposal for an iron frigate costing £36,000.

On completion, the *Guadalupe* sailed for Mexico under Commander Edward P Charlwood RN, a serving officer on leave. He joined the ship in 1841, watched the final stages of completion and remained in command for the next two years, a period which included the Mexican expedition against Yucatan when she and the *Montezuma*, also built by Laird, came under fire from both ships and forts. Baxter suggests that the construction of these two ships in British yards and their operations under the command of officers of the Royal Navy with largely British crews could have raised interesting points of international law.[24]

On his return to England, Charlwood reported to the Board on the advantages of iron ships in war, a report which was subsequently repeated to a parliamentary commission in 1847.[25] He said, 'For general purposes, I am decidedly of the opinion that in several points iron is much preferable to wood for steam vessels'. He then listed what he saw as the important advantages of iron ships: buoyancy; roominess, due to thin sides and shallow beams; watertight bulkheads which make iron ships much safer from the risks of grounding; and economy in timber, a material then becoming scarce. The only serious disadvantage was the problem of fouling.

A modern naval architect would agree with Charlwood on these points. Appendix 9 shows that an iron hull would weigh some 80 per cent of the corresponding wooden one and have about 20 per cent more capacity. The iron ship would be much more durable and would be more rigid, better able to resist the vibration caused by high-power machinery and the screw.

On the effect of shot he said, 'The damage is considerably less than is usually suffered by a wood vessel; and I should also consider that there were nothing like the number of splinters which are generally forced out by a shot sent through a wooden vessel's side'. Under questioning, Charlwood described his experiences under fire in the *Benbow* at the bombardment of Acre, where his ship had been repeatedly hit by shot, when the wood gave off enormous splinters. He thought that iron ships were much safer than the wooden walls.

During the Mexican campaign against Texas, the *Guadalupe* was under fire almost daily for four or five weeks and was hulled a number of times by 18pdr or 24pdr shot. The holes were clean punctures, rivets were only torn out for a few inches at most and the holes were easily plugged. There were few, if any, dangerous splinters.

During the action of 16 May 1843 the *Guadalupe* was in action with the Texan corvette *Austin* of 20 guns, hitting her about a dozen times with 68pdr shot and causing the Texan to withdraw. Charlwood thought his ship was a better gun platform than the wooden sloop *Salamander* on which he had served. He repeated that the iron ship, if properly built, of good iron, was safer than a wooden ship in a gale and was more 'buoyant'. There had never been any difficulty with the compass; it was a simple but lengthy job to adjust it and well within the capability of a naval officer instructed in the method.

Charlwood's meeting with Sidney Herbert on his return was reassuring, but did not affect the decision, already taken, to expand the programme of iron warship building. The new Board, under the Earl of Haddington, with Herbert as First Secretary, invited tenders from Ditchburn, Laird, Fairbairn and the Great Western Railway Company on 21 January 1843 for an iron war steamer of 200NHP. She was to carry a 32pdr (50cwt) at each end and a 32pdr carronade on each beam. Ditchburn and Mare's tender was accepted in April 1843 with a change in machinery from Maudslay to a Boulton & Watt set of 350NHP. *Trident*, as she was named, was the first seagoing iron fighting ship for the Royal Navy when she was launched on 16 December 1845. She was a typical paddler of the period with two masts and a single funnel abaft the paddle boxes, which carried box boats. Like many iron ships, *Trident* had a long life, finally being broken up in 1866.

Early in 1843 an even more ambitious step was taken when the Surveyor (Symonds) and the Steam Department (Parry) were instructed to draw up a specification for an iron paddle frigate. Laird was invited to tender using the engines which Forrester (Liverpool) had already under construction for *Janus*. Laird's tender was accepted in April 1843 and the lines were agreed in August. Originally to be called *Vulcan*, her name was changed to *Birkenhead* in February 1845 and she was launched two weeks after *Trident* on 30 December 1845. She entered service in 1846 as a brig but was soon converted to a barquentine.

Table 7.4 **HMS *Birkenhead***[26]

Displacement	1,918 tons, tonnage 1,405 (bm)
Dimensions	210ft x 37ft 8in (60ft 6in over paddle boxes) x 15ft 9in. Depth 22ft 11in
Machinery	536NHP Forrester side lever. 12–13 knots. Tubular boilers
Coal	500 tons
Armament	Four 10in, four 68pdr
Complement	250

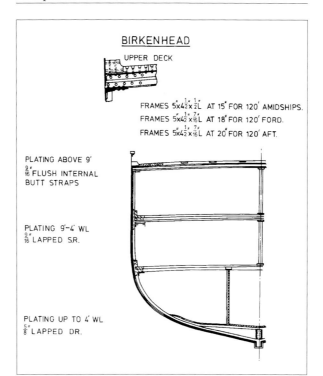

23. E C B Corlett, *The Iron Ship*, Bradford-on-Avon (1974, reprinted London 1990).

24. J P Baxter, *The Introduction of the Ironclad Warship*, Harvard (1933, reprinted Hamden 1968).

25. 1847 Committee.

26. E J Reed, *Shipbuilding in Iron and Steel*, London (1869).

Midship section of *Birkenhead*. (RINA)

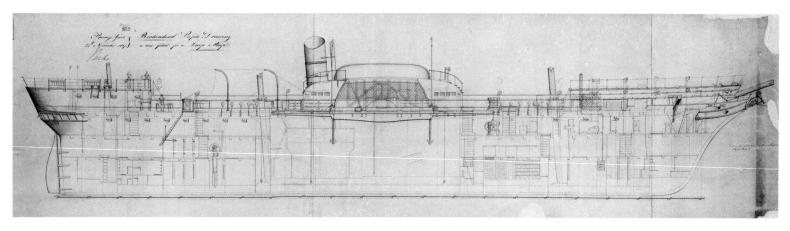

Profile draught of *Birkenhead* as fitted as a troopship in 1847. Originally the iron paddle frigate *Vulcan*, designed by Laird. (© *National Maritime Museum DR7360A)*

Laird had designed her with six bulkheads, watertight to the upper deck, with the exception of an opening between the engine and boiler rooms. There were iron stringer plates under the upper deck raising the neutral axis (about which the ship bends) and adding much to her strength. Side plating was ⅝in thick from the keel to the 4ft waterline, lapped and double riveted. From there up to the 9ft waterline, it was ⁵⁄₁₆in thick, single riveted, while the upper strakes were flush with internal butt straps.

Soon after entering service, the *Birkenhead* was used to tow the *Great Britain* off the shore at Dundrum Bay, where she had been aground for many months.[27] Soon afterwards she was placed in reserve until converted into a troopship in 1851. Alterations demanded by the trooping authorities included cutting large openings in the bulkheads to improve access and ventilation. Her armament was reduced to four small guns.

Following several uneventful voyages to Canada and Cape Town, she sailed from Queenstown (Cobh) on 17 January 1852 with 680 people on board. The troops, mainly young recruits, were carried on the lower and main decks, forward and aft of the machinery. The crew were in the forecastle and the officers of both army and Navy in cabins aft on the upper deck.

After leaving Simonstown, she sailed north for Algoa Bay where the troops were to be landed but, at about 0200hrs on 26 February, she hit a reef off Danger Point while steaming at 8½ knots. A pinnacle of rock pierced her bottom just in front of the foremast and, since her bulkheads were no longer watertight, the whole fore end of the ship flooded immediately, drowning most of the men on the lower troop deck. The loss of buoyancy forward caused intolerable stresses in the hull amidships; the plates fractured and she broke in half. On the after end, the troops fell in, facing inboard, while women and children were placed in the boats, an exhibition of courage and discipline often quoted by Victorian writers and owing much to the training given during the voyage by Major Seton. He was afraid that the two small boats would be swamped if too many people tried to get into them at once and kept the troops in rank until the water

27. Corlett, op cit.

The loss of the *Birkenhead* on the night of 26 February 1852, shown ten minutes after striking the rock. The breaking up of the hull did nothing to enhance the reputation of iron ships. (© *National Maritime Museum neg 2126)*

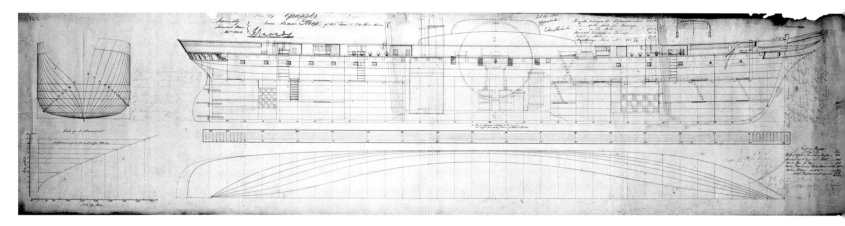

rose over the deck. All those in the boats were rescued, together with sixty-nine who swam ashore and about thirty who clung to the mast of the sunken ship, still sticking out of the water. Of the 648 on board, a total of 193 were saved. The remains of the ship were sold at Cape Town for £164 13s 6d.

There were many rumours that *Birkenhead* was carrying a large quantity of gold and several attempts have been made to explore the wreck. In 1958 a diver named Decker found that the ship was in three sections and was able to find and explore the two forward parts at a depth of 95ft. The after part, where the gold was believed to be, was not located. He reported that the guns were still in position close to the paddles and many fittings were recovered. It is not known (1986) whether the after section has been located, but no find of gold has been reported.

The iron screw frigates

The Board, with Sir George Cockburn as senior naval member, continued to enlarge the iron fleet. Sir George, well known for his harassment of the US coastline in 1814, culminating in the burning of a few public buildings in Washington, was a complex character. While there are many apparently well-founded stories of his personal dislike for the new technologies of the machine age and the new men who worked them, it is also clear that he realised the value of screw propellers and iron hulls and actively promoted their introduction.

An order for a few small iron sloops followed. Tenders were accepted from Napier for the first three on 16 January 1844 and from Ditchburn and Mare for three more. The following month it was decided that *Lizard* and *Torch* should be to lines by the surveyor with 150NHP side lever engines. *Jackall* and *Harpy* would

Grappler. Profile draught for the iron paddle sloop designed and built by William Fairbairn. The rapid corrosion of her hull contributed to the Admiralty's decision to give up the construction of iron fighting ships. (© *National Maritime Museum DR08213*)

Fairy. A small Royal Yacht used mainly for river service. She was among the first iron ships and a very early screw steamer. The Palace seemed to be encouraging new technology. (© *National Maritime Museum F2856-001*)

Fire Queen, a small iron paddler, purchased in 1847. (© *National Maritime Museum D0666*)

have the same lines, but direct acting engines of the highest power available, while *Bloodhound* (Napier) and *Myrmidon* (Ditchburn) would have 150NHP engines and lines by the builders. No accurate trials data are available by which the merits of these designs can be compared. All six ships seem to have had a long life: *Torch* and *Myrmidon* were sold, but not broken up, in 1856 and 1858; the others were broken up between 1886 and 1909. They cost £13,000 to £16,000 each. Two of them went into battle, as described a little later. *Harpy* had a stranger fate; she was used in 1892 by the War Office for tests of the Zalinski dynamite gun and other weapons.

A small packet, the *Princess Alice*, was purchased from Maudslay in January 1844, and then in May of that year Fairbairn was asked to design an iron paddle sloop to accept the 220NHP Maudslay engines ordered but not used for the *Trident*. His tender was accepted in November and she completed in 1846 as the *Grappler*.

She had an unusual construction with special plates rolled so that they were some 60 per cent thicker at the edges to compensate for the material lost in the rivet holes, even with the rivet heads countersunk (see drawing in Hayward[28]). She spent her first commission based on Sierra Leone, returning to England in June 1849. Her bottom was extremely foul after three years in warm water. More serious was the leak which had developed on the way home, which was found to be due to electrolytic corrosion caused where a copper pipe was attached to the iron hull. The Board paid a special visit to inspect the damage, as the whole subject of iron ships was under review. After they left, further areas of serious corrosion were found around some copper bolts and, later, many plates well away from copper fittings were found to be badly pitted and beginning to leak. It was decided to remove her machinery and sell the hull for scrap; after removing items of value, the dealer resold the bare hull for conversion to a sailing ship.

The next iron ship was the *Fairy*, described as a tender to the Royal Yacht. Since she was also one of the earliest screw vessels, it would suggest that the Palace as well as the Board was demonstrating interest in, and support for, new technology.

Towards the end of 1844 tenders were invited from ten builders of iron ships for an iron second-class screw frigate and, alternatively, for an iron first-class sloop. In November, four firms were selected and, after development of their proposals, orders were placed in February and March 1845. These four ships, described in Table

Table 7.5 **Iron Screw Frigates**

Frigate	Builder	Laid down	Displacement (tons)	Dimensions	Sold, etc
Greenock	Scott	3 Sep 1845	2,065	213ft x 37ft 4in x 15ft 6in	1873
Megaera	Fairbairn	Aug 1845	2,025	207ft x 37ft 10in x 16ft	1871
Simoom	Napier	Oct 1845	2,920	246ft x 41ft x 17ft 6in	1887
Vulcan	Ditchburn	12 Mar 1846	2,474	220ft x 41ft 5in x 17ft 6in	1867
Great Britain	Patterson	1839	3,675	289ft x 50ft 6in x 12ft	–
Himalaya	Mare	1852	4,690	340ft x 56ft 2in x ??ft	1940

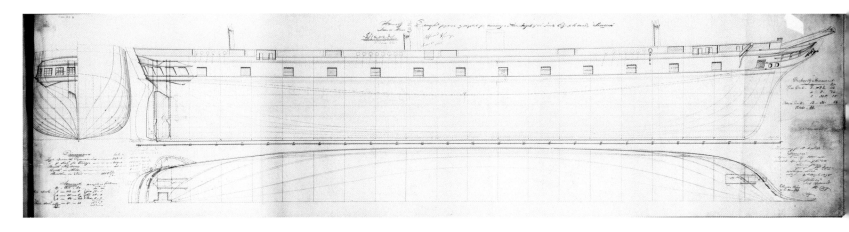

7.5, were among the largest iron ships built up to that date, even though not quite as big as Brunel's *Great Britain* with which they are compared.

Greenock was laid down in 1845 as the *Pegasus*, renamed in 1846. She carried another link with her builders in her figurehead, a bust of John Scott. Like all these early iron ships, she was massively built.[29] She had a Scott, Sinclair, two-cylinder, horizontal geared engine of 656NHP. The engine took some 21ft out of the 72ft length devoted to machinery, the four box boilers, each with four grates, taking the rest. Her armament was probably intended to be ten 32pdrs, but by January 1848 it was shown as four 68pdrs, two 56pdrs and four 32pdrs on the spar deck with four more 32pdrs on the main deck, but no armament was ever installed.

Megaera, ordered from Fairbairn, was in trouble from the beginning as he was getting into financial difficulties and sold about half his Millwall yard just as *Megaera* was started.[30] The contract specified a price of £21 15s 0d per ton for the hull, a remarkable reduction from that being quoted only a few years earlier.

Work was suspended in 1847 but was restarted later and she was launched in May 1849; a happy day for Fairbairn, since he could at last dispose of the rest of his loss-making Millwall yard. After the launch, *Megaera* was towed down river to Woolwich Dockyard for installation of her machinery, a 350NHP set by Rennie. By February 1850 she was complete and was docked for bottom painting, starting sea trials at the end of March. On completion of trials she was put 'in ordinary' at Sheerness, but six weeks later instructions were received to bring her forward as a relief for the *Cambrian* on the East Indies Station. However, before she was ready it was decided that iron ships were unfit to fight and, like the other iron frigates, she became a troopship. She was left with six of the fourteen guns for which she was designed.

Megaera remained in service until 1871, when she

Simoom. Sheer elevation and lines. One of the largest iron ships in the world, she was ordered as a frigate but converted into a troopship. (© *National Maritime Museum DR7274*)

28. R Hayward, *The Story and Scandal of HMS Megaera*, Buxton (1978).

29. J M Maber, 'The iron screw frigate *Greenock*', *Warship 23* (1982).

30. Hayward, op cit.

Himalaya. She was a new and big P&O liner, bought as a troopship during the Crimean War. Opponents of iron ships forecast a short life for her but she survived as a hulk until sunk by German dive-bombers in 1940. (© *National Maritime Museum N05466*)

Oberon. One of three large iron packets authorised in 1845 for use on the mail service between the Ionian Islands, Malta and Greece; later reclassified as a third-class sloop. *(© National Maritime Museum PW5616)*

31. W Pole, *The Life of Sir William Fairbairn* (1877, reprinted Newton Abbot 1970).

sprang a serious leak while crossing the Indian Ocean and was beached on the island of St Paul. The subsequent inquiry blamed poor maintenance and old age, though one may note that the only two large iron warships with serious corrosion problems were the two built by Fairbairn.[31]

Simoom was the biggest of the quartet and was originally intended to have an armament of twelve 32pdrs on the main deck and two 68pdrs (112cwt) and four 32pdrs on the upper deck. She cost £95,000 to build. She had a long life in service as a troopship, being broken up in 1887. *Vulcan* also became a troopship, later being sold as the *Jorawur* in 1867.

In 1854, the Admiralty bought the iron steamer *Himalaya* from the P&O line as a transport and she is sometimes described as a frigate. Of 3,438 tons, she was among the world's very largest ships when launched in 1853. Howard Douglas was opposed to the purchase and forecast a short life for her. She was paid off in 1894 and, serving as a hulk at Portland, was sunk by dive-bombers in June 1940.

Seven smaller iron war vessels were ordered in 1845, while in 1846 the Admiralty ordered three big and fast iron packets. Two smaller iron packets followed in 1846, together with the only iron sailing warship, the brig *Recruit*. She was traded back to Mare in part exchange in 1849 and later became a screw merchant ship, the *Harbinger*.

The Admiralty built no more iron ships until the Crimean War and very few even then. The complex story of the loss of confidence in iron will be told in the next chapter.

Condemnation of Iron Ships | *Eight*

Beaucoup de préjuges, de doutes raisonnables et de difficultés réelles.

Dupuy de Lôme, 1842[1]

DURING 1845, prejudice, reasonable doubts and real problems all became apparent, and many people began to suggest that the iron warship had not been adequately tested and proven against the effects of gunfire. Murray, Fairbairn's deputy, himself an iron shipbuilder, began to press for tests,[2] as did Colonel Dundas RA. The author of *Naval Gunnery*, Sir Howard Douglas, an arch opponent of iron ships, tells a somewhat different story, inaccurate in the dates, but probably correct in essentials.[3] Lieutenant Walter, the inventor of a rubber compound, Kamptulicon, which he believed would be successful in preventing holes in iron hulls, was yet another urging tests.[4]

Eventually, Sir George Cockburn agreed to a test programme which was carried out at Woolwich Arsenal in 1845–6. The trials were held in conditions of secrecy, which was most unusual at that time. Rear Admiral Bowles, himself a Lord Commissioner, told the Parliamentary Commission in 1847 that he was not aware of any tests.[5] No official records of these tests have been found, but the accounts referred to in the previous paragraph and that by Hosean[6] are in agreement, and the description which follows should be essentially correct.

Trials began in August 1845 and continued for some months. The target represented the side of an iron ship or, in some tests, both sides and the deck of such a vessel. Linings of wood or Kamptulicon were also tried. The gun was a 32pdr, firing at a range of 30–40yds, with reduced charges to obtain realistic striking velocities for different ranges.

Number 1 target was built up of three thicknesses of ⅛in plate, double chain riveted together. It was 6ft square and only one shot was fired. This made a clean hole the size of the shot, and none of the rivets was started. Number 2 target was made of a single thickness of ⅛in plate, flush jointed and single riveted, with frames 9in deep connected to the plate by double 6in x 3in reversed angle bars. One half of the target was lined at the back with Kamptulicon, which was intended to catch splinters. Two shots fired with a full 10lb charge went through both plate and lining, carrying the splinters along with them. The Kamptulicon almost completely closed the hole after the shot had passed, making it nearly watertight. The plates and bolts which held the backing were broken and seriously damaged.

Other rounds were fired with 8lb, 6lb, 4lb, 2lb and 1lb charges to simulate the effect of increasing range. The slowest shots still made a hole no bigger than the ball, but the edges were 'bent back with ragged radiating points'. Targets 3, 4 and 5 were formed of double and single ⅜in and 1½in plate and were fired at in much the same way and with much the same results.

There seems to have been general agreement that the holes made by high-velocity shot were clean and easily plugged. To deal with the jagged hole made by a nearly spent shot, the parasol plug was developed. This plug was made of sailcloth or rubberised fabric, in the form of a parasol or umbrella with a long handle, and was intended to be pushed out through the shot hole, opened and drawn back onto the hole so as to cover it. Dupuy de Lôme refers to this plug in his 1842 report and also refers to tests at Woolwich by that date.

Murray describes the problems of splinters:

> These experiments showed that shot, in striking plates of this thickness, was frequently though not invariably broken and the portion of plate taken out by the shot was broken into a number of small and most dangerous splinters. [7]

Low Moor iron was tried in comparison with targets of common boiler plate but the difference in quality of these two kinds of iron made no difference whatsoever in splintering or in the general effect:

> Layers of timber varying in thickness from 3in to 18in were then tried with a view of collecting and stopping the splinters. It was found that this was not effected with less than about 14in of thickness.

Wadding and packing of various kinds held in by a backing plate were also tried without success. Kamptulicon of a thickness equal to the wood (14in) worked well.

The effect of a glancing blow was studied by firing a 32pdr at 200yds with a 10lb charge. Under these conditions the shot, hitting between the frames, was not deviated and penetrated, making an elongated, clean hole.

The reverse side of the target was also fired at, to simulate a shot passing right through the ship and exiting through the disengaged side. The effect was much as in the previous tests, except that the rivets within a 2–3ft radius were loosened and the heads broken off some of them. When the reverse side of a target lined with Kamptulicon was attacked, it appeared that, with the larger charges, a somewhat bigger hole was made in the iron, though this was partially offset by the

1. S Dupuy de Lôme, *Mémoire sur la Construction des Bâtiments en Fer*, Paris (1844).

2. A Murray, *Shipbuilding in Iron and Steel*, London (1863).

3. H Douglas, *A Treatise on Naval Gunnery* (1855, reprinted London 1982).

4. G Walter, *Iron Steam Ships*, London (1850).

5. Select Committee 1847.

6. J C Hosean, *The Steam Navy and the Application of Screw Propulsion to Sea Going Line of Battle Ships*, London (1863).

7. Murray, op cit.

closing of the lining. A shot fired with a ¼lb charge merely bounced off the Kamptulicon without any penetration. With a ½lb charge the shot lodged in the lining.

The trials can be summarised as follows:

a. A shot fired at normal velocity would make a clean hole in ⅜in or ½in iron which could easily be plugged.

b. A nearly spent shot would still make a small hole but the edges would be jagged, making it more difficult to plug. It seems that the parasol plug should have been a good solution to this problem.

c. These conclusions were not altered by the quality of iron used.

d. Glancing shot caused no additional problems.

e. Shots hitting the reverse side made holes similar to those described in a. and b. but in addition rivets might be started over a 2–3ft radius.

f. A large number of splinters came from both the plate and, even more, from the broken shot. This result, too, was unaffected by the quality of the iron.

g. Fourteen inches of wood or Kamptulicon stopped almost all splinters. (Note that *Simoom* had 10in wood inside her frames.)

h. Kamptulicon was partially successful in sealing shot holes in the engaged side. Some increase in damage might occur when shot hit Kamptulicon before piercing the iron of the disengaged side. (Separate tests showed that Kamptulicon had very good strength and adhesion to iron. Its fire resistance, if any, was not measured.)

These trials continued through 1846 and were finally reported to Cockburn by 7 September 1846.

Contemporary interpretation of these tests was mixed. Douglas wrote: 'vessels entirely constructed of iron were utterly unfit for all the purposes of war, whether armed or as troopships'.[8] On the other hand, Murray wrote, 'I did not think that they [the Woolwich tests] were conclusive against iron vessels for ships of war'. Murray may have been right, but nor did the tests offer strong support for iron ships.

Parliamentary opposition to the iron fleet was growing, led by Admiral Sir Charles Napier, the leading Whig spokesman on naval matters. As mentioned previously, Napier had been the financial backer of the *Aaron Manby* as well as her first master and had lost his money in the venture, changing him into an outspoken opponent of iron ships.[9] While the main attack was on the alleged vulnerability of the iron ship to gunfire, there was also concern over the real and unsolved problem of fouling (Appendix 7).

There was no anti-fouling paint available when the first iron ships completed and copper sheathing could not be attached directly to an iron hull, as the two dissimilar metals act as an electric battery and cause very rapid corrosion of the iron. A single voyage to India could lead to a growth of barnacles 12in in length, reducing speed by about 2 knots. The Admiralty Chemist, W J Hay, recognised the value of copper oxide as a toxin and used it in his first anti-fouling paint in 1845. His own account describes successful trials on

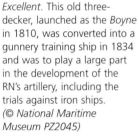

Excellent. This old three-decker, launched as the *Boyne* in 1810, was converted into a gunnery training ship in 1834 and was to play a large part in the development of the RN's artillery, including the trials against iron ships. (© *National Maritime Museum PZ2045*)

Rocket, *Fairy*, *Undine* and *Recruit* by 1847.[10] His rivals were less complimentary about his paint, one describing it as a good manure. It seems clear that Hay was on the right lines but unable to guarantee consistent success; this was a feature of anti-fouling trials until very recently (Appendix 7).

Hay's supporters claimed that the success, even if limited, tipped the balance in favour of retaining the existing iron ships. The Surveyor, Symonds, was called on to report on iron ships in July 1846. His reply was unfavourable, which was not surprising in the light of an entry in his diary a few months earlier: 'I have been ordered to report on the monstrous, iron screw vessels … Both were found wanting in displacement and volume and were three times mistaken'.

During July 1846 doubts and fears as to the viability of the iron fleet grew within the Board. There is no direct evidence as to the cause of these doubts, but it is likely that the government, which was losing its grip on Parliament, found preliminary reports of the Woolwich tests an inadequate response to the attacks of Napier and other critics.

On 27 July the Surveyor, still Symonds, was asked for his views on the fouling of iron ships. Since he was well known to be hostile to the programme and had not been consulted before, it must have been clear that his report would be adverse; perhaps that was what was wanted.

On the 30th of the same month, Captain Berkeley ordered the tender *Ruby* to be prepared for firing trials at the gunnery school, HMS *Excellent*.[11] *Ruby* had been built at Bristol in 1842 and had been used as a tender, first at Chatham and then at Portsmouth. From the start the correspondence files were full of complaints; she was too small to tow more than a lighter, her accommodation was inadequate even as a yard craft, and her machinery was unreliable. In later years she was mainly used to take shipwrights from Portsmouth Dockyard out to work on ships at anchor in Spithead.

After only four years of life she was worn out. Her plates, only ⅛in thick when new, were seriously corroded and the plates between beams were said to deflect so much that they were hardly safe to carry a man's weight. The survey reported:

Her state was very bad; the iron of which she was constructed was originally very thin, not thicker than a half-crown; the seams of rivets were many of them quite gone; the ribs were very far apart – I should consider it likely that they were about four feet apart, instead of being ten inches or a foot; the heads of her rivets were quite gone, especially internally, the deck was also partly removed for the purpose of lifting the machinery out previous to the experiment, and this made the vessel still weaker.[12]

This was the 90ft harbour launch which was to face the heavy guns of the gunnery training ship *Excellent* and become the focus of controversy ever since. She was placed broadside on to the guns at a range of 450yds and

A gun crew of HMS *Excellent*. From Howard Douglas's *Naval Gunnery*, 1855 edition.

shot from 8in and 32pdr guns were fired at her. The report states:

All the shot passed through both sides, the holes made on the first side being of the size of the shot, and generally smooth even when striking on a rib, but the damage done to the opposite side of the ship was very different as in the case when the shot struck on a rib the damage was very great. The iron sheets were torn off and injured to a considerable extent, and even when the shot passed clean through between the ribs, the holes made were of a difficult nature to stop, from their edges being turned outward. The splinters from the first side were few, but very severe.

The *Ruby* was then placed end on to the guns but the shot fired at her so tore the ribs and plates that it was evident that a similar vessel so situated would be in danger of being instantly sunk by one well aimed shot.[13]

A 10in shot with a 12lb charge passed through the bottom plates on one side, struck a rib on the other side, and made a hole 4ft x 3ft.

Captain Chads, of HMS *Excellent*, reached the obvious and unexceptionable conclusion that 'the above

8. Douglas, op cit.

9. *Life and Letters of Sir C Napier*, Naval Records Society.

10. W J Hay, 'The protection of iron ships from corrosion and fouling', *Trans INA*, vol IV (1863).

11. D Chads, 'Experiments at HMS *Excellent* on iron built ships'.

12. E P Halsted, 'Iron cased ships', *Journal of United Services Institute* (1861).

13. Chads, op cit.

Damage to *Ruby*, based on official drawings. *(RINA)*

HMS RUBY   6-7 AUG 1846
40 SHOTS FIRED FROM HMS EXCELLENT

STARBOARD SIDE TOWARDS GUNS

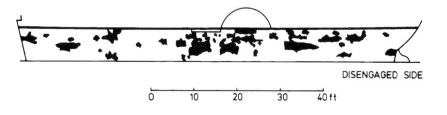

DISENGAGED SIDE

0   10   20   30   40 ft

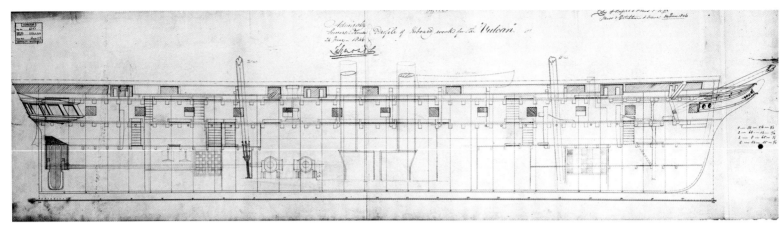

Vulcan. Profile draught of the ship as originally designed as an iron screw frigate, 1846. (© National Maritime Museum DR06397)

experiment clearly proved vessels of the *Ruby* class unfit for war purposes'. No other conclusion seems to have been drawn by anyone in authority, but the trial was used by those less responsible as evidence with which to attack the whole concept of iron ships.

The reason for this trial remains obscure. It did not need a trial to prove that a small launch was unfit for war. Those planning a trial must always consider what the possible outcomes may be and what can be learnt from them. It is most likely that someone decided to save money by expending an unwanted ship, rather than build expensive targets, but there is no evidence to support this suggestion, nor the alternative suggestion that the trial was set up to condemn the iron ship programme. The end came for *Ruby* on 7 August 1846 when her mutilated remains were sold for £20.[14]

The Board received the formal report[15] of the *Ruby* trials on 8 August and made their next move on the 27th. A letter was sent to the builders of the four iron frigates asking them to prepare, at their own expense, targets representing a section of the ship building at their yards. Scott & Sinclair (*Greenock*) estimated the cost at £1,500 to £2,000 which at £33 per ton suggests either a very large target or, more probably, reluctance to carry out the work. Ditchburn & Mare (*Vulcan*) pointed out that the *Ruby* was too small to teach any valuable lessons and suggested firing a few shots at *Sharpshooter* and *Rifleman*.

On 1 December 1846 the Board instructed Symonds to find out what costs would be incurred if the frigates were cancelled. HM Consul in New York was asked, by a letter dated 3 March 1847, to find out details of the US trials at Sandy Hook. That month a formal decision was made to complete the four screw frigates as troopships, and later it was decided to convert the *Birkenhead* in the same way.

The troopship conversion involved fitting smaller engines to provide more room for troops and a greater endurance under steam. With her original engines *Simoom* could carry 500 troops and coal for eight days' steaming at 10 knots, costing £60 per day. With the smaller engines, Edye claimed that she could carry 1,000 troops with twenty days' coal at 7¾ knots.[16]

As troopships, their official capacities were as listed in Table 8.1:

The change of engines and their subsequent destination has confused historians ever since. It is hoped (but with no great certainty) that the following table is correct.

The new engines were removed from the unsuccessful blockship conversions of frigates, discussed in Chapter 11.

November 1847 brought two more adverse reports on iron ships. Commander Slade of the iron brig *Recruit* said that she was worthless due to the effect of shot, sickness due to condensation and compass problems. Iron was, he thought, unsuitable for the construction of

Recruit. Structural drawing of the RN's only iron-hulled sailing ship. After less than two years in service, the brig was the subject of a highly critical report from her commander and was sold back to her builder. (© National Maritime Museum DR3742)

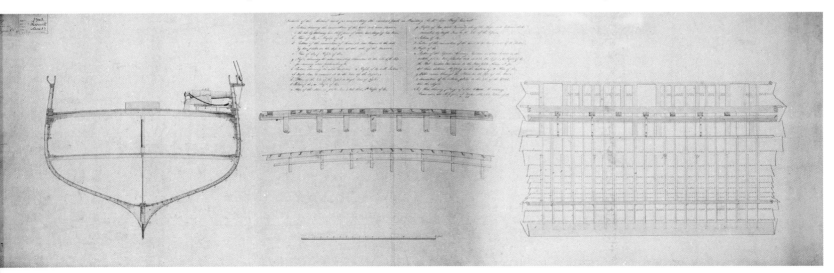

Table 8.1 **Troopship Capacities**

	Vulcan	*Megaera*	*Simoom*
Officers	27	26	29
Men	650	392	740
Ladies	5	6	8
Women	20	24	45
Children	30	48	80

Table 8.2 **Ships' Engines and their Destinations**

Ship	Original engine builder	Went to	New engine from	Builder
Megaera	Fairbairn	*Algiers*	*Forth*	Miller
Simoom	Napier	*D of Wellington*	*Eurotas*	Portsmouth
Vulcan	Rennie		*Seahorse*	Maudslay
Greenock	Scott Sinclair	*Hannibal*		Rennie

ships.[17] On the 15th, the Foreign Office received an alarming report that the iron gunboats *Harpy* and *Lizard* had been 'riddled by grapeshot' in the Parana River.

British and French ships operating several hundred miles up river in Uruguay became engaged with field guns at very close range. Wildly exaggerated accounts of the damage and casualties were written and are still quoted, such as that of Sir Howard Douglas:

> In consequence also of the ships being struck the splinters and rivets detached by the shot flew about like grapes and nearly all the men killed and wounded suffered from this cause.[18]

After reading this, one may be surprised to learn that after a heavy engagement with field guns at a range of 60yds, the casualties were *Lizard* (four killed, four wounded) and *Harpy* (one slightly wounded).[19]

Lieutenant Tylden of the *Lizard* says that his ship received seven shots between wind and water; nine cannon shot, fourteen grape and forty-one musket balls higher up; and seven shot in the funnel. He says, 'at the same time, the heavy shot and grape riddling the vessel from stem to stern, I ordered the officers and men to go below, but this step, I regret to say, had not the desired effect, two officers being killed in the gunroom'. After a further passage past the batteries on 4 June, Tylden sent home a grape shot which, on 21 April, had hit about a foot above the waterline and, after penetrating the iron side, carried on through the lining and two bulkheads before lodging in the opposite side.

Lieutenant Proctor of the *Harpy* says of the April action:

> One shot only, after passing through two floats and damaging a sector of the wheel, struck the iron hull

immediately outside an angle iron. The shot had not sufficient momentum to pass through the side but caused a split in the shape of a cross, breaking the said angle iron, which there is no doubt impeded the shot from passing through. It was necessary to rivet a patch of sheet iron, a foot square, over the part damaged.

There was no mention in either account of any casualties due to splinters. In fact, the resistance of these two small ships to field gun fire at close range is greatly to the credit of iron construction.

Even though iron was now out of favour, Mare offered a 50-gun iron frigate in June 1848 and in August the Board was given the chance to purchase the *Great Britain*. Neither offer was accepted, though a smaller iron ship from Mare was considered. Only in October 1848 was it decided to convert the *Birkenhead* for troop carrying.

There had been several other well-considered trials at HMS *Excellent* in the 1840s.[20] There were several tests of the effects of shot and shell on coal bunkers, and some very elaborate trials of the effect of the destruction of the funnel. In 1846 an old funnel, 3ft in diameter, was fired on at 600yds range by a 32pdr; after eight hits it was still standing, though the report points out that it would probably have fallen in a seaway. A broadside of fourteen guns was then fired, of which four shots hit (an interesting measure of accuracy), but the funnel still stood. Later, two or three shells hit the funnel, and 'afterwards, the braces on the weather side being shot away and there being a strong breeze, the funnel fell'. Further trials were carried out with a 4ft diameter funnel which was hit by fifteen bar shot and four round shot and remained upright. Various schemes were then tried for stopping the holes, the best being that of Thomas Brown, engineer of the *Bee*, attached to the Naval College. Two

14. Halsted, op cit.
15. Select Committee 1847.
16. Ibid.
17. Ibid.
18. Douglas, op cit.
19. Halsted, op cit.
20. Chads, op cit.

Megaera. Iron screw frigate, converted into a troopship and lost due to corrosion in June 1871. (© *National Maritime Museum DR3445*)

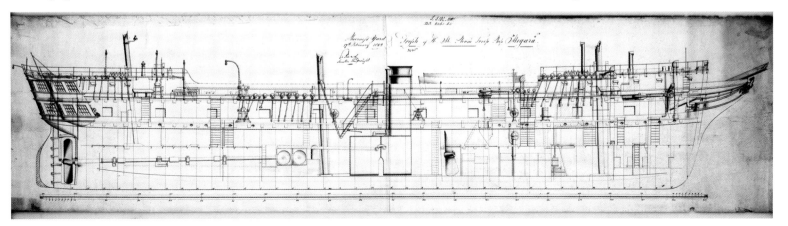

spring catches were attached to an iron plate, and the springs were pushed through the shot hole, fixing the plate to the damaged funnel. The security of this patch was proved by firing two shot through it without the patch being dislodged.

The integrity of the funnel was seen as very important since the draught of air which kept the boiler furnace going depended on the height of the flue. For the next part of the trials, five holes were cut in the funnel of the steam tug *Echo* and closed with Brown's patches. The holes were uncovered while the ship was at full power without any noticeable effect on the draught of air, power or fuel consumption. A similar trial was carried out in *Bee*, in which the funnel was removed entirely from just above the deck.

Arguments over the value of iron ships did not cease with the government's decision to stop building such warships. By 1849 the controversy centred on the use of iron for mail ships, which received a government subsidy in return for a promise that they could be used as auxiliary cruisers in time of war. It was argued, by Douglas and others, that the subsidy should not be paid to the owners of iron steamers since such ships were 'unfit for war'. Despite this argument, many of the big liner companies, the P&O in particular, were building considerable numbers of iron ships because of their commercial benefits such as lighter hulls, increased capacity and the need for rigid hulls to accept powerful machinery driving screw propellers.

Another committee was set up in April 1849 'to inquire into the practicability of procuring, by means of the commercial steam marine of the country, a reserve steam navy'. Anderson of the P&O said that his company had eleven iron ships and fifteen of wood. He also presented a table which showed that the overall proportion of iron ships was small (sixty-six out of 1,110, or 20,779 gross tons out of 255,321) but contained a much larger proportion of modern big ships.

In 1850 the Select Committee on Estimates was given a full account of the *Ruby* trials and for the first time it was appreciated how unrepresentative these trials had been. The committee concluded, 'that no vessel of that material [iron] intended for war had yet been subjected by experiment to any proof of shot whatsoever'. The Board had already realised that there was very little evidence on which to draw proper conclusions concerning the effect of shot on iron hulls and had initiated a new series of trials to be carried out by Captain Chads of *Excellent*. It would seem that those involved were unaware of the Woolwich trials, since there was a fair measure of repetition.[21]

These trials were carried out at *Excellent* between 1849 and 1851 in order to determine the effect of shot on iron ships.[22] The first series of tests, on 6 November 1849, was planned to compare the resistance of iron plates and timber to musket balls, canister and grape shot. The first trial used a marine's musket, charged with 4½oz of powder at a range of 50yds against targets of ⅛in, ¼in and ⅜in iron, and of 1in, 2in and 3in oak; the ⅜in iron and the 3in oak were proof against such

Megaera at sea in 1869. Her next voyage was to end in disaster when she had to be beached on St Paul Island in the Indian Ocean to prevent foundering. The corrosion of her plating was responsible for flooding beyond the capacity of the pumps. *(© National Maritime Museum PU6193)*

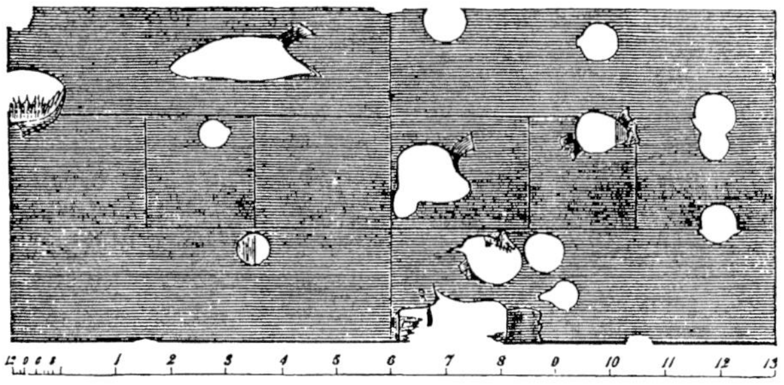

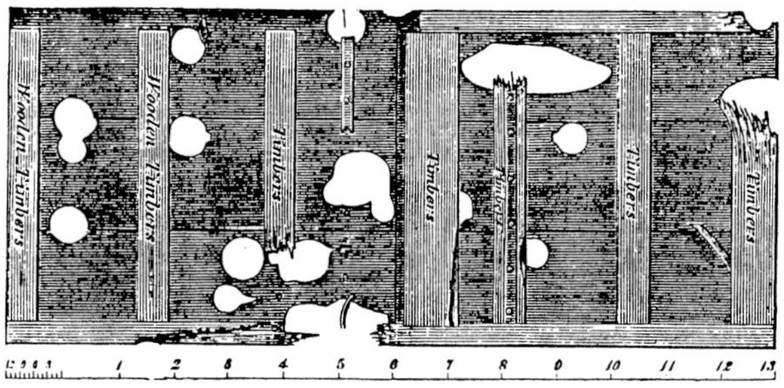

Left: Tests of 5 July 1851. The target seen from the outside which, for this test was covered half with ⅜in and half with ½in plate instead of the ⅝in used in the first series. Hits were made with 32lb solid and 8in hollow shot. *(From Howard Douglas's* Naval Gunnery*)*

Right: The same target was then turned and fired on with reduced charges to represent shot which had passed right through the ship and hit the farther side. There was serious tearing of the plate making jagged holes, difficult to stop. *(From Howard Douglas's* Naval Gunnery*)*

shot. In the next trial, case shot were fired from a 32pdr/56cwt gun with 6lb charges at ⅜in and ½in iron, and against 3in and 4in planks arranged 100yds from the gun. The thicker iron and timber stopped all shot, though the iron was cracked at the back. The next trial was of grape shot fired from the same gun with a 6lb charge at targets of ½in, ⅝in and ¾in iron, and 4in, 5in and 6in wood planks placed 200yds from the gun. All shots passed through, leaving jagged holes in the iron and the timber much splintered.

Captain Chads' conclusions on this series of trials were that:

a. Resistance to shot by iron and oak is in the ratio of their specific gravities, ie 8:1.
b. The holes in the iron were open and sometimes jagged, whereas those in the oak were always partially closed.
c. As far as this experiment went, it is perhaps doubtful whether iron or oak of the thickness used was the better, as the splinters from the iron, though fewer in number, were more severe than from the oak.

The next series of trials was much more significant. Two sections of a ship's side, each 10ft square, were built in Portsmouth Dockyard to the same design as the iron-work of the frigate *Simoom*. There was, however, no filling timber between the iron frames, nor was planking fitted inside the frames as in the actual frigate. The plates were of ⅝in iron and the frames were 4½in wide, 12in apart. The two sections of the ship's side were then placed 35ft apart between piles, firmly driven, at 450yds from the guns used, one behind the other and reversed so as to represent the two sides of an iron frigate.

Firing took place over several days in June 1850, and of the shots fired, only a few will be described in detail and the rest summarised. The first was a 32pdr shot fired with a 10lb charge from a 56cwt gun. It hit directly between two ribs, making a 6½in open hole. The shot broke up and the splinters from it, together with those torn from the plate, were numerous. The rear side was much struck and injured, two of the splinters having penetrated through, one of which made a hole 10in x 9in in the plate. Douglas quotes a letter from Captain Chads in which he says that seventeen 32pdr shot were fired with charges varying from 2½lb to 10lb and, of these, sixteen split and formed large and numerous splinters.[23] Hits on the ribs made much larger holes. Some rounds were fired from an 8in/65cwt gun and the solid 68lb shot produced results similar to, but more severe than, the 32pdr. A 56lb hollow shot broke up in a cloud of numerous splinters which flew between 100 and 300yds. Similar results came from a 10in/85cwt gun firing 56lb hollow shot.

Nine shells, with Moorsom's fuses, were fired from a 32pdr, some passing through intact plate and some going through earlier holes. Most of the shells broke in, penetrating the plate, but in all cases there was an explosion, sometimes of low order, generally not more than 4ft inside the target. Six shells with 3in fuses, but with the caps left on, were also fired. Four of the six hit undamaged structure and broke up without an explosion.

Five rounds of grape (forty-five 3lb shot in all) were fired from a 32pdr. Only five balls hit (at 450yds) but they all penetrated. Four hollow shot were fired from a 24pdr howitzer in a boat, with 2lb charges at a range of 50yds. Two hit ribs and split while the others made clean holes. Captain Chads drew the following conclusions:

a. All shot hitting ribs, and most in between, split.
b. Shot hitting between the ribs generally made a clean, open hole, slightly larger than the shot. Those striking the ribs made a much larger, jagged hole.
c. Hollow shot broke into many more splinters than those produced by a solid shot or those produced by a bursting shell.
d. Moorsom's fuses ignited the powder of a shell passing through ⅝in iron even if the shell was broken, but the breaking of a shell did not ignite the powder in it.

Finally, it appeared that the large, jagged holes would be difficult to stop and hence dangerous if near the waterline. 'Also, the numerous splinters would cause a few, well directed shot to clear away whole guns' crews and these two effects, more especially the last, must certainly condemn such ships as unfit for war purposes.'

Apart from a few reservations, which will appear later, one cannot dispute Captain Chads's conclusions from the evidence of this trial on the target as tested. However, the lack of the wood filling between the frames and the planking behind was a serious deficiency, particularly since the earlier trials at Woolwich had shown their value.

This deficiency was remedied in the next series of trials when a new target was made, representing the side of *Simoom* from just below the main deck to just above the upper deck. The iron structure was identical to that used in the previous series, but the space between the

21. Parliamentary Papers 1850.
22. Douglas, op cit.
23. Ibid.

ribs was filled in solid with 5½in oak timbers. Inside this, oak planking 4½in thick was arranged up to the port sill with 3in fir planking above. The timbers and planks were all bolted through the iron skin, making the target a genuine replica of one side of the *Simoom*. As before, the target was secured 450yds from the gun but this time there was no representation of the disengaged side of the ship.

Firing was carried out on 11 July 1850 when the following projectiles were fired: 32lb solid shot with 10lb, 6lb and 4lb charges; 68lb solid shot with 10lb charges; 8in 56lb hollow shot with 10lb and 5lb charges; and 10in 85lb hollow shot with 12lb charges. The holes made by the shot were not as irregular in shape as in the previous series, but were just as open. Very few of the splinters from the plate or from the broken shot were retained in the wood. With the smaller charges, the splinters were not so numerous but with the larger charges there were as many as in the previous series. The general conclusions were the same as before.

On 13 August a series of shots was fired against another target with ironwork similar to *Simoom*'s, but with fir planking 2in, 3in and 4in thick worked outside (nearest the guns) over different areas of the plating. Once again the results and conclusions were the same. Some solid shot were also fired against an all-timber butt representing a wooden line-of-battle ship and these gave rise to 'few, very few [splinters], in comparison'.[24] Another iron target was fired at on 10 October 1850. This time the inner side was lined with Kamptulicon. It did not prevent the shot breaking up, nor did the holes seal themselves.

In yet another series, on 5 July 1851, the target was built up with oak and fir frames, one half being covered with ⅜in iron and the other with ½in iron. Shot, both solid and hollow, hitting the thinner plate went through without splitting, but most broke up on the ½in plate. The target was then turned to represent the disengaged side and fired on with reduced charges. On 11 and 12 August a target was tried, made up of frames 4½in deep and ⅝in thick, spaced 11in apart, with 5in teak (10½in wide) outside and 2in teak (8⅔in wide) inside. A similar

butt, reversed, was also tried. A large number of splinters, both of wood and iron, were produced, the iron ones flying some 200–400yds, while the shot flew on for about 1,300yds.

Captain Chads's conclusions on this series were that 'it has been proved that the disastrous effects of shot upon iron are so great that it is not a proper material of which to build ships of war, and it has also been proved that these effects are not to be prevented'. Douglas spells out the same conclusion in more detail:

> If the iron sides are of the thickness required to give adequate strength to the ship (⅜in or at least ½in) the shot will be broken by the impact; if the iron plate be thin enough to let the shot pass into the ship without breaking, the vessel will be deficient in strength; the shot will do its own work, particularly in oblique or raking fire, more effectively than its splinters, and in passing out, make apertures which were more difficult to plug or stop than in passing in … the expedient of combining wood and iron makes matters worse. It is generally believed that iron vessels, however convenient or advantageous in other respects, are utterly unfit for the purposes of war.

This verdict was generally accepted by most of the more progressive builders of iron ships. Fairbairn told the Institution of Naval Architects, many years later, that 'the iron ship was even more dangerous under fire than one built entirely of wood'.[25] John Grantham, another pioneer, wrote:

> In the material points iron warships are deficient. The injury they would receive from shot is probably much greater than in timber built ships; and as there is no effective remedy against fouling, their employment on a foreign station, where there is no means of cleaning them every six months, is undesirable … I must state my conviction, that the result of careful experiments, and especially those conducted by Captain Chads, were anything but encouraging to the hopes entertained that iron ships would supersede wooden ships in the Navy.[26]

Edward Reed,[27] so critical of most aspects of Admiralty policy, accepted this verdict, as did his successor, Nathaniel Barnaby, who much later favoured composite construction for unarmoured ships for this reason.

The only naval architect critical of the Admiralty viewpoint was Scott Russell, who referred to 'seven years of tests on how to make iron plates not resist shot'.[28] Since he did not say how this was to be done, this argument can be dismissed as rhetoric.

Hindsight

The outcome of this first iron warship-building programme was seen as a failure but, 150 years later, it is hard to find fault with any of the actions taken by the Board. It was the Board who, by initiating work into the

A composite target tested in August 1851. It had similar iron frames to those of *Simoom* 11½in apart, but there was no iron plating. The skin was of 5in teak planking with an inner skin of 2in teak. Many splinters were formed of both wood and iron. *(From Howard Douglas's Naval Gunnery)*

Royal Charter. The rapid break-up of this iron ship when wrecked off Anglesey on 26 October 1859 was used as evidence of the unsuitability of the material for shipbuilding by iron's detractors. (© *National Maritime Museum neg 8954*)

correction of magnetic compasses, made the seagoing iron ship possible. Once the problem of navigation was solved, the introduction of iron ships to the Navy was cautious but steady. The success of the *Nemesis* encouraged the Board to believe that the problems of the iron ship had been solved and Charlwood's report on the *Guadeloupe* seemed to confirm this view.

There were two real problems left unsolved. The first was fouling and, though Hay's compound gave somewhat inconsistent results, these should have indicated that a solution was possible. The effect of gunfire on iron hulls was not ignored but it was believed that the experience of *Nemesis* and *Guadeloupe* had already demonstrated that iron ships stood up well to gunfire and were easily repaired if holed.

The Woolwich tests of 1846 were well planned and conducted but were not conclusive on the behaviour of iron. They did demonstrate that under some conditions the impact of a cannonball on a wrought iron plate would produce a lethal shower of splinters. It was also shown that a shot, particularly at low impact velocity, would make a jagged hole which was difficult to patch.

The decision to convert the iron frigates to troopships and to stop the building of iron warships was a political one with little evidence either for or against. It is worth noting that the smaller iron ships remained in naval service for many years, though they do not seem to have been in action.

The *Simoom* tests were also carried out scientifically and there is little with which one can disagree in Chads's report. One lesson which might have been accepted, as Captain Halsted pointed out, was that quite a thin iron plate (½in–⅜in) would break up all shells and ensure that there was no more than a low-order detonation. It would have been possible to fit such plates over much of the side of a wooden battleship with the loss of very few

guns as weight compensation. In this way, such ships would have been almost invulnerable to early shells and the thick wooden sides would have absorbed the splinters from broken shot. The weight of wooden hulls, machinery and coal required in 1845 was too much to allow for full armour.

The reason for the lack of success with these early iron ships seems to be that they moved too rapidly into a new technology which was not fully understood by the engineers of the day. Wrought iron is a strange material whose properties vary considerably in different directions. Tests on materials from HMS *Warrior* in 1984 (described in Appendix 9) show that:

a. Wrought iron has a very low strength at right angles to the plane of the plate. It is this 'through the thickness' strength which is most important in resisting impact.
b. All metals become brittle at low temperatures and the transition from ductile to brittle behaviour for wrought iron begins at +20°C.

It is a remarkable coincidence that the actions of *Nemesis*, *Guadeloupe* and *Harpy* were all fought in warm water where iron would behave well. It was much colder at Woolwich and during the *Simoom* tests. The rapid break-up of the *Royal Charter*, used by Douglas as an argument against iron ships, may also have been precipitated by the very low temperatures at the time (*Birkenhead* broke up in mild conditions).

In later years a few unarmoured iron warships were built but, in general, its use was reserved for armoured ships or as framing behind wood-planked composite ships. Wrought iron would not be accepted today as a suitable material for warship building, but nor would traditional wood construction.

24. Ibid.
25. W Fairbairn, 'The construction of iron plated ships', *Trans INA*, vol IV (1863).
26. J Grantham, 'The strength of iron ships', *Trans INA*, vol I (1860).
27. E J Reed, *Shipbuilding in Iron and Steel*, London (1869).
28. J Scott Russell, *Fleet of the Future*, London (1862).

Nine | Screw Propulsion

The introduction of the screw warship

The idea of a screw propeller was an old one; inventors had sought to use the Archimedian screw, used as a pump for centuries, or found inspiration in the windmill. Among many who made such proposals were Du Quet (1729), Daniel Bernoulli (1752) and Bramah (1785).[1]

A more practical proposal came from Lyttleton in 1794, who patented a three start screw of length equal to one complete turn, which was mounted in a frame outside the ship. This screw was driven by men at a winch connected to the screw by ropes and pulleys. Trials were carried out by Colonel Beaufoy at Greenland Dock, Deptford, but were not very successful, the best speed achieved being only 2 knots.[2]

A much more successful propeller was designed by Edward Shorter of Middlesex who obtained a patent for a 'perpetual sculling machine' on 1 March 1800.[3] The two-bladed propeller was carried over the stern on a long inclined shaft with a universal joint near the ship, the weight of the propeller being taken by a float. In 1802, Shorter's propeller was tried on the transport *Doncaster* in Gibraltar Bay. With eight men on the capstan which operated the propeller, the transport covered two miles at a speed of 1½ knots. The master, John Shout, and Captains Aylmer and Keats of warships in company, wrote enthusiastically to Shorter. A further trial was carried out at Malta in the presence of Admiral Bickerton who wrote to Shorter on 4 September 1802, 'I think the plan a good one and that it may in many instances be useful'.[4] Shorter seems to have been well aware of the advantages of using a steam engine to drive the propeller but this was never tried.

A prize was offered in 1825 for the best way of driving a ship without paddles and this was won by Commander Samuel Brown RN. He fitted a '12hp gas vacuum engine' into a small launch driving a two-bladed propeller at the bow. Though a speed of 7 knots is said to have been achieved, the scheme was not followed up, perhaps because of the inefficiency of a bow propeller.[5]

The credit for designing a screw propulsion system that worked and for overcoming all the real and imaginary problems falls to two very different men: Francis Pettit Smith and Captain John Ericsson. Their inventions were truly independent, almost simultaneous and since these two rivals became friends, they each contributed to the other's success.

Ericsson was born in the province of Varmiand, Sweden, on 31 July 1803. As a child he was fond of mechanical toys and was making his own designs by the time he was ten! These efforts persuaded Count Platen

to obtain a cadetship for Ericsson in the Corps of Mechanical Engineers in which he worked as a surveyor during the building of the Gota canal. In 1826 he came to England and developed a number of schemes for engines and boilers including a railway engine, the *Novelty*, the great rival of the *Rocket* in the Rainhill trials.

On 13 July 1836, a patent was taken out by 'John Ericsson, Engineer', of London, for an improved propeller suitable for a steam engine described as consisting of:[6]

> two thin broad hoops, or short cylinders, made to revolve in contrary directions round a common centre, each cylinder with a different velocity from the other; such hoops or cylinders being also situated entirely under the water at the stern of the boat, and furnished with a series of short spiral planes or plates, the plates of one series standing at an angle, the exact converse of the angle given to those of the other series, and kept revolving by the power of a steam engine.

During 1836 Ericsson experimented with a model boat some 2–3ft long to test his propeller. The model boat had an engine supplied with steam through a rotating arm from a boiler at the centre of a circular pond. These tests were very satisfactory and in 1837 a launch, the *Francis B Ogden*, was built on the Thames and launched on 19 April 1837. She was 45ft long, 8ft wide and had a draught of 3ft. The pair of contra-rotating propellers had a diameter of 5ft 2in, a total length of 2ft 2in and weighed 615lb. The engine had two cylinders with a stroke of 14in and a bore of 12in. It ran at 60rpm with a steam pressure of 50lb/sq in (very high for its day).

This launch seems to have been very successful from the first trial on 30 April 1837 when she reached 10 knots. A schooner of 140 tons was towed at 7 knots and the American packet *Toronto* at 4 knots. After several other successful trials during the summer, Ericsson invited the Board of Admiralty for a demonstration. The strange story of this trip, in which the Admiralty barge was towed behind the *Francis B Ogden*, is told by John O Sargeant in his Boston Lyceum lecture of December 1843.[7]

> The barge contained Sir Charles Adam, Senior Lord of the Admiralty; Sir William Symonds, Surveyor; Sir Edward Perry, the commander of the second British North Pole Expedition; Captain Beaufort, the Hydrographer of the Navy, and other scientific and naval officers.
>
> In anticipation of a severe scrutiny from such a distin-

guished personage as the Chief Constructor of the British Navy, the inventor had carefully prepared plans of his mode of propulsion, which were spread on the damask cloth of the magnificent barge. To his utter astonishment, as we may well imagine, this scientific gentleman did not appear to take the slightest interest in his explanations. On the contrary, with those expressive shrugs of the shoulder and shakes of the head which convey so much without absolutely committing the actor – with an occasional, sly, mysterious, undertone remark to his colleagues – he indicated clearly that though his humanity would not permit him to give a worthy man cause for unhappiness, yet he 'could if he would' demonstrate by a single word the utter futility of the invention.

Meanwhile, the little steamer proceeded at a steady progress of 10 miles an hour through the arches of the London and Southwark bridges towards Limehouse, and the steam engine manufactory of Mr Seaward. Their Lordships, having landed and inspected the huge piles of the marine engines intended for His Majesty's steamers, with a look at their favourite propelling apparatus, the Morgan paddle wheel, re-embarked and were safely returned to Somerset House by the noiseless and unseen propeller of the new steamer.

On parting, Sir Charles Adams, with a sympathising air, shook Ericsson cordially by the hand, and thanked him for the trouble he had been at in showing him and his friends this interesting experiment, adding that he feared he had put himself to too great an expense and trouble. Notwithstanding this ominous ending of the day's excursion, Ericsson felt confident that their Lordships would not fail to perceive the importance of the invention. To his surprise, however, a few days afterwards a letter written by Captain Beaufort, at the suggestion, probably, of the Lords of the Admiralty, was put into his hands, in which that gentleman, who had witnessed the experiment, expressed his regret that their Lordships had been very much disappointed in its results. The reason was altogether inexplicable to the inventor, for the speed obtained at the trial far exceeded anything which had been accomplished by a paddle steamer on so small a scale.

An accident soon relieved his astonishment. The subject having been started at a dinner table where a friend of Ericsson was present, Sir William Symonds ingeniously remarked that 'even if the propeller had the power of propelling a vessel, it would be found altogether useless in practice because, the power being applied in the stern, it would be absolutely impossible to make the vessel steer'.

This is a strange story. Symonds was no supporter of new technology but nor was he stupid. His reaction to Smith's demonstration only a few months later was cautious but sensible. Bourne suggests the following explanation for Symonds's strange rejection of Ericsson's work.[8] Some paddle steamers whose bows had been lengthened had been found difficult to steer; they had

Robert F Stockton, Ericsson's demonstration ship. The half model is mounted in a case with an engraving of the ship as a backdrop. (© *National Maritime Museum F7780-001*)

tended to turn away from the wind, pivoting about the paddles which were then well aft of amidships. Possibly, Symonds reasoned that if putting the propeller a little abaft amidships caused so much trouble, then moving it right to the stern would make steering impossible. Ericsson's decision to tow the Admiralty barge would then be construed as an attempt to conceal this fault by using the barge as a drogue. Ericsson was not an easy man to deal with and his brash manner may have upset the Board.

Ericsson found a new sponsor in Captain Robert F Stockton USN, the US consul in Liverpool. He ordered an iron ship, 70ft long, 50ft beam with 50NHP. This vessel, the *Robert F Stockton*, was launched at Liverpool in July 1838, and underwent trials in September. The engine was direct acting and was connected to the propeller without gearing. During one of Ericsson's earlier trials, Smith had suggested that contra-rotating propellers were unnecessary and that performance would be better with one only. The *Stockton* was so designed that she could steam using one wheel or both, as required, and since Ericsson in later designs used one screw only, it may be deduced that Smith was right. Pettit Smith, too, was to find his vessel went better with half its original propeller.

In December 1838 the *Robert F Stockton* arrived in the Thames and on 12 January 1839 she was demonstrated to some thirty scientists who found her more than satisfactory. On the 16th she towed four coal

1. G L Overton, *Marine Engineering*, Science Museum, London (1935).
2. B W Bathe and D Mackintyre, *The Man of War*, London (1968).
3. Overton, op cit.
4. E Shorter, Correspondence, Naval library.
5. J Bourne, *A Treatise on the Screw Propeller*, London (1852).
6. R Taggart, 'The early development of the screw propeller', *Naval Engineers Journal*, Washington (May 1959).
7. Ibid.
8. Bourne, op cit.

barges lashed alongside, giving a total beam of 59ft, at 5½ knots. In April 1839 this ship, under the command of Captain Crane, crossed the Atlantic under sail alone. She was sold in 1840 to the Delaware and Raritan Canal Company and was renamed *New Jersey*. She remained in service for many years as a tug on both the Delaware and Schuylkill rivers.

Once in the USA, Ericsson continued with the development of the screw and, due largely to his efforts, there were forty-one screw merchant ships in service by 1843. He also designed the *Princeton* for the US Navy, the first screw warship to go into service. She had a length of 164ft, a beam of 30ft 6in, a mean draught of 17ft and a displacement of 673 tons. The engines of *Princeton* were designed to lie below the waterline for protection. In October 1843 *Princeton* was tried against Brunel's paddler, the *Great Western*, and beat her.

There is still one last twist to the story of Ericsson's involvement with the Royal Navy. When he departed from England, he left his patents in the care of Count Adolph E Rosen. The first order was from France in 1843 for the 44-gun frigate *Pomone* with 200NHP machinery. In 1844 the Royal Navy ordered a set of 300NHP engines and a screw propeller for the frigate *Amphion*. These two ships were the first European warships with direct-acting horizontal engines arranged entirely below the waterline. They also had horizontal double-acting air pumps with canvas valves to reduce the shock incidental to high speed operation. Both vessels were said to have been successful on trials,

reaching about 7 knots (*Amphion* 6.75 knots), but since the required speed was only 5 knots, it is clear that money was wasted on unnecessarily large engines.

Francis Pettit Smith

Smith was born at Hythe, Kent, on 9 February 1808 where his father had been postmaster for forty years. The younger Smith became a sheep farmer but by 1835 was working at Hendon, where he developed an interest in ship propulsion. The next year he was given support by Wright's Bank and by Thomas Pilgrim, an engineer, and obtained a patent on 31 May 1836. His clockwork-driven model boat, fitted with a wooden screw, was demonstrated at the Adelaide Gallery, where it was seen by Sir John Barrow, the influential Second Secretary, the senior civil servant of the Admiralty.[9]

The tests of the model were so satisfactory that Smith and his backers decided to build a 6-ton boat with about 6NHP to demonstrate the value of screw propulsion. This boat, the *Francis Smith*, was fitted with a wooden screw of two complete turns, 2ft in diameter and 2ft 6in long. The screw was carried on a horizontal shaft, driven by bevel gearing and a Z-drive, from an engine with a single cyclinder, 6in diameter and 15in stroke.

Table 9.1 *Francis Smith*[10]

Tonnage	6
Dimensions	31ft 11 in x 5ft 6in x 2ft 8in draught

Pomone. The propeller for this French frigate was the first export order for Ericsson's screw in 1843. His agent in England, Count Rosen, designed twin rudders to operate ahead of the multi-bladed propeller, but on trials the ship proved impossible to steer. The entire stern was rebuilt and replaced with an axial rudder set conventionally abaft a two-bladed screw in a hoisting frame, as shown in these drawings. (*Atlas du Génie Maritime*)

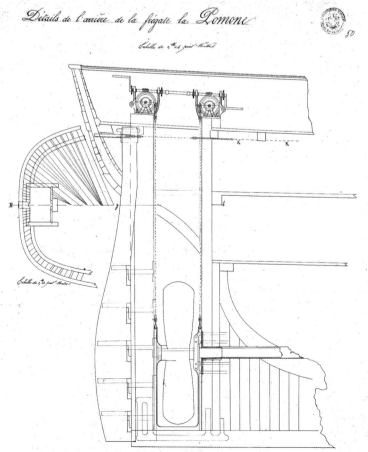

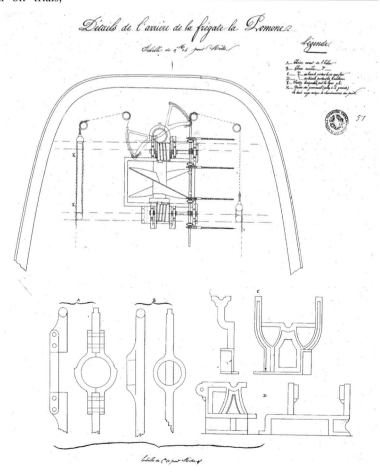

The *Francis Smith* was first demonstrated on 1 November 1836 on the Paddington Canal, and was used there and on the Thames until September 1837. During one run in February 1837, the propeller hit some debris in the water and half of it broke off, the speed of the boat increasing. In consequence, a new propeller was made with a length of a single turn. She was able to tow the *Great Western* into the East India Dock on one occasion.

Smith then decided that it was necessary to demonstrate his screw at sea, since it was being alleged that it was suitable only for river use. One Saturday evening in September 1837, he took the *Francis Smith* from Blackwall to Gravesend and, after taking on a pilot at 0300hrs, continued to Ramsgate. He arrived during morning service and was later able to show his boat to his banker, Wright, at Dover.

From Dover, Smith steamed on to Hythe and back to Folkestone, covering five miles in three-quarters of an hour on the return trip. On 25 September the little launch set out to return to London. It was rough and stormy, but the screw worked well under these conditions and favourable reports reached the Admiralty from coastguards who had watched her.

In March 1838 the Admiralty asked for trials of the *Francis Smith* under their supervision, only six months after their rejection of Ericsson's propeller. These trials were successful and, as Bourne says, 'the adoption of the propeller for naval service was deemed not an improbable contingency'.

Before reaching a decision on screw propulsion, the Board asked for a demonstration on a vessel of at least 200 tons. Smith formed the Screw Propeller Company, with backing from the bankers Wright and Currie, to

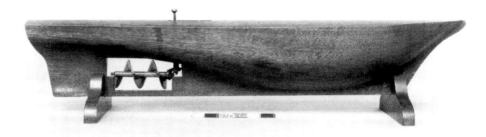

Francis Smith. A model of Smith's propeller trial launch. Note the long screw. (*Science Museum*)

build such a ship. The *Archimedes* was designed by Edward Pasco and laid down by Henry Wimshurst early in 1838.

Table 9.2 **Archimedes**

Tonnage	237
Dimensions	125ft (oa) x 22ft 6in x 9ft forward, 10ft aft
Depth	13ft
Machinery	J G Rennie, direct acting, 2-cylinder, 37in diameter, 36in stroke, 26rpm Pressure 6lb/sq in, 80NHP Weight 64.4 tons. Geared 25:133.3
Cost	£10,500

The combined length of the engine and boiler rooms was 39ft. Though contemporary prints show her as carrying twelve guns, there is no record of armament and this may have been artistic licence, or added to encourage sales of the ship. She was built of fir and rigged as a three-masted schooner. Rennie said, 'The lines fore and aft are beautifully run and the vessel is well calculated to go through the water both with steam and under sail'.[11] Smith believed that the Admiralty had promised to buy her if she reached a speed of 5 knots.[12]

She was launched on 18 October 1838 and made her first voyage during 1839. The first propeller fitted consisted of a screw thread, 7ft in diameter and 8ft long (pitch), the helical surface making one complete turn. It was made from wrought iron with sixteen arms driven onto the shaft, arranged at appropriate angles. Sheets of iron, ¼in thick, were wrapped over both sides of the arms and riveted to them.[13]

It was soon found that the diameter of the propeller was too great for the engine to drive it at the correct speed, and the diameter was reduced in stages to 4ft 9in. Later, the propeller was altered to one of two blades, each forming a single half-turn. The blade area of the new propeller remained the same at 33sq ft, quoted as one-quarter of the vessel's midship section. Step-up gearing with two wooden (hornbeam) cog wheels and iron pinions, held in an iron frame, turned the propeller five and a third turns for every engine revolution (screw rpm 138 at full speed).

After trials on the Thames and Medway, the *Archimedes* went to sea on 15 May 1839, making the voyage from Gravesend to Portsmouth in twenty hours

9. Bourne, op cit.

10. Descriptive catalogue, 'Marine Engineering', Science Museum, Item 272, Inv 1857–60.

11. E Chappell, 'Papers relating to Smith's patent propeller', London (1840), supplement to *Mechanics Magazine* (18 Feb 1859).

12. N P Burgh, *A Practical Treatise on Modern Screw Propulsion*, London (1869).

13. Ibid.

Francis Pettit Smith, portrayed with a model of the *Archimedes*, his demonstration ship. (© *National Maritime Museum PY5593*)

Archimedes, Smith's demonstration ship. The illustration includes a row of guns but it seems most unlikely that any were carried. She is shown off the North Foreland in heavy weather during her inaugural voyage from Gravesend to Portsmouth. (© *National Maritime Museum PY0211*)

against wind and sea. At Portsmouth she was tried against HMS *Vulcan*, a paddle steamer of 140NHP and a tonnage of 720. The report by Admiral Fleming and Captain Crispin on these trials, still using the original long propeller, was very favourable.

Soon after this trial there was an accident to the boiler and *Archimedes* had to return to London where it took five months to fit a new one. Soon after this repair was completed, she broke the crankshaft on the way to the Texel for a demonstration to the Netherlands navy. The engine was repaired by Miller, Ravenhill and Co and it was at this time that the propeller was altered. The changes were proved in Barking Creek on 30 April 1840 where she reached a speed of 8½ knots.

A series of trials were then carried out for the Admiralty by Captain E Chappell, who had been super-intendent of the Packet Service for thirteen years, and by Thomas Lloyd, the chief engineer of the Woolwich Steam Factory. They found she would answer her helm and 'obey all necessary movements' when advancing, stopping or backing as well as any paddle steamer. It must be realised that few engineers and others outside the Admiralty had any expectation that screw propulsion would be successful. Bourne records his own doubts at this date and there were several unfavourable reviews in the press.[14]

On 3 May, *Archimedes* left her moorings and reached Gravesend, twenty miles away, in an hour and forty-five minutes. On the following day the trials team was joined by Admiral Otway, commanding the squadron which was at anchor off Sheerness, and he was able to prove her

manoeuvrability for himself as he steered her in and out of the line of anchored warships. There may have been yet another propeller change at Ramsgate before the series of trials began at Portsmouth later in the month.

Before then she was visited by Rennie, who said:

> She was visited by all naval authorities, both scientific and unscientific, and there appeared to prevail but one opinion as to the efficiency of the principle for naval warfare. By this arrangement the engines are completely protected from shot by coal boxes on each side while the propeller from being wholly immersed under water is out of reach of shot. The funnel is the most vulnerable point but it might be easily replaced, in case of accident, by having a spare funnel below, constructed on the tele-scopic principle.

(See Chapter 8 for tests on the effect of shot on funnels.)

Archimedes – trials at Dover, April-May 1840

During these two months a series of races were held over the cross-Channel course, in which *Archimedes* was pitted against a series of the fastest mail packets on the Channel route.

Archimedes first beat the *Ariel* by six minutes to Calais, averaging 9½ knots, and on the return run won by five minutes, both ships using sail as well as steam. The next trial was with the *Beaver* which was beaten to Ostend by four minutes, but on the way back *Beaver* won by nine minutes at 9¼ knots.

14. Shorter, Correspondence.
15. See model of *Widgeon* in National Maritime Museum.
16. Chappell, op cit.

Table 9.3 **Mail Packets**

	Length (ft)	Breadth (ft)	Tons (bm)	NHP	Mid section area (sq ft)	Speed (knots)
Ariel	108	17.3	152	60	95	10.4
Swallow	107.6	14.8	133	70	84	10.4
Beaver	102.2	16	128	62	84	11.2
Widgeon	108	17.1	162	90	95	10.3
Archimedes	106	21.1	237	80	143	

Under steam alone, there was little to choose between *Archimedes* and *Swallow*, with a slight advantage to the screw. *Archimedes* was then tried against *Widgeon*[15] and the results are contained in the following report, dated at Dover, 2 May 1840, the first official trial report on screw propulsion.[16]

Dover, May 2nd, 1840

Sir,

In pursuance of the instructions of the Lords Commissioners of the Admiralty, as conveyed to us in your letter of 25th ultimo, directing us to examine and report on the principle on which the *Archimedes*, steam vessel, is propelled, we beg to state that we have made such experiments as were practicable, and we request that you will be pleased to submit to Their Lordships the following report.

On our arrival at this place we made arrangements with Commander Boteler, by which the *Widgeon* sail steam packet was placed at our disposal. The following statement shows the comparative size, power and immersion of the two vessels.

Name	Tonnage (bm)	Diameter of cylinder (in)	Length of stroke	Draught
Widgeon	162	39	37	7ft 3in
Archimedes	237	37	36	9ft 4in

The *Widgeon* is the fastest packet on the Dover station. She has 10 horsepower more and 75 tons burthen less than the *Archimedes* and the mean draught of the former is 2ft 1in less than that of the latter.

EXPERIMENTS

1. Our first was on a run of 19 miles upon a WSW course from Dover Roads, with a light breeze aft, and smooth water, but without sails. The engines of the *Archimedes* worked 27 strokes a minute and the speed of the vessel was 8¼ knots per hour. The *Widgeon* performed the whole distance in six minutes less than *Archimedes*.

2. In returning the above 19 miles to Dover Roads, against a moderate headwind, without sails, the engine of the *Archimedes* worked 27 strokes per minute and her speed was 7½–8 knots per hour. The *Widgeon* performed the distance in 10 minutes less than the *Archimedes*.

3. The third experiment was a run of 10 miles, from the Dover Roads to the Calais Roads, in a perfect calm, with the sea smooth as glass. *Archimedes'* engine worked 27 strokes per minute and her speed was 8½–9 knots per hour. The *Widgeon* performed the distance in 34 minutes less than the *Archimedes* and the whole time occupied by the latter was 2hr 9½min.

4. In returning the above 19 miles back to Dover Roads the weather was dead calm and the sea as smooth as before. The French mail packet, called *La Poste*, started at the same moment. Speed of the *Archimedes* and her engine as before. *Widgeon* ran the distance in four minutes less than the *Archimedes* and the *Archimedes* in 25 minutes less than *La Poste*. The latter has engines of only 50 horses aggregate power.

5. On this trial there was a fresh breeze at east and

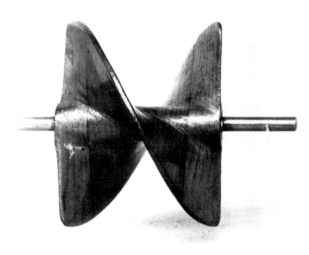

Some of the propellers tried on *Archimedes*. (Science Museum)

moderate sea. Both vessels set the whole of their sails, the *Archimedes* carrying much more sail than the *Widgeon*. The run was as before, from Dover to Calais, 19 miles close hauled. *Archimedes'* engine from 27 to 28 strokes and her speed 9–9½ knots. *Archimedes* ran the distance in nine minutes less than the *Widgeon*.

6. In returning to Dover with a fresh breeze abeam and all sails set, *Archimedes'* engine 28 strokes and her speed 10 knots, she performed the distance in 54 minutes less than the *Widgeon*.

REMARKS

These trials clearly prove that the speed of the *Archimedes* is slightly inferior to that of the *Widgeon* in light airs and calms, and in smooth water; but as the steam power of the former is 10 horses less and her burthen 75 tons more than the *Widgeon*, it is evident that in these vessels the propeller power is equal, if not superior, to that of the ordinary paddle wheel. In this respect, therefore, Mr Smith's invention may be considered completely successful. It is also plain from the second trial that in steaming against even a light air of wind the low mast and snug rig of the *Widgeon* gave her an advantage over the *Archimedes*, with loftier masts and heavier rig, and although the prevalence of calms prevented us from trying them further upon this point in blowing weather, we are satisfied that in strong breezes the advantages of *Widgeon's* low rig would be still more apparent. On the last two trials, however, the power of the sails acted strongly in favour of the *Archimedes* as she then beat the *Widgeon* and made the passages between Dover and

Model of a propeller in nine adjustable sections, allowing various configurations of blades. According to a contemporary note dated 1835 on the model, 'The screw of the *Archimedes* was built up from this model.' (© National Maritime Museum L1478-002)

Calais in less time than it has ever been performed by any of Her Majesty's mail packets. The *Archimedes* went upon this occasion from Dover to Calais in 2hr 1min and returned in 1hr 53½min.

There are two points of great practical interest respecting the screw propeller which ought not to pass unnoticed. First, the noise made by the spur wheels used in giving the necessary velocity to the propeller shaft. Second, the liability of these wheels to rapid wear and to accidental derangement. The noise alone, we conceive, would prevent its being applied to any of Her Majesty's packets in particular. Mr Smith, however, proposes to obviate this objection by substituting spiral gearing in place of the present cogs and a model of this method will be submitted to Their Lordships with this report. As it is the intention of Mr Smith shortly to make trial of this alteration, we abstain from giving any reports on its merits at present.

It is, however, in propelling ships of war that the value of Mr Smith's invention will probably be experienced. In such cases the rumbling noise in the ship made by the spur wheels is of no great moment, even if it cannot be overcome; for outside this vessel, the noise is not audible to so great a distance as that made by the common paddle wheel. A ship fitted with the screw propeller may be used either as a sailing or steaming vessel, or as both, if required; for we ascertained by experiment that the engine can be connected or disconnected with ease, and in any weather in two or three minutes. In carrying a press of sail, the inclination of the ship does not diminish the propelling power of the screw, nor lessen the ship's way, as with the ordinary paddle wheel. The getting rid of the paddle boxes also leaves the broadside battery altogether clear of obstruction, and in boarding an enemy's vessel would allow of the ships lying close alongside of each other. In conclusion it is proper to state that the operation of the screw facilitates the steering and accomplishes the backing of the ship as easily as the common paddle wheel.

> We have the honour to be, Sir,
> Your most obedient servants
> Captain E Chappell, T Lloyd
> The Secretary of the Admiralty

This letter is quoted in full in a paper by the Steam Department, Somerset House, dated May 1850. The Steam Department comments are also important and interesting:

It is obvious that in the *Widgeon* and *Archimedes*, which differed materially both in size and form, an exact comparison could not be made between the performance of the screw and that of the paddle but the results of the trials clearly showed, especially when the peculiar fitness of the screw for war purposes was taken into consideration, the propriety of trying this new instrument in a less equivocal manner.

With this view the *Rattler* was ordered to be built; and

that the experiment might be conclusive, so far as a trial between two vessels could make it so, she was constructed on the same lines as the *Alecto* – the after part being lengthened for the insertion of the screw – and fitted with engines of the same power and on a plan which had been previously tried in paddle wheel vessels.

The actions taken by the Admiralty are the subject of the next chapter, but first the remaining career of the *Archimedes* will be outlined. After the trials were over she circumnavigated Britain with Captain Chappell and Pettit Smith on board, calling at every port of importance to demonstrate the success of the propeller to shipowners, engineers, etc. Next came a record passage to Oporto in sixty-eight and a half hours, followed by visits to Antwerp and Amsterdam. Bourne says, 'Everywhere the vessel became an object of wonder and imagination'.

During her British cruise, *Archimedes* had visited Bristol and Captain Guppy, who was working with Brunel on the *Great Britain*, sailed with her to Liverpool. Later, Brunel himself hired the *Archimedes* for more detailed trials with eight different propellers, three by Woodward and the others by Smith. Brunel reported these trials to his directors in October 1840, recommending that the *Great Britain* be changed from paddle to screw propulsion.[17] Perhaps the most fascinating passage of this paper is where this great and imaginative engineer expresses his initial surprise at the efficiency of the screw.[18]

The basis of this report is not entirely correct, as shown by Corlett,[19] since Brunel, like all engineers of the day, believed that the resistance of a ship depended on the area of its midships section. Brunel's engineering intuition led him to sensible conclusions on the suitability of screw propulsion, as will appear in considering his contribution to the Navy's first screw ships.

It seems that *Archimedes* was used for some other trials since Taggart mentions a trial in which she lost a tug-of-war against the paddler *William Gunston*.[20] In July 1842 the *Archimedes* was offered to the Admiralty for £3,000. The offer was rejected as there was no use for such a small ship. By June 1846 *Archimedes* was offered for sale as a 'yacht, tender or letter of marque' (perhaps she did carry guns!).[21] Smith believed that the Admiralty had promised to buy her if she proved successful and, as a result, the Screw Propeller Company failed, leading to Smith's personal financial disaster, discussed later.

17. Chappell, op cit.
18. I Brunel, *The Life of I K Brunel*, London (1870, reprinted Newton Abbot 1970).
19. E C B Corlett, *The Iron Ship*, Bradford-on-Avon (1975).
20. Taggart, op cit.
21. *The Times*, 23 Jun 1846.

Widgeon. One of the fastest paddle packets on the Channel run and more powerful than *Archimedes*, she was just able to beat the screw ship in races across the Channel. (© *National Maritime Museum F7784-002*)

Ten | HMS *Rattler* and Other Early Screw Ships

1. PRO Adm 12/375.
2. PRO Adm 12/375, letter of 28 May 1840.
3. PRO Adm 12/375.
4. See model in Science Museum reserve collection.
5. L T C Rolt, *Isambard Kingdom Brunel*, London (1970), pp283–4.
6. Brunel manuscripts, Bristol University. These consist of notebooks and letter books. They will be referenced as 'Brunel' with date if that is not clear in the text. Note: the dealings between Brunel, Smith and the Admiralty departments are complex. There was initial misunderstanding and quarrelling between all concerned and it has not been easy to resolve apparently contradictory accounts. The main sources are the PRO summary letter books, the Brunel manuscripts and accounts by Rolt (n5) and Bourne (n16). In general, a single reference number will be given for each paragraph and the note below will list, briefly, the sources for that paragraph. The main facts to remember are that *Rattler* completed quickly and was a success and that the main players, Lloyd, Smith and Brunel, seem to have become friends.
7. Brunel notebook.

The building of the *Rattler*

The Admiralty report on the trials with *Archimedes* was followed by a letter from Mr Caidwell of the Screw Propeller Company, enclosing copies of the ship's log during trials with *Ariel* and *Beaver*.[1] Captain Chappell and Mr Lloyd were invited to discuss their report with the Board. Admiral Sir Edward Codrington also wrote to the Board on 28 May 1840, saying that 'the screw is well adapted for ships of the line'.[2]

The Board seems to have been convinced that the screw propeller was the way ahead for the Royal Navy, but they were understandably less certain of how to move forward. An imaginative first step was taken in September 1840 when it was decided that the new instructional tender for the naval college, *Bee*, should have a screw. In November, the Surveyor was told to discuss with Captain Chappell and Mr Ewart, chief engineer of Woolwich, the best way of 'fitting the Archimedean screw'.

Lord Minto minuted in November that the screw could be fairly tested only if fitted to a vessel similar to one already tried with paddles, and that 'the experiment may be prudently tried if the question of gearing is satisfactorily determined'. Presumably, this question was satisfactorily resolved as on 14 December approval was given to the building of a sister to the *Polyphemus* (paddle), to be fitted with a screw.[3] The next day, Seaward was asked to tender for an engine of 200NHP, as fitted in *Polyphemus*,[4] but geared up in speed to suit a propeller. Seaward submitted his drawings on 8 January 1841 and saw no difficulty in fitting suitable gearing.

During March, Sir Edward Parry, controller of steam machinery, suggested to the Board that the advice of Isambard Brunel be sought. Brunel records that his meeting with Parry on 20 March was 'very agreeable'.[5] Parry had read Brunel's report on his own trials with the *Archimedes* and apparently agreed that Brunel should superintend the building of a screw vessel for trials. Brunel was led to believe that 'he would have full authority without the intervention of any government official and report direct to Parry on the Board'.[6] Though there were obvious advantages in harnessing Brunel's genius and drive to the naval screw programme, there were also drawbacks. It is always difficult for someone outside government to have authority, particularly when the spending of public money is involved. Furthermore, Smith had already been given the post of consultant. Much unnecessary ill will was generated between these two eminent engineers and also with

Thomas Lloyd, chief engineer of the Woolwich Steam Factory, another outstanding engineer.

Brunel's first action was to arrange trials of the paddler *Polyphemus*, both as a basis for comparison with the screw steamer and to provide data for the design of the screw itself. These trials were held off Southampton on 2 May and involved Brunel, as well as Claxton and Guppy for the *Great Britain* design team. The *Polyphemus* was tried at three engine speeds, with one run in each direction over a mile determined by cross bearings of prominent buildings on shore.[7] On the 28th of the same month Brunel wrote that he proposed to drive the propeller shaft using 'drums and straps' (belt drive).

On 28 July 1841 Brunel wrote a very strong letter to Parry, complaining of interference. He accepted that his plans had to be submitted to the Surveyor but objected very strongly to them being passed to Woolwich. On the other hand, the Board had formally requested the Surveyor's comments on the plans and his only source of professional advice was at the Steam Factory. The Surveyor's office completed the drawings of the new ship by 16 July.

Brunel wrote again on 3 July, pointing out that it would be necessary to try propellers of different diameters and that it would be desirable to try the propeller at different positions along the shaft, varying the clearance behind the stern post. For this reason it would be necessary to build the ship with a very large aperture in the stern, about 10ft 6in long and 11ft 6in high, and to accommodate such a large hole the run would have to be lengthened by 6–10ft. Admiralty records attribute the proposal to lengthen the run to Thomas Lloyd and it may be that Brunel's indignation at the release of his drawings to Woolwich was because he suspected plagiarism. It is more likely that Lloyd's proposal was completely independent; he had a longer experience of screw propulsion than Brunel and was to show a very keen interest in the effect of stern shape on the efficiency of the screw. The idea of designing the stern aperture to take propellers of different diameters, in different positions, is an obvious one to engineers of the ability of Lloyd and Brunel, and there is nothing improbable in suggesting identical, independent solutions to the same problem.

Brunel was now involved in the selection of the machinery for the ship. Initially, he saw three contenders, Seaward's *Gorgon* design, Maudslay's double cylinder, or the steeple engine of Forrester. The main factor in the choice was the need to get in a drum 12ft in diameter on the engine output shaft, if possible

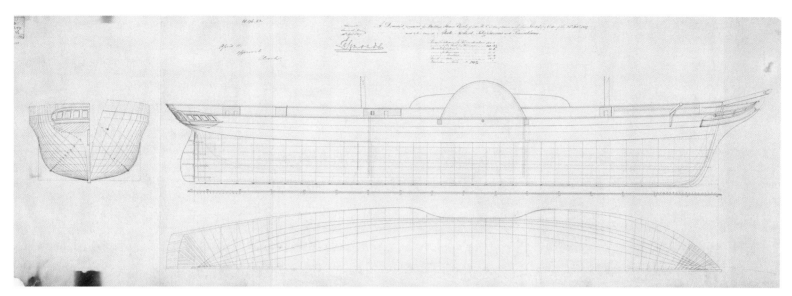

Original draught of *Polyphemus*, a paddle sloop used by Brunel in trials to estimate the power required in *Rattler*. (© National Maritime Museum J7829)

without cutting a hole in the upper deck. Further examination ruled out the Seaward design and tenders were invited from Maudslay and Forrester on 22 July. When their proposals were received in September, Maudslay was marginally the cheaper at £9,270, much to Brunel's delight, as he considered their engine to be better than Forrester's.

Later in the year, Brunel had further thoughts on the size of aperture required, and as a result of trials in *Archimedes* suggested an aperture only 5ft long and height from waterline to keel. He was asked to show the Board a model of his proposals but refused, saying that a model was not needed. Board members of that era were not accustomed to reading drawings, and expected models from which to make a judgement. Obviously, someone made a model from his drawings, which made him angry when he saw it, as he claimed it did not properly represent his ideas.[8]

At the end of 1841 someone suggested that time and money could be saved if the paddle steamer *Acheron* was converted to take a propeller instead of building a new ship. Woolwich Dockyard, which had been told in November to reserve a slip for the new screw vessel, was instructed on 13 December that *Acheron* was to pay off for conversion. Brunel heard of the change of plan at a meeting on 5 January 1842 and immediately objected, saying that a conversion would be more expensive and would not save time. A few days later, on 17 January 1842, he wrote at length to the First Naval Lord, Cockburn, stating the objects of the trial as he perceived them and why they could be achieved only if a new ship were built.[9]

Brunel began by asserting that the trial was not required to show that the screw would propel at about the same speed with the same power as the paddle, as this had already been demonstrated. The aspects which still needed demonstration were the sailing qualities, with and without the use of engines, without stopping to disconnect the shaft, and the performance of the screw in heavy seas, particularly against a headwind which would reduce the speed by 2–3 knots. The

performance of a screw steamer must be compared with a paddler in all these conditions and it must be with a steamer designed for the screw. *Acheron*'s form was distorted by the paddle sponsons and she was too full aft to get a good flow into the screw. In the next few days Brunel also wrote to Barrow and to Smith objecting to *Acheron*, and the Screw Propeller Company (Smith) wrote to the Board as well, setting out their objections to a conversion.[10]

Laird's introduced a further possibility on 15 January by suggesting that an iron ship be built for the trial as it would be better for the screw. This idea was rejected on 24 February. However, on 19 February the Surveyor was instructed to look at the possibility of converting a steamer under construction, rather than the *Acheron* as Brunel 'considers her too full aft'. On the 14th it was finally decided that a new vessel should be built at Sheerness, of the *Prometheus* class but adapted for screw propulsion. She was said to be 'in lieu of the *Rattler*', and was to use such parts of the frames provided for the original *Rattler* as was feasible. The new ship also took the name *Rattler*, a historic name for small ships and not a facetious reference to the noise of her gearing, as has been alleged (she did not have gearing at this time).

In February the Board told Brunel to communicate with Smith. In his reply he said he saw no reason to deal with Smith, but had told the latter that he would receive any communication. His letter to Smith was terse to the point of rudeness.[11]

Unfortunately, no one told Brunel that it was now intended to build a new ship and in March he wrote to Parry complaining that he had had no reply to any of his letters. There is no evidence that even this drew a formal reply, but there must have been a verbal response. The Surveyor sent the revised plans to Sheerness on 5 April and instructed Lang, the master shipwright, to work with Smith.[12]

Relationships were still somewhat strained between all concerned. In August it was Smith's turn to complain to the Board that Brunel had no right to interfere, and the following month Lang wrote that work had been

8. Brunel letter, 3 Jul 1841; PRO 12/375 of 20 Dec 1841.

9. Brunel letter, 10 Jan 1842, 17 Jan 1842; PRO 12/375.

10. Brunel letter, 7 Feb 1842, 16 Feb 1842.

11. PRO 12/402.

12. Brunel letter 7 Mar 1842; PRO 95/88 5 Apr 1842.

suspended because of Brunel's delay in supplying information. In August, Maudslay was ordered by the Board to accept Brunel's plans.[13]

By March 1843 the Screw Propeller Company were informed that their design of propeller was to be fitted

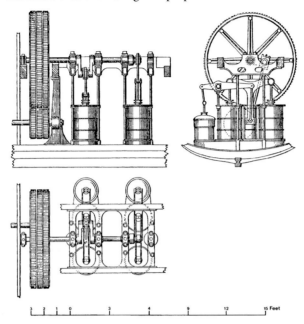

Right: *Rattler*'s Maudslay engines.

Below: *Rattler*, an original drawing showing the machinery and propeller arrangements. (© *National Maritime Museum DR3617A*)

but they were to work with Brunel. The propeller itself was to be made by Maudslay, despite some doubts as to whether this would infringe Briggs's patent. Maudslay were slow in making the propeller, and in September Brunel wrote to Smith suggesting a formal Admiralty complaint to Maudslay. The threat of such action seems to have been enough, as on 24 September the machinery was tested in the East India Dock. Relations between Smith and Brunel had improved greatly as a letter from the latter on 31 October, though disagreeing with Smith on technical matters, was written in a very friendly style.[14]

There is no doubt that there was much ill-feeling between almost everyone concerned in the early days, quite largely due to the divided authority between the enthusiastic Steam Department and the doubting Surveyor's Department. However, even though Brunel was frequently annoyed by Admiralty actions, his papers do not support the version put forward by Rolt in his well-known biography of Brunel, which shows the great man struggling alone against a hostile and reactionary Admiralty. Rolt copied this story from the biography of Brunel's son, another Isambard, who no doubt remembered the curses of his father in the heat of the moment. It is interesting that the complaints are directed at everyone, even Brunel, who was thought to be delaying

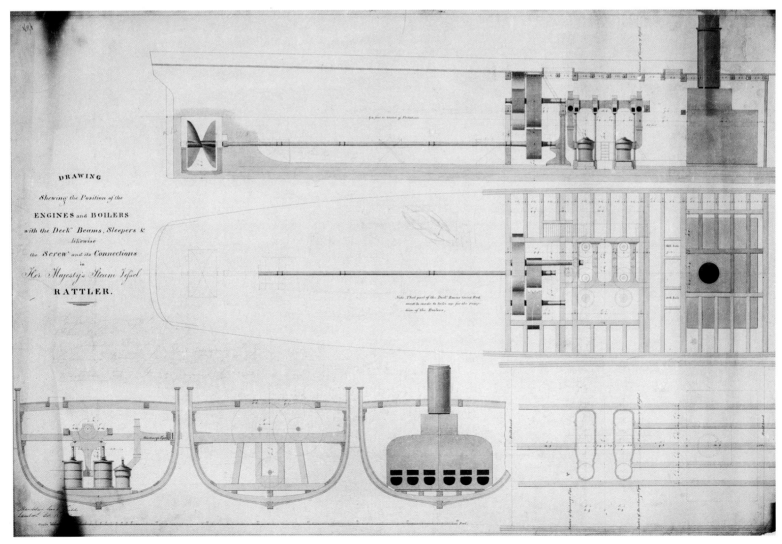

the project. All concerned were in a hurry to get the *Rattler* to sea.

While it is convenient to follow the story of *Rattler* through to the end, it must be appreciated that there were many other activities related to screw propulsion taking place at the same time, both within the Admiralty and outside. These will be discussed later, but the chronology given in Table 10.1 should be kept in mind while following the *Rattler* trials.

The trials of *Rattler*

Rattler left Blackwall for a proving run to Greenhithe and back on 30 October 1843. The propeller was a Smith design of 9ft 2in diameter, lift pitch and a length of 5ft 6in (half a turn of the screw). She carried 80 tons of coal and 60 tons of ballast and was not rigged at that date, giving draughts of 9ft 2in forward and 11ft 2in aft. The *Rattler*'s engine was worked up to 22 rpm, giving a speed of 8 knots. Brunel noted that the engines had not reached their calculated speed and it was decided to cut 3in off the forward end of the screw and 12in off the aft end.[15]

On 4 November the Surveyor wrote to Brunel and Smith informing them that the *Rattler* would leave from Blackwall for formal trials at 0930hrs the following day, 5 November. Smith, Brunel and Lloyd were all on board and now in harmony. The speed was measured using the 'mean of means' from either six or eight runs in opposite directions over the mile, which eliminated the varying effect of tide. The engine speed was 23–24rpm geared up 4½ to 1 to the propeller. Further trials were held on 8 November and on the 16th, by which date the propeller had been reduced in length to 3ft.

That was the last trial of 1843; during the winter the *Rattler*'s bottom was sheathed with copper at Brunel's suggestion. The outer edge of the rudder was tapered off. The 1844 series began on 3 February, Brunel noting that the slip was increased and suggesting that the coppering had had a favourable effect in reducing ship resistance. (In fact the slip, at 24 per cent, was only slightly greater than in one of the early trials.) It is also recorded by Bourne that *Rattler* raced the *Polyphemus*, her paddle half-sister, on the same day, with *Rattler* reaching 9¼ knots compared with 8+ knots for the paddler of considerably less indicated power.[16]

Between February 1844 and January 1845 there were twenty-eight official trials in the Thames, covering test of propellers from different manufacturers, with various numbers of blades and with the geometry altered. The position of the shorter screws within the stern aperture was also varied and its effect noted, as a result of which it was apparent that a fairly short aperture was sufficient. These trials are recorded in some detail by Bourne and, together with the somewhat similar trials in *Dwarf* during 1845, represent a careful and valuable technical appraisal of screw propulsion.[17] It is incorrect to suggest that this year of trials was an example of Admiralty procrastination.

Table 10.1 **Key Dates for Screw Propulsion**

1840 Sept	Order for the tender *Bee*
1842	Contract signed to purchase the yacht *Mermaid*
1842 Oct	Trials of *Bee*
1843 May	Trials of *Mermaid*, purchased in June as HMS *Dwarf*
1845 Jan	SS *Great Britain* sails from Bristol to London, Lloyd on board (favourable report)
1845 Apr	Trials of the Royal Yacht *Fairy*, iron screw steamer
1845	Trials of various propellers in *Dwarf*
1846	Trials of variations in stern lines in *Dwarf*

Table 10.2 *Rattler* **Propeller Trials 1844-5**

Propeller designs	Smith, Woodcroft, Sunderland, Steinman and Hodgson
Number of blades	2, 3 & 4
Pitch	11–26ft
Diameter	8ft 2in–10ft
Position	10in forward of centre of aperture to 1ft 2in aft
Gear ratio	4½:1

It was clear that the length could be reduced to about one-third of the original half-turn, which greatly eased the problem of fitting a propeller in the stern of a ship and made it practical to hoist the screw out of the water when under sail. The Smith two-bladed propeller of 10ft diameter, 11ft pitch and 1ft 3in length gave the highest ship speed (10.07 knots) and it is now displayed at the Royal Naval Museum, Portsmouth.

Towards the end of April 1844 the Board agreed to Lloyd's proposal to fit a thrust meter to *Rattler* at a cost of £100. This was a simple mechanical balance which measured the actual force developed by the propeller. A few days later, the Board agreed to replace the belt drive by gearing which was ordered from Maudslay. It is likely that both the thrust meter and the gearbox were fitted in December 1844, though the records are not entirely clear.[18]

Early in 1845 *Rattler*, together with *Victoria and Albert* and the *Black Eagle*, steamed from Portsmouth to Pembroke.

When rounding Land's End, and steaming against a strong headwind, both these vessels, as might be expected,

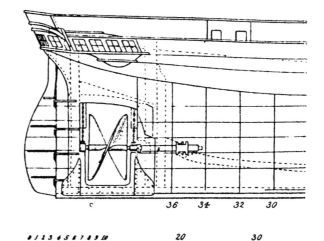

13. PRO 95/88, 9 Aug 1842, 18 Sep 1842.

14. Brunel letters, 19 Sep 1843, 24 Oct 1843, 31 Oct 1842; the letter of 31 Oct is important in the changing relationships.

15. Brunel notebook.

16. J Bourne, *A Treatise on the Screw Propeller*, London (1852); Brunel notebook; PRO 95/88 18 Nov 1843.

17. Bourne, op cit.

18. PRO 12/432; Brunel letters 30 Apr 1844; *Mechanics Magazine* (18 Feb 1859).

The final lines of *Rattler* showing the long aperture and propeller. The hoisting chains for the screw can also be seen.

Right: The most successful propeller in the trials was this Smith design, now in the Museum of the Royal Navy, Portsmouth. *(Science Museum)*

Far right: A model of *Rattler's* stern aperture as modified for the two-bladed screw and hoisting apparatus, 1844. *(© National Maritime Museum L2541)*

showed a great superiority, their power being much greater than *Rattler's* in proportion to their resistance, and their paddle floats being constructed on the vibrating [feathering] principle. This comparative failure of the *Rattler* made an unfavourable impression on the public mind as to the efficiency of the screw against wind and sea in heavy weather, and this impression still remains.

This comment, probably by Lloyd and written in 1850, shows the real difficulties in adopting screw propulsion when there was little or no understanding of the action of a propeller.[19]

Rattler and *Alecto*

In March 1845 the famous trials began in which *Rattler* competed against the similar paddle steamer, *Alecto*, in a series of races and towing trials.[20]

19. Brunel letter, 12 Feb 1842; PRO 12/449.

20. The description of the trials is based almost entirely on Bourne, op cit.

The power developed by the steam was measured by indicators in both ships, and in *Rattler* it was possible to use a dynamometer to measure the thrust in the propeller shaft. Mechanical losses in the engine, auxiliaries and shafting reduced the indicated power by 15–25 per cent to give the thrust power in the shaft.

At 0554hrs on 30 March 1845, a still, calm morning, the two ships left the Nore to race to Yarmouth using steam alone. Nearly nine hours after, at 1430hrs *Rattler* stopped her engines in Yarmouth Roads where twenty minutes later she was joined by the *Alecto*. *Rattler* had completed the course at an average speed of 9.2 knots while *Alecto* had managed 8.8 knots. However, the average indicated power of *Rattler* was 334.6ihp while that of *Alecto* was 281.2ihp. At speeds of this order, power is roughly proportional to the cube of the speed, and using this, it can be shown that at the same power as *Alecto*, *Rattler's* speed would have been only 8.7 knots, less than *Alecto's*.

The apparent clear victory for the screw is turned into a small advantage to the paddle on this first trial. (See Appendix 10 for a technical analysis of these trials.) Later the same day both ships left Yarmouth Roads, heading north with a moderate breeze from the south and calm water, the two ships under both sail and steam. After a run of thirty-four miles *Rattler* had gained thirteen and a half minutes in two hours forty-nine minutes, the mean speeds being *Rattler* 11.9 knots, *Alecto* 11.2 knots.

The following day both ships set off again under

Table 10.3 **Comparative Data**

	Rattler	*Alecto*
Dimensions	176ft 6in x 32ft 8in	164ft x 32ft 8in
Draught (fwd), aft, mean)	11ft 9in, 12ft 11in, 12ft 4in	12ft, 12ft 7in, 12ft 3in
Tonnage (bm)	867	800
Machinery	Vertical Siamese, Maudslay, 4-cylinder, 10in diameter, 200NHP, 360ihp, 25rpm, 9.1 knots	Direct, Seaward & Capel, 2-cylinder, 21/22in diameter, 200NHP, 280ihp, 14/18rpm, 8.5 knots

steam alone, against a strong headwind and sea. At 0922hrs the two ships were side by side, both at full speed, and the third race was on. At 1000hrs *Rattler*'s steam pressure fell and *Alecto* caught up, but by 1044hrs she had fallen back by about half a mile. The course was then altered to bring wind and sea on the port bow and the race continued until 1717hrs when *Rattler* stopped engines and anchored. Some thirty-nine minutes later *Alecto* arrived, having covered sixty miles at 7 knots instead of the 7½ knots of *Rattler*.

These were average speeds; the actual speed had varied considerably during the run. Initially, with a strong headwind, *Rattler* could only make 5.5 knots whereas later, with the wind moderating and off the port bow, she reached 8.8 knots. Against the wind *Rattler* was developing 364ihp and *Alecto* 250ihp. Due to the ship's motion in the seaway, the thrust in the shaft varied violently from a maximum of 5.7 tons to a minimum of 2.3 tons with a mean of 4.2 tons. When conditions changed and the speed rose to 8.8 knots, *Rattler*'s power rose to 388ihp with a mean thrust of 4.1 tons. The two ships then made a short run before the wind, under steam alone and with all spars struck. *Rattler* reached 10 knots with 369ihp and *Alecto* 292ihp.

A series of three trials was then run under sail alone. *Alecto* unshipped her paddle boards while *Rattler* merely set her two-bladed screw vertically behind the stern post. In the first trial with a moderate breeze from astern and calm water, *Rattler* gained a mile and a half in just under two hours, despite having accidentally set her screw horizontal for part of the run. It did not seem to make much difference.

The second sailing trial was in a moderate wind and a calm sea, *Rattler* gaining a short lead after a single tack in five hours. The last run under sail was with the wind abeam and under plain sail only. *Rattler* gained thirty-eight minutes in four hours with a mean speed of 8.5 knots.

A pair of trials were then held, in which each ship in turn towed the other. First, *Rattler* towed the *Alecto*, whose paddle boards were removed, at about 7 knots using 352ihp. In the second trial, *Alecto* towed *Rattler* (screw vertical) at rather less than 6 knots. Once again, *Rattler* showed to advantage, but this was largely due to her greater power.

Then on 3 April 1845 came the famous trial, portrayed in so many books, in which the two ships were fastened stern to stern for a tug of war. There were those who thought the victory was bound to go to the ship whose engines started first. *Alecto* was given every chance, started first and was towing *Rattler* astern at 2 knots before the latter ship started her engines. Five minutes later, *Rattler* had arrested her stern way and soon she moved ahead, pulling *Alecto* backwards, despite her thrashing paddles, reaching a speed of 2.8 knots. *Rattler* developed 300ihp while *Alecto* could only muster 141ihp. It is fairly certain, as will be discussed later, that the Board had decided in favour of the screw before this tug-of-war was held. In all probability, it was a spectacular public relations exercise, designed to convert remaining doubters.

Following this stunt, two useful runs were carried out in *Rattler* using reduced power (see Appendix 10.) The tenth trial was run with a moderate wind on the star-

The famous tug of war between *Rattler* and *Alecto*. The Board of Admiralty had been convinced of the value of screw propellers some time before and had already ordered many screw ships. (© *National Maritime Museum PY0923*)

board bow over a distance of seventy-two miles. *Rattler* at 9.07 knots beat *Alecto* at 8.19 knots by some fifty minutes. The indicated powers were *Rattler* 324ihp, *Alecto* 246ihp. Against a strong wind and a heavy head sea, *Alecto* beat *Rattler* for the first time by half a mile in seven hours. *Rattler* lost steam pressure, since it was necessary to close the engine room openings which reduced the draught to the boilers and hence affected the pressure. This reduced her speed to 4.2 knots at 22rpm. *Alecto* had excess steam and had to blow some off. The twelfth and last trial was under steam alone during the return from Yarmouth to Woolwich, but was abandoned when *Alecto* had a boiler accident, *Rattler* being in the lead at the time.

Soon after the trials were over, in July 1845 *Rattler* towed the *Erebus* and *Terror* (themselves fitted with auxiliary screws) to the Orkneys on their way to Sir John Franklin's ill-fated Arctic voyage.

The *Erebus* had a 25NHP engine which came from a locomotive on the Greenwich railway. The propeller could be hoisted out of the water through a well. Hot water from the boiler was circulated to the mess decks and other parts of the ship for heating. The forward 20ft of the hull was sheathed in iron for protection, it being noted that any barnacles which grew would be removed in passing through ice. In fact, barnacles, etc, do not grow at low temperatures; one may also wonder if the iron resisted impact for long at these low temperatures.

Further developments and trials

In order to understand the significance of the trials using *Rattler* it is necessary to look at the dates when

Table 10.4 **Orders for Screw Ships**

Four iron frigates	Feb–Mar 1844
Amphion	Jun 1844
Dauntless	Aug 1844
Fairy and three more small ships	1844
Arrogant, *Termagant*	Feb 1845

operational screw ships were ordered – see Table 10.4.

During January 1845, Lloyd and Commander Crispin had travelled from Bristol to London in the *Great Britain* and had reported favourably on her.[21]

Before the races with *Alecto* in March 1845 there were four more orders for screw ships, including *Niger*, destined herself for another series of propeller trials. Very soon after the trials, the first screw battleships (blockships) were approved in August–September 1845. It is clear that the trials with *Rattler* in early 1844, sometimes dismissed as time wasting, had convinced the Board that the future lay with the screw. The races against *Alecto* confirmed this view and provided some information useful in designing future propellers.

There are still a number of other trials which must be mentioned before the operational screw fleet can be discussed. These trials were needed, not because the Admiralty had much doubt, but because there was no theoretical understanding of propeller action; every new design was a matter of trial and error. There was no way of scaling test results from models.

The first ship with a screw to be ordered for the Admiralty was the instructional tender, *Bee*, and she was the first, by a long way, to run trials. For teaching purposes she had both a screw and paddles, worked off

Sir John Franklin's exploration vessels *Erebus* (seen here in 1846) and *Terror* were among the first ships fitted with screws. They also had heating in the mess decks supplied from the boiler. (© *National Maritime Museum BHC3325*)

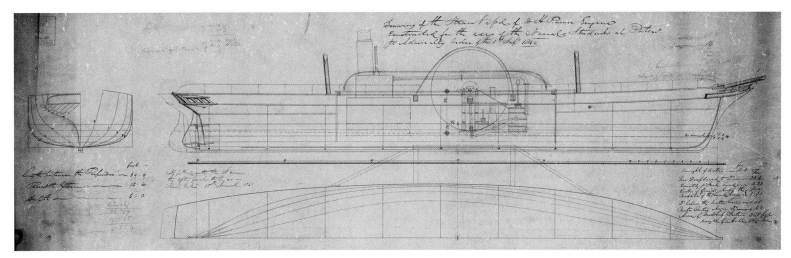

Above: Admiralty draught for the *Bee* showing the original paddle-only configuration, with the later modification to the stern lines for the additional screw propulsion. *(© National Maritime Museum DR6753)*

the same engine, which could be worked in opposition. She was launched at Chatham on 28 February 1842.

Table 10.5 *Bee*

Tonnage	43
Displacement	28 tons
Dimensions	63ft x 12ft 2in x 3ft 2in mean draught
Machinery	Beam engine, 10NHP
Propeller	3ft diameter, 3ft 9in pitch

Bee ran her screw trials on 25 October 1842 in the Thames, making 6.8 knots at 48rpm. Later, she was tried with the paddles and screw working in opposition, when the paddles drove her ahead despite the stern thrust of the screw. The rotational speed of the propeller was too low for it to perform well despite a 5 to 1 gearing up. This must surely be the most bizarre trial of all time! She was tried with a variety of propellers by Rosen (unsuccessful), Bloxland, etc.

Another early screw trials ship was the *Dwarf*. She was designed by Rennie in 1840 as the yacht *Mermaid* to try a 'rotary' engine by Galloway. Wright's bank lent the money for the *Mermaid* to be built at Ditchburn and Mare, but problems with the novel engine delayed acceptance and the bank, having already suffered heavy losses from the financial failure of the *Archimedes*, finally collapsed. The problem with the engine seems to have been with the seals to the rotor.

Sir John Rennie and his brother persuaded Sir

Table 10.6 **HMS** *Dwarf* [22]

Tonnage	164 (bm)
Displacement	98 tons (trial)
Dimensions	130ft x 16ft 6in x 5ft 6in mean draught
Machinery	John & George Rennie, 2-cylinder, vertical geared, 49in diameter, 2ft 8in stroke, 90NHP
Trials	216ihp = 10.54 knots at 35.5rpm and 8lb/sq in
Propeller	5ft 8in diameter, 8ft pitch, 1ft length

Left: 'Push me – pull you': the training ship *Bee* was the first ship to be ordered for the Navy with a screw propeller. She also had paddle wheels worked off the same engine and the two propulsors could be worked in opposition. In these circumstances the paddle usually won because the shaft did not turn fast enough for good propeller efficiency. *(IWM)*

George Cockburn to buy the *Mermaid* for the Navy, provided that she achieved 12 knots on trial. This was an extremely onerous condition as it is likely that no steamship had reached such a speed when the contract was signed on 7 March 1842. Official trials were held on the Thames on 15 May 1843 when, without rigging, the mean of six runs was 10.5 knots. Despite the failure to reach the contract speed she was accepted into service as HMS *Dwarf* on 22 June 1843. One unofficial report claims a speed of 12.14 knots on 15 May; perhaps this was with the tide and used to justify acceptance.

The propeller was of cast iron, moulded in loam, without using a pattern. The mould was shaped by an iron template, cut to a curve formed from a solid cone revolving on its axis during the perpendicular descent of a tracer.

During 1845 some twenty-five trials were run in the hope of determining the proper pitch and length of a propeller in relation to its diameter. Most of these trials used a screw of 5ft 8in diameter (one of 4ft 5¼in), with three different pitches (8ft, 10.23ft and 13.23ft). Length was varied from 1ft to 3ft 1¾in. The results showed that the shorter propellers were most efficient but little else could be deduced, then or now. A dynamometer was installed to measure thrust, but it was so unreliable that the results could not be used. Though these trials were not particularly useful, for reasons beyond the state of

21. PRO 12/449.

22. See model in National Maritime Museum.

knowledge in 1845, the Admiralty deserve all praise for their efforts.

The overall efficiency of a propulsion system does not depend on the propeller alone but is affected, for better or for worse, by the mutual interference between hull and propeller, known to modern naval architects as 'hull efficiency'. Lloyd and Brunel were aware of these effects and in 1846 Lloyd arranged an ingenious trial on *Dwarf* to investigate the effect of changing stern shape. As built, she had a very fine run but for the trial this was filled out with three layers of planking, care being taken to maintain a fair shape with no roughness or discontinuity which could add to the drag. Prior to this change of shape, the speed was 9.1 knots at 32 engine rpm. With the stern made bluff by the thick planking, the speed was reduced to 3.25 knots, the engine being unable to turn at more than 24rpm.

One layer of planking was removed and the speed rose to 5.75 knots at 26.5rpm; with all the planking removed the speed was restored to just over 9 knots. This trial had a major influence on the early screw warship programme, with many ships being altered on the slip to give them finer stern lines. The problem is a difficult one and the obvious solution did not always work. There was little further requirement for the *Dwarf* in the Navy and she was sold for scrap in 1853.

In 1847–8 the effect of stern shape was again investigated using two near-sisters, *Sharpshooter* and *Rifleman*, the former having much finer stern lines. Both ships originally had 200NHP Miller & Ravenhill geared engines. The results of comparative trials were seen at the time as strongly supporting the fine stern, but re-examination shows that the advantage was not as great as Bourne believed. In the first trial *Sharpshooter* was 1.7 knots faster but in a later trial, with rig as in *Rifleman*, she lost 0.6 knot of this advantage.

Rifleman was then rebuilt with a fine stern and reached 9.5 knots with the same power as *Sharpshooter*. Both ships were later re-engined and carried out numerous other trials. A further comparison was made between *Teazer* with a full stern and *Minx* with finer lines. There were so many differences between the state

of the ships that conclusions are hard to draw. It seemed that the evidence favoured fine stern lines and *Teazer* was rebuilt with a finer stern. A comparison of results before and after shows the value, in this case at least.

Table 10.7 **Trials in *Teazer***

Stern shape	Date	Speed (knots)	ihp
Full	Jun 1847	6.32	176
Fine	Oct 1848	7.69	128

In the earlier of these two trials she had a 120NHP Miller & Ravenhill engine, replaced before the second trial by a 40NHP Penn oscillating engine. She was not rigged in either trial.

Minx was used for a lengthy series of propeller trials, first with a 100NHP Miller & Ravenhill, then with a 10NHP Seaward & Capel high pressure engine (60lb/sq in). Of these, the most interesting is one in which the propeller was arranged abaft the rudder. As would now be expected, this was a little less efficient, since a rudder behind a screw can take some of the rotation out of the slipstream, recovering energy which otherwise would be lost. It may be doubted if the two trials were sufficiently comparable to show a real difference.

Also in 1847–8, some thirty-three trials were carried out in *Minx* with the first engine. In the fourth set, the effect of altering blade area was studied, the results generally confirming the advantage of a small area but showing that carrying this philosophy to extremes showed the opposite. At the end of the first series, the original propeller was replaced and a trial run made to show the effect of three months' fouling. The effect was 0.25 knot loss of speed, barely measurable.

A novel propeller by Woodcroft was tried with its pitch increased from the forward side to the after end. This gave the highest speed of all, 8.1 knots (160ihp), with the propeller the right way round, but only 6.8 knots when it was reversed. Designs by Atherton, the new chief engineer of Woolwich, with pitch reduced near the boss to eliminate centrifugal effect, were tried with moderate success.

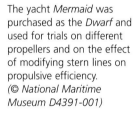

The yacht *Mermaid* was purchased as the *Dwarf* and used for trials on different propellers and on the effect of modifying stern lines on propulsive efficiency.
(© *National Maritime Museum D4391-001*)

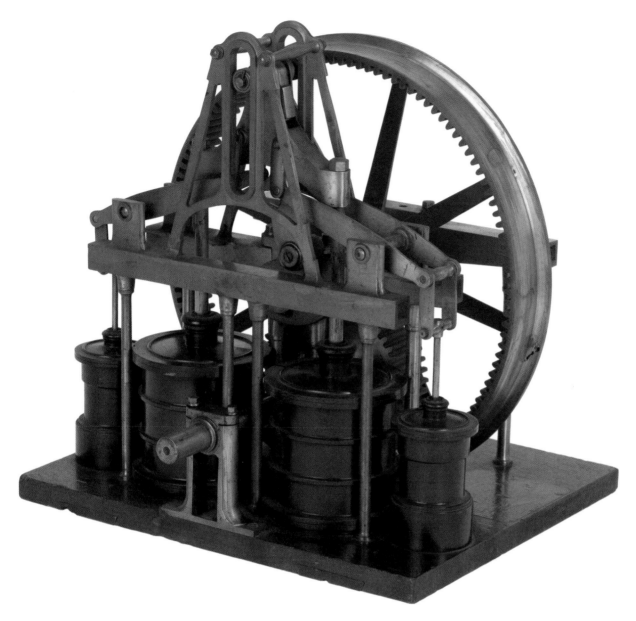

Geared screw engines by William Fairbairn proposed for *Sharpshooter* and *Rifleman*, 1846. Propellers needed to turn more rapidly than early direct-drive machinery could manage so they were geared up: in this case, a large wheel with interior teeth engages a smaller cogwheel within, saving overall space on the system of external cogs. (© *National Maritime Museum L2406-001*)

In each set a variety of pitches were tried and there were frequent retests of earlier screws, partly to see the effect of fouling. It is, perhaps, not too unkind to suggest that the main conclusion should have been that moderate changes in shape had virtually no effect on efficiency. A thrust meter was fitted and the results suggest that only one-half to two-thirds of the indicated power in the steam was converted into useful thrust. The rest went on overcoming friction inside the engine and transmission, propeller losses and in interaction with the hull.

It is worth noting that the rivalry between individual propeller designers was extremely bitter and there were many allegations of infringement of patent. In September 1851 the Admiralty finally resolved the dispute by awarding the very large sum of £20,000 to be shared between the rivals in settlement of all claims. Overall, the first and most successful designer was Pettit Smith but he did not do well financially.[23]

Smith lost much of his own money in the problems of the *Archimedes* and was unsuccessful in the various court actions over patents. It was said:

As is usual in such cases both parties went into a court of law where both the judge and the counsel were supremely ignorant of everything relating to the matter in dispute, and the usual legal sophistries were employed to show that Mr Smith had done nothing whatever of a useful character.[24]

Smith himself wrote in 1854:

The idea of using the screw as a propeller is at least a century old, and within that period has had its hundred votaries, each in turn nursing it as the offspring of his own fertile imagination until compelled by the failure of repeated tests to abandon it in disgust … I as conscientiously believed myself to be the first discoverer.[25]

Smith's story was to have a fairly happy ending. In 1855 he was granted a Civil List pension of £200 pa and two years later a national subscription was held on his behalf from which he received £2,678 and a service of plate. Many of those who had taken part in the technical revo-

23. PRO 12/561, 29 Sep 1851.
24. *Illustrated London News* (26 Apr 1856).
25. *Mechanics Magazine* (Apr 1854).

lution in the Navy contributed: Lloyd, Brunel, Atherton, Scott Russell, Froude, Isaac Watts, etc. In 1860 Smith was made director of the Patent Office museum (now the Science Museum), inheriting the magnificent collection of models of early screw propellers. He was knighted in 1871.

Niger and *Basilisk*

There were many propeller trials still to come, and, indeed, such trials continue to this day, but one may see just one more as belonging to the pioneering age. *Niger* was ordered early in 1845 as a screw ship and in March 1846 the Board approved the building of *Basilisk* with paddles, to be as similar as possible to *Niger*, for yet another set of comparative trials. These were finally held between May and August 1849 and may demonstrate the truth of a belief that it is even more difficult to stop a programme of trials once approved than it is to obtain the approval in the first place. However, the trials were carried out with great care and zeal and form a useful record of the state of the art of the day.

Niger had a propeller of 12ft 6in diameter, 17ft pitch and a length of 2ft 10in, driven directly from the engine at about 70rpm. *Basilisk* had wheels of 22ft 1in diameter, with floats 9ft 6in wide and 2ft 3in deep. The floats were reefed, or drawn in to the centre, to give an effective diameter of 21ft during the trials.

Three series of trials were carried out:

a. Under steam alone. These included individual trials at three draughts and at reduced power, towing trials and a tug of war.
b. Sail and steam together. Individual runs at two draughts.
c. Sail alone at three draughts.

This time the paddle steamer had more power and, in consequence, *Basilisk* had a speed advantage under steam at deep draught of from 1–12 per cent. Corrected to the same power, this implies an advantage to *Niger* of from 0.5–3 per cent, well below the accuracy of measurement. At the intermediate draught *Basilisk* had a negligible advantage, both as recorded and when corrected to equal power. At the lightest draught, even corrected for power, *Basilisk* was 4.7 per cent faster than *Niger*.

Under sail and steam combined there was nothing to

Another tug of war – between *Niger* and *Basilisk*, which in this case proved little. (© *National Maritime Museum PY0944*)

choose between the two ships, but winds were very light and too much significance should not be read into the results. Under sail alone, *Niger* won all the races, whatever the wind directions, but by a narrow margin. The real advantage of the screw lay in weight and arrangement. *Niger*'s hull was 95 tons lighter than that of *Basilisk* as no special stiffening was needed to support the propeller shaft, while a considerable amount of support was needed for the paddle shaft and sponsons. In addition, the screw machinery was 54 tons lighter. The screw machinery lay well below the waterline (top of engine 4ft 2in below water) while the top of *Basilisk*'s engine was 6ft 8in above the waterline.[26]

Towing trials

Niger was able to tow *Basilisk* at 5.6 knots with 594ihp, while *Basilisk* towed *Niger* at 6 knots with 572ihp. The screw seemed to use more power for less speed, but *Basilisk* was the heavier ship. The tug of war finished with *Niger* towing *Basilisk* backwards at 1.47 knots with 188 more indicated power. A repeat had the screw pulling the paddle at 1.1 knots with 530ihp, as against 342ihp for *Basilisk*. *Niger*'s fuel consumption seems to have been about one-third greater than that of the *Basilisk*, but this was due to her inefficient engines. All in all, these thirty-three trials were very much a wasted effort and a fine example of how a full-scale trial can absorb effort without a clear result unless it is very care-

Table 10.8 *Niger* and *Basilisk*

	Niger	*Basilisk*
Tonnage (bm)	1,072	1,031
Displacement (tons)	1,496	1,710
Length	194ft 4in	190ft
Beam	34ft 8in	34ft 5in
Draught at quoted displacement	15ft 3in/16ft 3in	15ft 4in/16ft 6in
Engine builder	Maudslay	Miller
Machinery	400NHP	400NHP
	4-cylinder horizontal	2-cylinder oscillating
Max ihp (before 1850)	790	1,033

fully planned. The trials of *Niger* and *Basilisk* were the only such wasted effort in the whole screw programme.

Another comparison of the paddle and screw was carried out in 1854 to decide on which type of propulsion caused least vibration. *Himalaya* was compared with *Victoria and Albert* and as a result the new Royal Yacht, *Osborne*, was given paddles.[27]

The screw programme in hindsight

Trials with the *Archimedes* were sufficient for Brunel to commit the future of his company to the screw in one single ship, the *Great Britain*. One may well ask whether the Surveyor, Symonds, should have recommended a similar policy to the Board. Before looking at the technical arguments it is as well to remember that *Great Britain* was a commercial failure partly because her power was not well matched to her size and speed.

Following the trials of *Archimedes* and *Widgeon*, it was clear that there was not much to choose between paddle and screw propulsion as then used. (Modern screws are considerably better than the best paddle.) It would have been reasonable to assume that the infant screw was capable of more development than the well-known paddle. The real advantages of the screw lay mainly in the arrangement of the ship. Paddle boxes were a great handicap to the warship; they reduced the number of positions for broadside gun mountings, and the wheels were thought to be vulnerable to gunfire. (But see Chapter 6; they were less vulnerable than expected.) The paddle boxes added to wind and wave resistance and were liable to cause slamming in beam seas, which might damage the wheels. Most of these points were covered by Lloyd and Chappell in their report and they also mentioned, less realistically, the difficulty of boarding from a paddler.

The paddle is very sensitive to the immersion of its floats, giving the best performance when the top of the lowest board is just in the water surface. There were many things which could go wrong. The designer might miscalculate the weight of the ship so that she floated deeper in the water than intended. More difficult was the problem of allowing for the change in water level caused by the bow wave. Then, too, the weight of the engines could cause the centre of a weak ship to sag by several inches, again sinking the wheels too deep. When

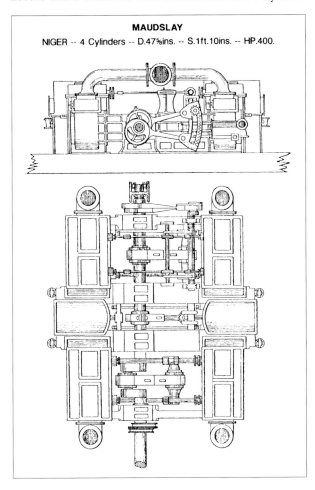

MAUDSLAY
NIGER -- 4 Cylinders -- D.47⅝ins. -- S.1ft.10ins. -- HP.400.

26. E P Haisted, 'Screw fleet of the navy', *Journal of the United Services Institution* (1850).
27. PRO 593/54.

Left: *Niger*'s four-cylinder Maudslay engines.

The British and French fleets becalmed in the Baltic, 1854. The British screw ships are getting up steam to tow the French sailing ships of the line. (© *National Maritime Museum PY8322*)

the ship was rolling, the immersion would differ from side to side and the resulting changes in thrust would make the ship yaw.

On the other hand, the screw had some positive virtues. It was entirely underwater and so protected from shot, the low shaft line making it possible to protect the machinery in the same way. It was much easier to sail a screw ship; the propeller was turned so that its two blades were behind the stern post. (It was the fact that the screw was totally hidden behind the stern post that led to the heavy vibration which was the one drawback of the early screw ships.) In a paddler, the lower boards had to be removed, with all the toil and danger which that involved, or a reefing mechanism fitted, increasing the risk of action damage. Finally, the screw ship, with its funnel lowered, looked exactly like a sailing ship and this may have helped in winning over the few remaining diehards.

Why, then, did the Admiralty hesitate? There were certainly some unresolved problems on the design of the propeller itself; the choice of diameter, pitch and length was unclear, though the *Minx* trial, in particular, could have been read as showing that, within quite broad limits, details of the geometry did not matter. A more

serious problem was due to the effect of weakening the stern post by cutting a hole for the shaft combined with the forces associated with vibration. It was this which almost caused the loss of the *Royal Albert* in 1856 by uncontrollable flooding through the worn stern gland.

The resources available for warship building in the 1840s were not large and a reluctance to commit them all to a novel device like the screw is understandable. After all, that great pillar of free enterprise, Samuel Cunard, built his last paddler, the *Scotia,* as late as 1861 and did not convert her to the screw until 1879. In practice, any delay in adopting the screw had few consequences. After 1840 the new paddlers built were five First Rate frigates, twelve Second Rate frigates and twenty-one sloops.

These ships gave good service in the Crimean War and elsewhere. All in all, the screw programme was well planned and executed with a sense of urgency tempered with realism. The technical driving force was Lloyd, supported by Brunel and Smith – what a pity it is that their early quarrels are remembered, rather than their later friendship and success. The technical team were encouraged, even pushed, by the Board and credit is due to Cockburn, Herbert and Corry.

Introduction

The first half of the 1840s was a period of innovation. The screw propeller had been a great success but the iron hull had been a failure. Symonds's extreme attitudes had been discredited and he was on the way out, but there were still many ships under construction to his design style.

A new Board under the Earl of Ellenborough was formed in January 1846 but it had a short life, as Peel's government fell in July of that year, George, Earl of Auckland becoming First Lord. Corry, one of the drivers of the technical revolution, was replaced by H G Ward. The new Board had to decide on the fate of both the iron ships and of the Surveyor, Symonds. They also had to decide what was to be done with the large number of Symondite sailing ships under construction.

Though the government was pledged to economy, the Navy Votes remained higher than in the previous decade (Table 11.1).

To clarify the confusions of the period a short chronology is provided (see Table 11.2).

The strategic background

During 1844–5 there were a number of events which caused both Britain and France to believe that war was almost inevitable. The British were particularly alarmed by a pamphlet written by the Prince de Joinville, son of Louis Philippe. His work '*Notes sur l'état des forces navales de la France*' suggested that the introduction of the steamship could help France to defeat her historic enemy. In some ways the pamphlet was a restatement of Paixhans's ideas of twenty years earlier, but the new author's connections gave added authority to his views.

De Joinville suggested that earlier British victories had been due to greater numbers of ships and men and to superior British seamanship. He then argued that France should build a large force of small, fast steamers, well armed with shell-firing guns; this was an early form of the philosophy advocated by the *Jeune Ecole* at the end of the century. A little thought on each side of the Channel would have shown the weakness in the argument. Britain's industrial might was so great compared with that of France that any attempt to implement de Joinville's plan could easily be countered by a British building programme. The inaccuracy of long-range gunfire, particularly with shells, discussed in Chapter 6, was another factor which should have been seen as discrediting the plan.

The French were alarmed by the visit of the Tsar of Russia to London in June 1844, while Britain was even more upset by French action in Algeria and by the imprisonment of a missionary in Tahiti.[1] Following the French bombardment of Tangier on 22 August 1844, their ambassador to London said, 'War is now generally regarded as inevitable.' Tension eased a little in October when Louis Philippe visited Windsor as a guest of Queen Victoria, but there was another crisis in 1845 and in the following year Anglo-American relations were strained by the opening of the Welland Canal which bypasses Niagara between Lakes Erie and Ontario.

In this tense political atmosphere, the British suffered from the recurring nightmare that French steamships would land an invasion force of some 30,000 men in a single night. It was an unrealistic fear, as the problems of landing troops in the Crimea were

Table 11.1 **Navy Votes**

Date	Total (£m)	New work (£ 000)	Men (x1,000)
1842	7.0	194.5	43.1
1843	6.4	234.9	40.2
1844	6.5	298.9	38.3
1845	7.3	486.4	40.1
1846	7.9	526.8	43.3
1847	7.7	559.6	45.0
1848	7.9	688.6	43.0
1849	7.0		40.0
1850	6.7		39.0
1851	6.5		39.0
1852	6.7		39.0
1853	7.2		45.5

Table 11.2 **Chronology**

Year	Month	Event
1845	Apr	*Rattler/Alecto* tug of war
	Aug	Blockships ordered
1846	Jan	Haddington replaced by Ellenborough
	Jun	*Amphion* ordered
	Jul	Government falls, Auckland First Lord
	Jul	Iron programme stopped
1847	Jun	Thomas Lloyd becomes Chief Engineer
	Jun	Symonds resigns
1848	Feb	Baldwin Walker becomes Surveyor
	Jun	Isaac Watts becomes Assistant Surveyor
1849	Jan	Sir Francis Baring First Lord
1852	Mar	Northumberland First Lord
1853	Jan	Graham First Lord

1. C J Bartlett, *Great Britain and Sea Power*, Oxford (1967).

An attempt to defuse Anglo-French tensions: the state visit of King Louis Philippe to Britain in October 1844. On arrival at Portsmouth in the paddle frigate *Gomer*, the French king was greeted by HMS *Victory* with yards manned and dressed overall, perhaps a pointed reminder of a previous conflict.
(© National Maritime Museum PX9823)

to show (Chapter 12), but the armies and navies of both countries, lacking trained staff officers, believed it to be possible.

This fear led the government in 1844 to set up a Commission on Coast Defences. Their principal task was to investigate the state of defences of the Royal Dockyards and to suggest improvements in their protection against a sudden assault. They found deficiencies everywhere they went: 'Sheerness was so defenceless that it could be captured by three steamers and the Thames up to Tilbury was equally defenceless.'[2] Pembroke, too, was vulnerable and both Portsmouth and Plymouth were in need of considerable strengthening. While most of the recommendations were for conventional forts, the commission also proposed some mobile batteries. This recommendation was quickly followed up and led directly to the first steam battleships.

The blockships[3]

The original concept for these floating batteries, or blockships as they soon came to be called, was for some elderly Third Rates and frigates to be given minimal steam power and a jury rig so that they could move to their stations in any weather and transit to a different port. It is certain that they were envisaged from the start as screw ships,[4] even though *Rattler's* comparative trials with *Alecto* had yet to begin. The blockships were to have a speed of 5–6 knots, three weeks' provisions and water, with reduced scales of naval and ordnance stores.

The proposed disposition of these ships is given in Table 11.3.

The use of tugs was considered, but rejected in favour of self-propelled ships for quick response and reliability.[5] The first batch of ships to be chosen was found to be in an unsatisfactory condition and, after various other suggestions, other ships were allocated on 2 September 1845 (see Table 11.4). A few days later *Forte* (44) was added to the list.

By this time it had been decided that the blockships

Table 11.3 **Proposed Disposition**

Solent and Isle of Wight	2 liners, 4 frigates
Medway	2 frigates
Plymouth	2 liners, 2 frigates
Pembroke	2 liners

Table 11.4 **Revised Allocations**

Chatham	*Hogue* (72), *Eurotas* (44)
Sheerness	*Blenheim* (72), *Horatio* (44)
Portsmouth	*Edinburgh* (72), *Ajax* (72)
Plymouth	*Seahorse* (44)

should have a full sailing rig, though on a reduced scale. There are suggestions both by Edye[6] and Fincham[7] that this change was at the instance of the secretary, Corry, who was a strong advocate of the steam battleship. Since they were now to be seagoing ships, the need to select vessels in good material condition was apparent.

It was decided to fit 450NHP engines in the Third Rates and 350NHP in the frigates. There was no rational method of deciding on the characteristics of the propeller or on the benefits of modifying the stern to give finer lines, as some suggested. Symonds was sounding a sensible note of caution when, in January 1846, he proposed that one ship of each category should be completed and tried before too much work was done on the others. Eventually it was decided that *Blenheim* and *Ajax* were to be advanced and that the frigate blockships should await the trials of *Amphion*.

Fincham had argued that there was no real evidence that finer stern lines, which would be expensive, would make any difference to the performance of these ships. Accordingly, *Ajax* was given engines without alteration to her lines while *Blenheim* was lengthened 5ft. All four battleships started their conversion in the hands of contractors and were completed by dockyards.

Ajax was the first to complete, by one day, on 23 September 1846, becoming the world's first steam battleship. *Blenheim*, however, has the honour of being

Three of the Royal Navy's pioneering screw ships in action in the Baltic during 1855: left to right, *Cornwallis*, *Amphion* and *Hastings* (two second generation blockships and the first screw frigate). (© *National Maritime Museum PU9050*)

the first such ship to go to sea, also by the margin of a single day. The cost of *Ajax* was little more than that of a major refit: some £23,000 for hull work and £21,500 for machinery. *Blenheim* was much more expensive: hull £43,000, engines £23,600 and masts £8,200.

The additional hull cost must have been due mainly to the work involved in altering the stern, though making good defective structure may also have been different in the two ships. It is often claimed that it would have been almost as cheap to build a new ship but, comparing the cost with purpose-built liners, the probable cost of a new blockship would have been some £120,000. The original estimate for a floating battery was £11,600, a quite unrealistic figure, less than the cost of the machinery and allowing nothing for making good aged and defective hulls.

Trials of the first two ships justified Fincham's simple approach. On their first trials with virtually the same power and, initially, propellers of the same diameter and pitch, *Ajax* made 6.5 knots and *Blenheim* 5.7 knots. After *Ajax*'s screw had been reduced in pitch by two degrees she made 7.0 knots. Other trials data for all four liners can be found in Table 11.5.

It should be appreciated that the scientific conduct of speed trials was in its infancy. The measured speeds were probably accurate only to within about a quarter of a knot, there was an unknown and variable difference between indicated and shaft horsepower and the amount of fouling on the bottom was not recorded. It is not even certain that the effects of tide, currents and wind were eliminated. Even allowing for all these unknown factors, there is no clear advantage for the lengthened ships. With modern knowledge, it is clear that the lengthening was too small to have had any effect. In all four ships, the stern was so bluff that there would be a large mass of 'dead' water behind it, affecting propeller performance. Many years later, the great hydrodynamicist William Froude described how he was able to swim in the propeller hoisting trunk of a blockship with the ship under full sail.[8]

Table 11.5 **Blockship Trials**

Ship	Lengthened by (ft)	Machinery	ihp	Speed (knots)
Ajax	–	Maudslay 2-cylinder horizontal	931	6.8
Blenheim	5	Seaward & Capel 4-cylinder direct connecting rod	938	5.8
Edinburgh	–	Maudslay	963	8.9
Hogue	8	Seaward & Capel	797	8.3

The blockships completed at a displacement of about 3,000 tons, carrying 212 tons of coal, provisions for eight weeks and fresh water for five weeks. The machinery occupied a lot of space and the armament was reduced in number from seventy-two to sixty guns, though these were of much larger calibre. The crew must still have been very cramped.

Gun deck	Twenty-eight 32pdr/56cwt
Main deck	Twenty-six 8in/53cwt
Upper deck	Two 68dpr/95cwt pivot, four 10in/67cwt

The lower deck ports were 6ft above the waterline.

Bearing in mind the limited role for which they were intended, these four ships must be considered very successful. Even seen as full seagoing battleships, their promise was such as to lead directly to the construction of fast liners such as *Agamemnon* and all of them gave good service in the Baltic during the Crimean War.

By the time that the war was over, their original concept had been forgotten and they were condemned by Sir John Pakington and Sir Charles Napier as unfit for the line, poor steamers and not very good under sail. Pakington even said, 'They might, perhaps, be useful as floating batteries'! (ie, their intended role of fourteen years earlier). They were finally scrapped in the mid-1860s after nearly twenty years' service as steamships. The frigates, discussed later, were not nearly so successful. Five more Third Rates were converted to blockships during the war, but for a very different role (Chapter 12).

2. Commission on Coastal Defences, 1844. Membership comprised Captain Sir Thomas Hastings, Colonel Sir George Hoste RE and Colonel Mercer RA.

3. D K Brown, 'The first steam battleships', *Mariner's Mirror*, vol 63 (1977). Later research has revealed several detail errors.

4. Select Committee 1847.

5. Ibid.

6. Ibid.

7. J Fincham, A *History of Naval Architecture*, London (1851).

8. W Froude, 'Apparent negative slip in screw propellers', *Trans INA*, vol VIII (1867).

The last sailing ships

A large number of sailing ships of rates from Fourth to First were started in the early 1840s; few, if any, completed as sailing ships and most were considerably modified.[9] The first set of changes came in about 1847, as a result of the work of the Committee of Reference, and involved alterations to the form and proportions. Symonds's excessive beam was reduced, length generally increased and a fuller midship section adopted.

These changes were first implemented while John Edye was still the senior assistant surveyor. His was a complex character and there are insufficient data to do him justice. He raised numerous objections to iron hulls and to what he saw as the over-rapid introduction of screw propellers, but his objections were neither silly nor trivial. He was opposed to the School of Naval Architecture, yet his own published works include tables of dimensions and weights which paralleled much of the work of the school. The increasing use of iron diagonals, though proposed by Seppings and used by Lang, was extended by Edye. A loyal supporter of Symonds, he seems to have been quick to discard the main features of Symonds's system as soon as he had authority. From 1832 Edye prepared all drawings of every ship and wrote the specifications to his own hand. He was clearly cautious and also competent; the Royal Navy owes him much.

Screw frigates

There are three threads to the story of the screw frigate. The first was the development of the iron frigate, most of which were screw ships. Next came the development of the frigate blockships, followed by the design of the *Amphion*. It is convenient to complete the blockship story first, though there were considerable interactions with *Amphion*.

The four frigate conversions were finally ordered in September 1845. *Horatio* was the only one completed to the original plan. She was converted in Chatham Dockyard and moved in December 1849 to the East India Docks to have her Seaward engines installed. She left the following May for Sheerness, making about

8½–9 knots with some overheating of her machinery.

The only sketch found of *Horatio* shows her as a rather ugly vessel with very tall lower masts and a big funnel between the main and mizzen masts. The others do not seem to have completed as blockships but were converted differently during the Crimean War (Chapter 12).

Table 11.6 **Armament of *Horatio***

1852	Main deck	Eight 32pdrs, twelve 8in
	Upper deck	Four 10in
1853	Main deck	Eighteen 8in
	Upper deck	Four 10in

It is sometimes said that their engines took up so much space that no coal could be carried. This cannot be literally true since *Horatio* remained in active service as a steamship for some time, but there was probably a real space problem. *Horatio* handled well under both sail and steam and her captain was pleased with her.

A 36-gun frigate (*Ambuscade*) of Seppings's design was laid down at Chatham in 1830. She was still on the slip in May 1844 when Lang, the master shipwright, was asked if there was weight and space available for a 300NHP engine. The engine was to be similar to that designed by Ericsson and Count de Rosen for the French frigate *Pomone* and was to be built by Miller & Ravenhill. It was a two-cylinder, horizontal, return piston rod engine driving the screw without gearing. The propeller was a two-bladed, 15ft design by Ericsson. The engines were quite low, keeping them below the waterline. The hull, too, was altered, being lengthened 18ft with a new shape of bow which enabled a 32pdr bow chaser to fire directly ahead. The name, too, was changed, to *Amphion*.

Her engines developed 592ihp, giving a speed of 6.8 knots on trial. Her first captain, Cooper Key, complained frequently of her lack of power and of her under-pitched propeller.[10] It would seem that, in the original concept, the machinery was intended as an auxiliary only, to be used in a calm or contrary winds. Since frigates were required to make long voyages, which could be accomplished only under sail, the concept of

9. David Lyon & Rif Winfield, *The Sail & Steam Navy List: All the Ships of the Royal Navy 1815-1889*, London (2004).

10. P H Colomb, *Memoirs of Admiral Sir Astley Cooper Key*, London (1898).

Edye's draught for the 90-gun *Hannibal*, 1847, one of the last pure sailing line of battleship designs. She was converted to screw during construction and completed in 1854. *(© National Maritime Museum J1617)*

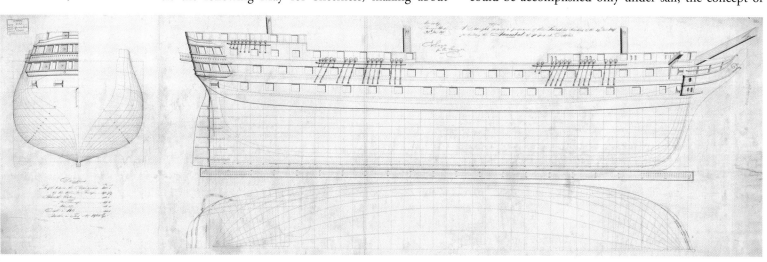

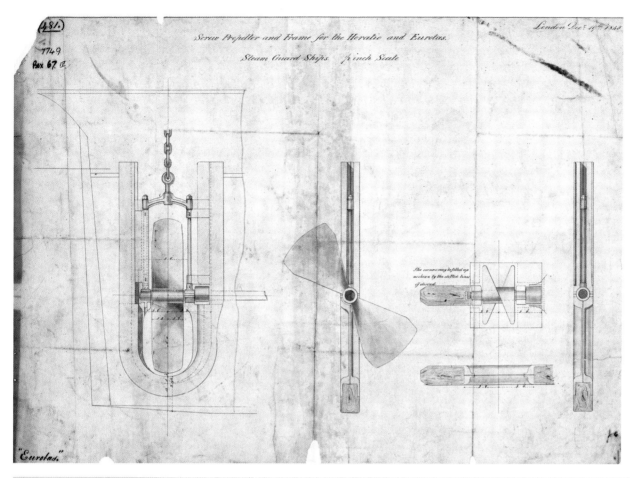

'Screw Propeller and Frame for the *Horatio* and *Eurotas*, Steam Guard Ships.' Official plan dated 19 December 1845. (*© National Maritime Museum J0693*)

Arrogant, the first screw Fourth Rate and one of the first two ships with Penn trunk engines. (*© National Maritime Museum A8115*)

A contemporary model of a Penn trunk engine. *(Rijksmuseum, Amsterdam NG-MC-528)*

auxiliary machinery was valid in the light of contemporary fuel consumption and, indeed, was used by Brunel in the *Great Britain* for this reason. In August 1844 the Surveyor was instructed to prepare a number of alternative designs for paddle or screw frigates. Even though this was before the *Rattler/Alecto* trials, the choice was for a screw ship designed by Fincham. *Dauntless* was originally ordered from Deptford and transferred to

Portsmouth in February 1845. Her original trials in 1848 were disappointing as she only managed 7.4 knots. It was decided to lengthen the run by 9ft 6in to improve the flow into the propeller and it appears at first sight that the change was very successful since on new trials she made 10 knots. However, this speed was reached only at much greater power and rpm than in the first trial and, in 1854, at roughly the same power as in 1848, her speed was still about 7½ knots.

Arrogant, ordered in February 1845, was another attempt at giving some auxiliary power to a sailing ship. The secretary, Sidney Herbert, was keen to increase rapidly the number of steam warships in the Navy and

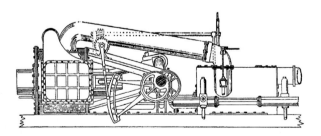

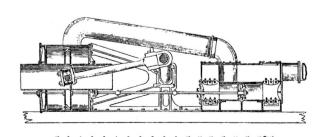

The first of the very successful Penn trunk engines. A drawing of those fitted to *Arrogant*, screw frigate.

Table 11.7 **Early Wooden Screw Frigates (excluding blockships)**

	Order (as steam)	*Completed*
Amphion	May 1844	Oct 1846
Dauntless	Aug 1844	Aug 1848
Vigilant	Aug 1844	Cancelled
Arrogant	Feb 1845	Sep 1852
Termagant	Feb 1845	1853
Phaeton	Apr 1845	1859*
Curacoa	Nov 1850	1854
Tribune	Feb 1851	1854

*Work delayed

hence wished to reduce the cost of individual units. *Arrogant* was one of the first two ships to receive the novel and very successful Penn trunk engines, in her case of 360NHP. On completion, she was tried with three different propellers with pitches of between 15ft and 15ft 5½in. This difference was too small to make any significant difference and the recorded speeds are the same within the limits of accuracy of speed trials.

The sequence of early wooden screw frigates is shown in Table 11.7. Most were originally ordered as sailing ships, but plans were changed at such an early stage that they were effectively new designs.

Two more, *Euryalus* and *Imperieuse*, are dealt with in a later chapter with their sister ships.

This programme shows a speedy initial response, but a failure to build in sufficient numbers, particularly in the light of the growing number of steam merchant ships which might require protection.

A well-qualified Select Committee sat in 1849 'to inquire into the practicability of providing, by means of the commercial steam marine of the country, a reserve steam navy, available for the national defence when required'.[11] The membership included shipowners, naval officers and enthusiastic politicians, including Corry.

Captain Chads' evidence was perceptive, and clearly showed the problems of converting merchant ships into warships. He pointed out that commercial ships did not carry enough canvas to keep up with the fleet under sail, nor did they carry enough coal to give satisfactory endurance when steaming. Guns smaller than 32pdrs were of little value but, with mountings, these weighed 4–5 tons, while 8in or 68pdrs totalled 6–7 tons each and a 10in pivot about 10 tons. The master shipwright

Table 11.8 **Merchant Steamships 1 Jan 1849**

Gross tonnage not exceeding	Wooden hull		Iron hull		Total	
	Number	Tons	Number	Tons	Number	Tons
100	498	29,828	31	2,059	529	31,887
250	260	41,637	12	2,102	272	43,739
400	127	39,161	9	2,710	136	41,871
600	66	32,845	5	2,613	71	35,458
1,000	66	46,777	1	798	67	47,575
1,000+	27	44,324	8	10,517	35	54,841
Total	1,044	234,572	66	20,799	1,110	255,371

of Portsmouth thought he could convert a passenger liner in about a fortnight. He would remove all cabin partitions on the middle deck, which was usually strong enough to mount heavy guns on the broadside. The masts were satisfactory, but stiffening (carlings) would be required under the pivot guns forward and aft. It would be best to remove the spar deck, but this was not essential.

The committee does not seem to have looked very hard at how many suitable ships were available. Since Table 11.8 lists only twenty-seven ships of over 1,000 tons (the committee saw iron ships as unsuitable) there can have been very few suitable for conversion to effective cruisers.[12]

The screw battleship

The first design for a screw battleship was prepared by John Edye in 1846. She was ordered in April 1847 as the 80-gun *Audacious* to be built at Devonport. In November her name was changed to *James Watt* and the

11. Select Committee 1849.

12. D K Brown, 'Armed merchant ships – a historical review', RINA Symposium, *Merchant Ships of War*, London (1987).

Tribune, an early second-class screw frigate. (© National Maritime Museum F8958-003)

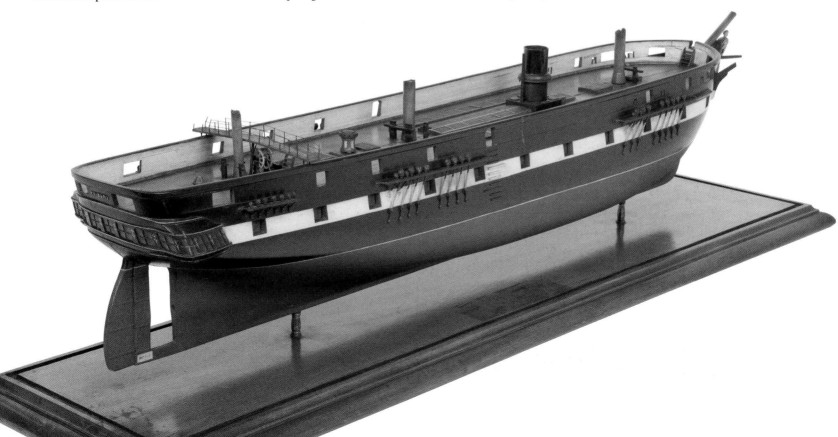

Sans Pareil, converted into a steam battleship while building and not very successful. Able to carry only 70 guns, she was the smallest screw liner. (© *National Maritime Museum D1269*)

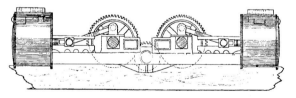

SEAWARD
TERMAGANT & EUPHRATES -- 4 Cylinders -- D.62ins. -- S.3½ft. -- HP.620.

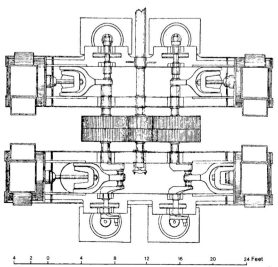

The Seaward engines of *Termagant*.

drawings were sent to the Committee of Reference the same month but she was never started.

In October 1848 it was decided to convert the *Sans Pareil*, ordered in 1845 from Devonport. She was lengthened by 18ft aft and given the 350NHP engines out of *Eurotas*. These Boulton & Watt engines developed 622ihp and gave her a trial speed of about 7 knots and proved most unreliable. Even after re-engining in 1854 she was still considered unsatisfactory.

Although both Lord John Hay and Baldwin Walker told the Select Committee on Estimates in 1848 that the steam battleships were fit to serve only as batteries in narrow seas, it was also decided that all ships of forty guns and less should be steamers. The trials of *Blenheim* in the summer of 1848 were most successful and further strengthened the case for steam battleships, even though the First Lord, Baring, was still in 1849 calling for more trials to compare paddle and screw propulsion. However, the *Blenheim* trials were seen as decisive and approval was given for a screw battleship. Isaac Watts told the committee of 1848:

The principal reason which occurs to my mind is to be found, I think, in the result of the trial of the *Blenheim* when Admiral Chads took her out from Cork on an experimental trial. He reported very favourably of her and, as far as I am aware, that led to placing the screw in line-of-battle ships.[13]

Chads told the 1849 Committee, 'I am satisfied that no fleet ought to be without them; it has opened up the whole system of our tactics and it will change all our tactics in the navy.'[14]

The Admiralty order for building *Agamemnon* was dated 3 July 1849. Watts said that 'the design was completed on 15 December 1847', which makes it fairly certain that she was built to Edye's design for the original *James Watt*, though the drawing was signed by both Edye and Watts. Watts said that she was laid off and the keel laid within about two months of the order (actually four months) and continued:

> She was a much larger ship, she was much longer, and with a much fuller midship section than it was the custom to build line-of-battle ships at that time, with a view to her receiving the larger engines of 700NHP, which were made for *Vulcan* and not put into her.

Today's designer of a steel warship would choose about the same prismatic coefficient, but would adopt a greater length (about 290ft), but with heavy machinery and a heavy wooden hull, still weak in comparison with the steel construction, such a length would not be practical. For its time and purpose, the proportions and form of *Agamemnon* appear well chosen.

Edye's evidence to the 1848 Committee throws a fascinating light on how the size of the engines was chosen. 'The engineer is furnished with a skeleton scale drawing of the cross-section of the engine room, and he is directed by the Admiralty to furnish an engine that can go into that space, the weight not to exceed a certain weight that is given.' John Field, in his evidence to the same committee, added that the height of the centre of gravity and the draught of the ship was also given 'and we have to adapt our machinery to this without

knowing what the head or stern of the vessel may be'. It was a crude approach, but there was still no way of doing better. Design was evolutionary, one ship being a little bit bigger, a little bit faster than its predecessor, allowing the use of very simple design rules.

The French had taken a slight lead, thanks to Dupuy de Lôme. Their first sizeable steamship was the 36-gun frigate *Pomone*, launched in 1845, with a 220NHP Ericsson engine and screw giving a speed of about 7 knots. In April 1847 Dupuy de Lôme proposed a battleship in which steam would be the prime mover, with sail as an auxiliary. His ambitious plans were rejected at first, but with the support of the Prince de Joinville they were finally accepted and his ship was laid down on 7 February 1848. Initially named *24 Février*, she was changed to *Napoleon* before launch on 16 May 1850. The *Napoleon* was completed for sea in July 1852.[15]

Thomas Lloyd and Isaac Watts visited France in 1851 and reported the progress on *Napoleon* when they returned. As a result, work on the *Agamemnon* was hastened and she was launched on 22 May 1852 and completed in October of that year, only a few months behind *Napoleon*. There were some revisions to the plans: eg, one dated 28 June 1849, and new Penn engines were ordered. She had the same machinery arrangement as *Ajax* and *Sans Pareil* with boilers and

Table 11.9 Comparison of Form with a Typical Third Rate Sailing Liner

	Agamemnon	Vanguard
Length (L)	230ft	190ft
Beam (B)	55ft 4in	56ft 9in
Max section area (A)	1,060sq ft	895sq ft
Displacement (W)	5,080 tons	3,680 tons
Draught (T)	23ft 4½in	21ft 9in
Length/beam ratio (L/B)	4.16	3.35
Mid section area coefficent $C_A = A/(B \times T)$	0.82	0.73
Prismatic coefficient $C_p = \dfrac{W \times 35 \ (cu \ ft)}{A \times L}$	0.73	0.76

13. Select Committee 1847.

14. Select Committee 1849.

15. R Estienne, 'Dupuy de Lôme et le *Napoleon*', *Marine et technique aux XIXe siècle*, Paris (1987).

Agamemnon. Internal profile draught. (© *National Maritime Museum DR7484*)

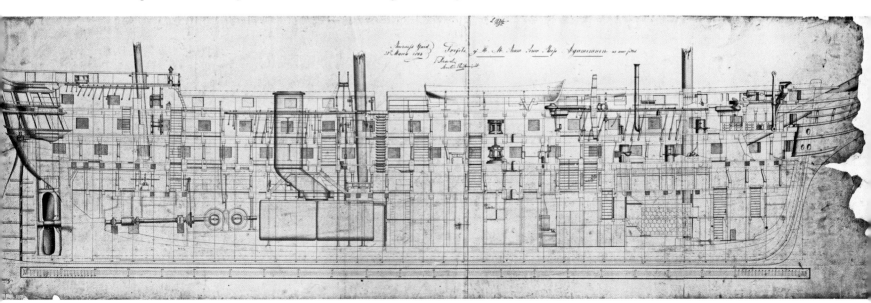

Table 11.10 **Comparison of *Agamemnon* and *Napoleon***

	Agamemnon	*Napoleon*
Tonnage, displacement	3,074, 5,080	– , 5,120
Length, beam, draught	230ft x 55ft 4in x 24ft 1⅛in	234ft 5in x 55ft 1½in x 25ft 4in
Mid section area	1,060ft	1,070ft
Metacentric height	Unknown	4.89ft
Boilers	Tubular	8 rectangular
NHP, ihp	600, 2,500	900, 2,200
Speed	11.4 knots	12.1 knots, claimed

Agamemnon. Designed by John Edye, she was a great success and was the prototype for the majority of purpose-built wooden steam battleships. (© *National Maritime Museum B1323*)

funnel between the main and mizzen mast. In consequence, she was inclined to trim by the stern and all other new construction had machinery forward of the main mast.

Agamemnon had the successful two-cylinder Penn trunk engines with 70¾in bore and 3ft 6in stroke working at 63rpm with 20lb/sq in pressure (safety valve setting). Her propeller was 18ft in diameter and 20ft 6in in pitch.

Napoleon's original engine was a two-cylinder horizontal by Moll with 98in bore and 5ft 4⅛in stroke working at 27½ rpm, geared up 1.8 to 1, and taking steam at 15lb/sq in. These engines were not very satisfactory and were replaced in 1861 by a two-cylinder Mazeline unit, also of 900NHP. The propeller had four blades and was 19ft in diameter and of 24ft pitch.

It is usually claimed that *Napoleon* was the more powerful ship on a comparison of nominal horsepower, 900 to 600. NHP was a fiction (see Appendix 1) and it was *Agamemnon* which had the greater power generated in her steam, ihp. From this had to be deducted the power used by auxiliaries, losses due to internal friction and losses in the shaft. It is not easy to accept that these losses were greater in the well-developed Penn engines than in the geared, and apparently unsuccessful, Moll engine. Almost certainly *Agamemnon* put more power into her screw.

The proportions and form of the two ships were very

similar. Matching propeller geometry to the characteristics of hull and machinery demanded luck as well as skill, but the British had more experience on which to build.

Agamemnon reached 11.24 knots over the Stokes Bay measured mile, the mean of several runs (probably four), which would largely eliminate the effects of tide and wind. Her sisters achieved very similar speeds, giving a fair measure of confidence in the results. *Napoleon* was not run over a measured distance. Her 'trial' consisted of a single run from Toulon to Ajaccio on 30 August 1852 in which she covered 119 miles at an average of 12.14 knots, logging 12.8–13 knots at a displacement of 5,074 tons. On 25 September she logged 13.5 knots, but the logs of those days were not very accurate (see Table 1.11).

In 1856 *Algesiras* carried out trials in opposite directions over a 13.5km course off Provence (without sails). Some of the runs were with only half the boilers lit but the maximum ihp recorded was 1,742 with a speed of 11.66 knots. Even 13.5km is too long for a trial distance, since currents and wind can change in the hour or so of each run.

The evidence that *Napoleon* was faster than *Agamemnon* is not convincing in the light of the greater power of the British ship. The ratio of the speeds claimed 12.14:11.24 knots is 1:08. For the same form – and there was not much difference – power would vary as the cube of the speed: ie, *Napoleon* would have needed 26 per cent more power than *Agamemnon,* or some 3,150ihp instead of the 2,200 or so developed.

Table 11.12 **Armament**

Agamemnon initially	One 68pdr, thirty-four 8in and fifty-six 32pdr
Napoleon	Eight 22cm (shell), fourteen 16cm (shell), fifty-eight 30pdr

Three more ships similar to *Agamemnon* were built together with a fourth lengthened by 4ft. The design was clearly seen as very successful and formed the basis for many later screw battleships, a great tribute to her designer, Edye.

By 1851 it was clear to the Board that the construc-

Table 11.11 **Other Recorded Speeds of Early French Screw Ships**

Ship	Displacement (tons)	Date	Run	Miles	Speed (knots)
Algesiras	5,121	5 –8 Aug 1856	Toulon-Algiers	193	13.01
Arcole	5,240	18–19 Sep 1856	Toulon	12	

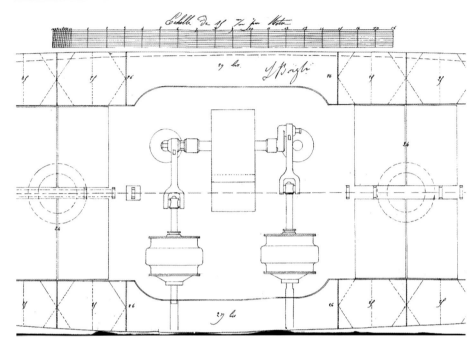

Plan view of the machinery layout of *Napoleon* as built. The rectangle between the two widely spaced cylinders represents the reduction gearing that gave so much trouble. The circles fore and aft of the engine room are the boiler uptakes that gave the ship her two-funnelled profile. *(Atlas du Génie Maritime)*

Official design draught for *Napoleon. (Atlas du Génie Maritime)*

tion of screw battleships was not proceeding fast enough and Baldwin Walker proposed to convert a number of the sailing liners then under construction. In particular, he wanted to combine the advantages of screw propulsion and the concentrated firepower of a three-decker. In December 1851, Watts and the master shipwright of Pembroke, James Abethell (1st SNA), inspected the 120-gun *Windsor Castle,* originally designed by Symonds and still on the building slip. As a result, drawings for a conversion were rapidly prepared and by 18 January 1852 they were approved. She was cut amidships and a new section 23ft long inserted while the stern was rebuilt and lengthened a further 8ft. She was launched on 30 September 1852, the day the Duke of Wellington died, and later that year she was given the name of the greatest British soldier of the century. This

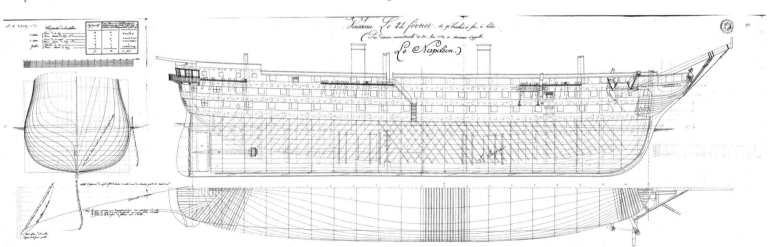

James Watt. This is the only time a major British warship has been named after an engineer. Despite her name, her engines were unreliable. (© National Maritime Museum BHC3423)

conversion was successful and a considerable number of other ships were converted on similar lines (as discussed in Chapter 13).

The number of screw battleships completed or converted before the Crimean War is given in Table 11.13, excluding the four blockships.

Table 11.13 **Screw Battleships Completed (cumulative)**

1851	1
1852	2
1853	7
1854	8

In the same period the French had completed nine steam battleships; no other power had even started one.

Guns and gunnery

Between the Battle of Waterloo and the start of the Crimean War there were a number of major changes and many minor improvements to the gunnery equipment and the training of gunners in the Royal Navy. The most important of these were:

a. Change to an all 32pdr armament
b. Introduction of shells
c. Tests against old ships of the efficacy of various projectiles
d. Improved training

At the end of the Napoleonic wars most ships had a mixed armament firing different-sized projectiles from a range of guns and carronades. Typically, a Third Rate would have 32pdr guns on the gun deck and either 18pdr or 24pdr guns on the upper deck. There would also be a number of carronades, usually 24pdrs or 32pdrs on the forecastle and poop. Other rates also had mixed armaments.

During the 1820s there were a number of proposals for a uniform armament of guns with the same bore firing a common shot. The length of the gun barrel would vary, the longest and heaviest guns being carried on the lower decks, but even the shortest guns on the upper decks were longer than the old carronade. The carronade did, however, remain in service throughout the period of this book.

The first and certainly the best known proposal for a uniform armament came from Paixhans with the publi-

Edgar. Although not apparent in this view, like *Agamemnon* she had her funnel and boilers abaft the main mast giving excessive stern trim. (© *National Maritime Museum PU6214*)

cation of his *Nouvelle Force Maritime* in 1822. This work was widely used and discussed in Britain; reviews appeared in *Papers on Naval Architecture* and the *United Services Journal*. A similar proposal was put forward by Colonel Monro in 1825. There seems to have been little dispute about the value of the change in gun size but it was some time before money and labour became available to carry it out.

Thanks largely to the improved foundry techniques introduced by Blomefield at Woolwich Arsenal at the end of the eighteenth century,[16] it was found possible to bore out many existing 18pdr and 24pdr guns to take 32lb shot. A start was made in 1830 when 800 Congreve 24pdrs and about the same number of Blomefield guns were converted to 32pdrs. 'Double shotting' was not recommended for these bored out guns and 'triple shotting' was prohibited. Careful trials had shown that multiple shots from the same discharge were of little value except at the closest range.

From 1838 onwards these converted guns were gradually replaced by a new range of 32pdrs weighing 42cwt, 45cwt or 50cwt, though some of the older weapons remained in use for many years. By the late 1830s it is likely that all ships in commission carried an armament almost entirely of 32pdrs.

British experiments with shell-firing guns began in 1824 and a few 8in/50cwt guns were introduced the following year and the 10in/65cwt was fitted in a few paddle steamers some years later. There was considerable opposition to the use of shells at sea due to the risk of explosion, by accident or enemy action, of one's own shells on a crowded gun deck. The spherical shell with an asymmetrical fuse was also much less accurate at longer range than a solid shot, since the out of balance weight of the fuse would make it fly out of true. Finally,

it was clear that the early time fuses were unreliable, sometimes exploding the shell too soon or, more often, not at all. By 1838 these fears and problems had been overcome, in part at least, and significant numbers of 8in/65cwt shell-firing guns appeared on the gun deck.

The paddle steamer, as it grew in size, led to a new range of weapons. Since the wheel and its surrounding box limited the number of guns carried on the broadside, there was pressure to carry bigger guns with greater lethality. In particular, heavy guns firing 42lb, 56lb, 68lb shot, and even more, were mounted at bow and stern.

During the war of 1812, the series of US victories in frigate duels, although broken by the *Shannon*'s defeat of *Chesapeake*, showed the Royal Navy that they needed to improve the training of gun crews and to develop mechanical aids to accurate gunnery. Sir Howard Douglas published the first edition of his *Treatise on Naval Gunnery* in 1817, which quickly became the training manual for gunners.[17]

The need for a specialist gunnery training school was gradually perceived and HMS *Excellent* was commissioned at Portsmouth on 19 January 1830, both for training and experimental work. Seamen gunners became a specialist and career rate with additional pay of 2–7 shillings a month. While there was some suspicion that officers' gunnery courses were too theoretical, the value of *Excellent* was soon appreciated. Both rate of fire and accuracy were much improved, as demonstrated during the successful and accurate bombardment of Acre in 1846.[18]

The exceptional figures in Table 11.14 are taken from *Excellent*'s trial records.

The normal crew on a 32pdr was fourteen men. There were enough men in the crew to man only one broad-

16. H M Baker, *The Crisis in Naval Armament* (National Maritime Museum monograph 56), London (1983).

17. H Douglas, *A Treatise on Naval Gunnery*, London (1820, 1855 and 1860 editions).

Table 11.14 **Rate of Fire**

Gun	Crew	Rounds	Time
32pdr/56cwt	13	11	7min 10sec
68pdr/65cwt	15	11	7min 40sec

A sectional model of the three-decker *Queen* of 1840. By this date most battleship guns were 32pdrs but of different lengths/weights, although a few 8in shell guns were being added on the gun decks. (© *National Maritime Museum D7870*)

side fully and a ship would prepare for action with half-crews on each side.

The accuracy which could be achieved in action is hard to determine. Guns mounted on a fixed base on land, firing at a stationary target, could achieve frequent hits out to 3,000yds (see Chapter 6); hence the belief in the superiority of forts over ships. Even in a slight seaway, the motion of the ship would degrade the accuracy of gunnery and it is likely that few hits would be scored at over 1,000yds.

From about 1829 tangent sights were introduced and these, together with the practice of measuring range by subtending the angle made by a known height on the enemy, improved accuracy, at least in good weather. From 1830 percussion locks replaced the old flint lock

firing mechanism and by improving the certainty of ignition also contributed to accuracy.

Detailed but important changes to gunnery were made elsewhere. The safety of magazines and the means of supplying charges to the guns were improved. Changes were made to the design of gun carriages to ease the task of training the gun.

The nominal weight of the gun (eg, 56cwt) referred to the weight of the barrel only. To this must be added the weight of the carriage, ammunition and miscellaneous gunner's equipment in order to understand the impact of the weapon on the design of the ship (see Appendix 5).

The *Prince George* trials

There were frequent trials of the penetration of shot against various targets representing the side of a ship, but in 1835 a more elaborate and realistic series of firing trials was carried out against the old three-decker *Prince George* (launched 1772). The majority of the firing was with solid or hollow shot, though a few shells were also used. The range was generally 1,200yds.

At this range it was found that an 18pdr/42cwt shot fired with a 6lb charge at two or three degrees' elevation would penetrate 21–23in. With the full charge of 10lb 10oz the gun recoiled 11ft and discharged the shot at a muzzle velocity of 1,680ft/sec, reduced to about 780ft/sec at 1,200yds.[19] Some solid shot were fired from a 68pdr (46in penetration) and also some hollow shot which went through 25–56in.

There were also some tests of ricochet firing, firing to skip off the surface, from 32pdrs and 68pdrs using both solid and hollow shot. The penetration was generally less, but still 30in or more.

A number of shell firings were also carried out, but available records are sparse. In the first trial, two time-fused shells were placed on board and detonated. While they caused considerable damage, there was no fire, much to the surprise of the trials team. A 32pdr shell fired against the side hit and penetrated below the water-line and, though it did not explode, caused severe flooding. Out of eighty time-fused shells fired, thirty-eight failed to explode. It was found that four out of five fuses failed to work after bouncing off the water, and one in three failed on hitting the ship's side. If the shell hit fuse foremost, which was generally the case, the remnants of timber would plug and extinguish the fuse.

These trials were taken seriously and led to the rapid introduction of the shell-firing gun. There was little concern for secrecy in those days and it is surprising that after the results of these trials were known, the effect of shells in the war with Russia was unexpected.

In May 1853, another trial was carried out against the *York* at 1,200yds, in which six 32pdr shells and six 8in shells, all with Freeburn's concussion fuses, were fired. All hit, ten functioned correctly, one broke on an iron knee and the other failed. On the other hand, by bursting on contact the damage was not severe.

In this history of the ships, little space can be devoted

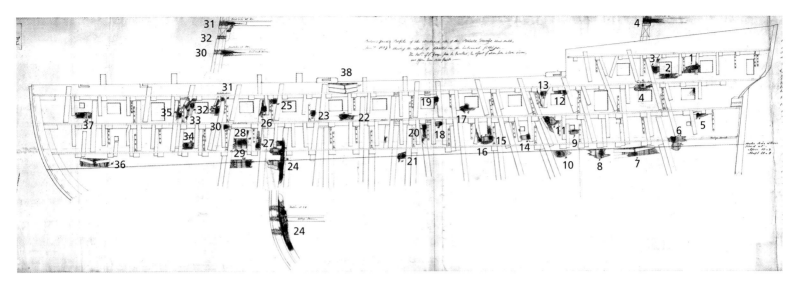

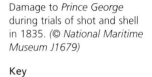

to gunnery. The principal sources, Douglas[20] and Robertson,[21] are neither comprehensive nor, it is suggested, entirely reliable. A good history of early nineteenth-century gunnery is long overdue.

Naval Review 1853

The new Navy was on show at a review at Spithead in August 1853. Bartlett rightly points out the significance of the occasion.[22] The paddle steamships were conspicuous with their large paddle boxes and tall funnels. Almost indistinguishable from sailing ships with their funnels lowered, the screw steamers represented the future.

There were no iron-hulled vessels and none with armour, but both would soon arrive. The Navy had changed greatly already; the war would speed the pace.

Damage to *Prince George* during trials of shot and shell in 1835. (© *National Maritime Museum J1679*)

Key
Knee and timbers damaged 1, 3, 4, 11, 14–16, 30–33
Planking damaged 2, 12, 17, 20–23, 34, 36
Unexploded shell damaged knee and timber 5, 18
Timbers severely damaged 6–10, 19, 25, 28, 29, 37
Shell damage to knee and timbers 13
Rider shot away 24, 26, 27, 35, 38

18. Bartlett, op cit.
19. R Estienne, 'Dupuy de Lôme et le *Napoleon*', *Marine et technique aux XIXe siècle*, Paris (1855 edition.)
20. R Estienne, 'Dupuy de Lôme et le *Napoleon*', *Marine et technique aux XIXe siècle*, Paris (1987).
21. F L Robertson, *The Foundation of Naval Armament*, London (1921).
22. Bartlett, op cit.

The review of the fleet in 1853. Paddlers are conspicuous but the newer screw ships looked little different from sailing ships. (© *National Maritime Museum PW6120*)

Twelve | The War With Russia 1854–1856

Introduction: technical developments[1]

Happily, major wars were rare in the nineteenth century and this war, more familiar as the Crimean War, saw the final replacement of the sailing ship in the Royal Navy by the steamship. As such, it was almost the only chance to evaluate the developments described in earlier chapters. The war saw the introduction or extended use of whole fleets of steamships, armoured ships, shells, rifled guns and mines. There was an enormous building programme with the use of 'mass production' techniques. For these reasons, Antony Preston has described the war as 'The last old-fashioned war for the army and the first modern war for the navy'.

For the navy, it was a worldwide war, with the major effort in the Baltic, and with significant operations in the China Sea and White Sea as well as in the Black Sea. There were no fleet actions, nor were there any significant encounters at sea, and hence the lessons learned must be treated with caution. It is a complicated war to follow, unfamiliar to most students of naval history, and for which there are few good references.[2] It will be necessary to sketch in the operational scene but this cannot be a

history of the war with Russia. A chronology is included to show the timing of naval operations in the Baltic and Black seas and their relationship with army operations.

The fleets

The war brought the two largest fleets in the world into conflict with the third, Russia. The overall strength of the allied fleet seemed overwhelming.

Table 12.2 **The Fleets 1850**

	Britain	France	Allied	Russia
Line of battle	86	45	131	43
Frigates	104	56	160	48

Since the main allied fleets were deployed far from their home bases, in the Baltic and Black seas, their local superiority was much less than indicated by this table. On the other hand, the Russians had no steam liners and few steam frigates. It was the allied supremacy in steam

The junction of the British and French fleets in the Baltic, 12 June 1854; the flagships are saluting one another with their national colours. The principal Royal Navy ships are steamers whereas the French line of battle comprises sailing ships. (© *National Maritime Museum PY8240*)

Table 12.1 **The War with Russia 1853–1856**

Chronology

Date	Black Sea, including army	Baltic and elsewhere	Date	Black Sea, including army	Baltic and elsewhere
1853	Preliminary operations		31 Aug	French embark (sail 5 Sep)	
31 May	Russian ultimatum to Turkey		7 Sep	British sail from Varna	
8 Jun	British fleet approaches Dardanelles		14 Sep	Landing	
2 Jul	Russians invade Moldavia		20 Sep	Battle of the Alma	
5 Oct	Turkey declares war		23 Sep	Russians block Sevastopol	
28 Oct	Turkish Army crosses Danube		26 Sep	Fleet meets army at Balaclava	
30 Oct	British fleet enters Bosphorus		27 Sep		Fleet withdraws for winter
30 Nov	Battle of Sinope		17 Oct	Bombardment of Sevastopol	
1854 3 Jan	Allied fleet enters Black Sea		25 Oct	Battle of Balaclava	
3 Mar		Baltic fleet leaves Spithead	5 Nov	Battle of Inkerman	
			14 Nov	Great Storm	
19 Mar		Baltic fleet at Wingo Sound	22 Dec	Lyons replaces Dundas	
			24 Dec	Bruat replaces Hamelin	
26 Mar	Fleet arrives at Baltchirk		1855 2 Feb	Formal renewal of blockade	
27 Mar	Declaration of war (reaches Dundas 9 Apr)		22 Feb	Cruise to Anapa	
			28 Mar		Baltic fleet sails
6 Apr	*Furious* fired on at Odessa		Apr	Night attacks on harbour forts	
17 Apr	French troops reach Gallipoli		3 May	Kertch expedition sails and recalled by cable	
27 Apr	Bombardment of Odessa		22 May	Kertch expedition sails again	
28 Apr	Reconnaissance of Sevastopol		25 May	Capture of Kertch and Yenikale	
5 May		Gulf free of ice	26 May	Squadron enters Azov	
12 May	*Tiger* lost		31 May		Off Kronstadt
12 May	32,000 French, 18,000 British troops land at Gallipoli		9 Jun		*Merlin* and *Firefly* mined
1 Jun	Danube mouth blockaded	*Lightning* surveys Bomarsund	18 Jun	Unsuccessful attack on Redan	
			28 Jun	Death of Lord Raglan	
13 Jun		French fleet joins	19 Jul		Off Helsingfors
21 Jun		Bomarsund shelled	9 Aug		Attack on Sveaborg
21 Jun		Off Kronstadt	8 Sep	Capture of Malakov	
6 Jul	Orders to invade Crimea		9 Sep	Evacuation of Sevastopol	
24 Jul	Dundas & Bruat recce Cholera epidemic				Fleet withdraws
8 Aug		Landing at Bomarsund	17 Oct	Bombardment of Kinburn	
16 Aug		Surrender of Bomarsund	1856 25 Feb	Peace conference opens	
			29 Feb	Armistice in Crimea	
21 Aug		Kola	30 Mar	Treaty of Paris	
30 Aug		Petropavlovsk	23 Apr	Victory Review	

men-of-war which allowed them to dominate the seas, almost without opposition. This supremacy was not at first apparent to the British government, who feared that the numerically stronger Russian force in the Baltic might be able to defeat the allied squadron and launch an invasion of Britain.

The outbreak of war and the opening moves

The reasons for this war are complicated, but the major cause was Russia's desire for free access to the Mediterranean. Turkish weakness seemed to offer an opportunity, and excuses were provided by alleged persecutions of religious and ethnic minorities in the Turkish Empire. Britain and France had no wish to see the

Russian Empire extend to the Mediterranean and offered support to Turkey.[3]

Negotiations or, perhaps more correctly, threats, bluff and counter-bluff, occupied the early months of 1853, culminating in an ultimatum addressed to the Sultan on 31 May. On 2 July the Russian army crossed the Pruth into Moldavia and, after futile negotiations, Turkey declared war on 5 October.

The initial British and French counter-moves were cautious. The British Mediterranean fleet moved towards the Dardanelles as early as June, but it was 22 October before the allied fleet moved up to Constantinople. Some ships went up the Bosphorus but did not enter the Black Sea as neither of the allies had yet declared war.

1. D K Brown, 'The Royal Navy in the Crimean War', *Marine et technique au XIXe siècle*, Paris (1987). Note: the paper was based on an early draft of the book and this chapter is altered and expanded in the light of discussion.

2. Sir W L Clowes, *The Royal Navy. A history from the earliest time to the present*, London (1903); this is by far the best readily available account of the operations.

3. R L Ffrench-Blake, *The Crimean War*, London (1971).

Sinope

The war between Turkey and Russia appeared to be limited to the Danube principalities and it is likely that the Turkish Admiral Osman Pasha believed that there was an implicit truce at sea when he anchored his frigate squadron off Sinope in early November 1853. He had six sailing frigates, with his flag in the 60-gun *Avni Illah*, three corvettes and two small paddle steamers. Their largest guns were 24pdrs and the Turks were poorly trained and unready for war. The anchorage was protected by eighty-four guns, some possibly landed from the squadron.

Russian scouts reported the Turkish ships and Admiral Nakhimov decided to attack with his fleet, vastly superior in numbers, size and guns.

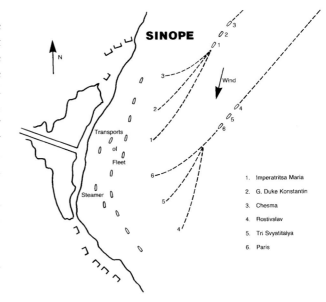

Table 12.3 **The Russian Fleet**

Line of battle, 120-gun	3
84-gun	3
Frigates	2
Steamers, small	3

Two of the 120-gun ships each carried fourteen 60pdr shell-firing guns and there were ten more such weapons in other ships.

Nakhimov closed to attack at 1230hrs on 30 November with his liners in two columns. Firing began about 1330hrs and went on until nightfall when the Turkish ships were largely destroyed. They lost some three thousand men (75 per cent) and the only ship to escape was the paddler *Taif*. The Russian losses were thirty-seven killed and 229 wounded. Reaction abroad was one of surprise, shock and horror. There were emotional articles alleging Russian breach of truce – there was no truce – and of firing on survivors in the water. It was believed that the destruction was mainly caused by the Russian shells, though the evidence on this point is far from clear. Douglas quotes a letter from General Paixhans in which he says that the Russian report specifically refers to the destruction of the Turkish frigates by shells.[4] Correspondence with the French ambassador to Turkey confirmed the destruction of the bigger Turkish ships as being due to fire following the explosion of shells.

Most writers were unaware of the effects of shells as demonstrated by the *Prince George* trials[5] and by corresponding French trials at Gavre.[6] The Turks were perhaps also unaware of the destruction of a squadron of their own fleet at the Liman River (Azov) in 1788 by a flotilla of Russian oared gun boats using shells and commanded by General Sir Samuel Bentham.[7]

4. Sir H Douglas, *A Treatise on Naval Gunnery* (1860 edition).

5. Sir H Douglas, *A Treatise on Naval Gunnery* (1855 edition; reprinted London 1982).

6. J P Baxter, *The Introduction of the Ironclad Warship*, Harvard (1933).

7. F L Robertson, *The Evolution of Naval Gunnery*, London (1921).

The battle of Sinope evoked a passionate reaction. This French print quotes Lord John Russell's description: 'Butchery decorated with the name of victory.' (© National Maritime Museum PU5897)

The British fleet entering the Baltic. Left to right: *Leopard, Vulture* (distant), *St Jean d'Acre, Royal George, Duke of Wellington, Princess Regent, Cressy, Impérieuse, Arrogant, Edinburgh, Hogue, Blake, Ajax, Euryalus, Dauntless, Neptune, Monarch, Amphion* (foreground), *Bulldog* (distant). (© *National Maritime Museum PY8333*)

This skirmish at Sinope had effects out of all proportion to its operational significance. Napoleon III directed his *chef du materiel*, Dupuy de Lôme, to develop the design of steam, armoured batteries. Politically, war was now inevitable and both Britain and France declared war on 27 March 1854. The news reached Admiral Dundas at Baltchirk in the Black Sea on 9 April and Admiral Napier in the Baltic on the 4th of that month.

The Baltic 1854

The first problem facing the Board was to choose a commander-in-chief. Promotion by seniority, the long years of peace and very limited retirement schemes led to very elderly admirals. J W D Dundas in the Black Sea was born in 1785 and the final choice for the Baltic, Sir Charles Napier, was only a year younger. It was a war of young technology and old men. Manning the fleet posed even more problems, as pay and conditions were not good enough to attract sufficient high-quality volunteers, while the use of the press gang, still legal, was unacceptable. In consequence those who joined were mainly landsmen, pensioners and the unemployable.

Table 12.4 **The Baltic Fleet**

Steam line-of-battle ships	9
Steam blockships	4
Sailing line-of-battle ships	7
Screw frigates	4
Paddle frigates, small steamships	11

By February 1854 the fleet was assembling and the newly entered men were being hurriedly trained. On 11 March Queen Victoria reviewed her ships from the yacht *Fairy*. The Queen then led the first squadron to sea as far as St Helens and by 1600hrs the fleet was out of sight. A second squadron under Admiral Corry was also given a royal send-off on 16 March.

Admiral Napier's instructions can be summarised as follows.

a. Prevent any Russian ships leaving the Baltic.
b. Reconnoitre and, perhaps, attack the Aaland islands.
c. Avoid getting involved with Denmark or Sweden.
d. Look into Reval and other fortified towns.

These were amplified in a private letter from Sir James

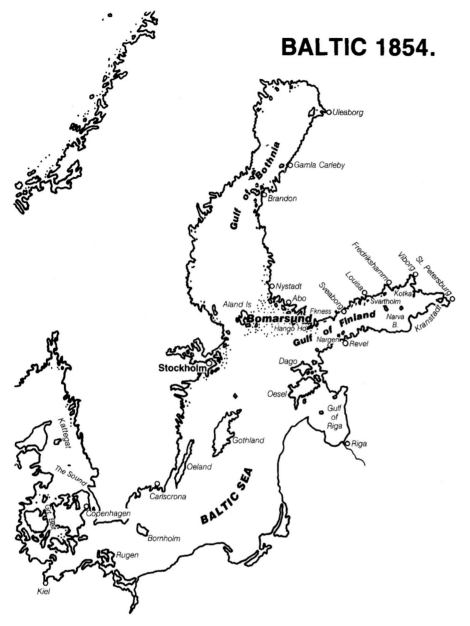

BALTIC 1854.

The Baltic.

operations, much effort was put into training inexperienced officers and men in gunnery and sail handling, to such an extent that there were shortages of both shot and powder. The standard of seamanship was poor and there were accidents and near-collisions. Even the smallest ship required four minutes to take in two reefs[10] and steam was used often to offset poor sailing.

The hydrographer to the Baltic fleet, an outstanding captain called Sulivan, gives some interesting impressions of the sailing qualities of the ships of the fleet, but as with all such accounts, they reflect the skill of the captains as much as the quality of the ship. The *Duke of Wellington* was said to sail beautifully, particularly off the wind, when the blockships had difficulty in keeping up, even under full sail. On another occasion when it was 'blowing a good topgallant breeze' (Beaufort force 5–6, wind speed 15–20 knots) on a wind, *Edinburgh* and *Hogue* were able to keep up, *St Jean d'Acre* was nearly as good as the *Duke* while *Neptune* 'is an astonishing ship'. She was one of the fastest and with a regular, well-trained crew was the crack ship. *Boscawen* was also fast – Sulivan gives the praise to Symonds even though she was much modified from the Symondite form. *Cressy* was not outstanding, though better than some of the blockships. *Edinburgh* and *Hogue* were considered much better than the other two. *Hogue* had some difficulty in holding a course. Sulivan did not think highly of *Austerlitz*, the only French steam liner, describing her as 'a lump of a ship, not nearly as handsome as our 90-gun ships, she looks like one of our blockships enlarged'.

In June, Sulivan, as hydrographer, took *Lightning* to reconnoitre Bomarsund, which was bombarded later in the month by three paddle frigates – Sulivan says that the value of the damage inflicted was less than the cost of the shells fired! It was clear that shore batteries now had an effective range of some 1,500yds and that the British 68pdr could hit, occasionally, out to 4,000yds.

The sailing ships were left to blockade Sveaborg while the steam fleet moved up to Kronstadt. Sulivan and others climbed up the Tolbukin lighthouse off the western end of the island to inspect the Russian fleet of sixteen liners and a few frigates. These were protected by massive granite forts with three or four tiers of guns and there was as yet no way of attacking Kronstadt.

Bomarsund

There are some 280 islands in the Aaland group with the main fort of Bomarsund on Aaland itself. It was a granite structure with eighty guns commanding the sound and further guns on the inland face. Two smaller forts and a battery provided additional support. Sulivan found an uncharted channel and led the four blockships with two screw frigates to attack from the rear. A French army of 9,000 men, together with a smaller British force, was landed and Fort Tzee surrendered to the French on 13 August and Fort Nottich to the British two days later. One of *Blenheim*'s 10in guns had been landed and this gun, together with those of the fleet,

Graham in which he said, 'I rely on your prudence in not knocking your head against stone walls prematurely, or without the prospect of a great success'.[8] Napier was at anchor near Copenhagen when news reached him of the declaration of war and he was joined there both by his sailing squadron and by the French ships under Vice Admiral Parseval-Deschenes with one steam liner, eight sail of the line and nine smaller ships.

Table 12.5 **Baltic – Balance of Forces**

	Britain	France	Allied	Russian
Steam liners	13	1	14	–
Sailing liners	6	14	20	27
Total			34	27

The allied fleet then moved up the Baltic, blockading Riga and attacking coastal villages and shipping. These minor attacks achieved little of military value and alienated potentially friendly inhabitants.[9] During these

opened fire on the main fortress on 16 August. No great damage was done but the garrison surrendered. The operation demonstrated the value of the mobility of a steam fleet, particularly its ability to strike from an unexpected direction. The effect on morale of the concentrated fire from the numerous large guns was also shown, as was the inability of ships' guns to do much harm to fortifications.

The fort was then blown up, with the exception of a line of seven casemates left to test the effectiveness of naval gunfire. The *Edinburgh* began shooting at 1,060yds, firing 390 rounds.

Table 12.6 **The *Edinburgh* Firing**[11]

Lancaster 95cwt	100lb elongated shell
68pdr/95cwt	Solid shot
32pdr/56cwt	Solid shot
10in shell gun	84lb hollow shot
8in shell gun	56lb hollow shot

Lightning leading the fleet through the Ango channel to attack Bomarsund (1855). Behind *Lightning* follow *Ajax, Blenheim, Alban* (distant), *Amphion*; over the island are the masts of *Hogue* and *Edinburgh*. In this one picture one can see the Royal Navy's early paddle steamer, the first four steam battleships (blockships) and the first screw frigates, representing much of the technical development described in this book. (© *National Maritime Museum* C0716)

8. *Life and Letters of Sir James Graham*, Naval Records Society.
9. B Greenhill and A Giffard, *The British Assault on Finland*, London (1988).
10. H N Sulivan, *Life and Letters of Admiral Sir B J Sulivan*, London (1896).
11. Douglas (1860).

A birdseye view of the bombardment of Bomarsund in August 1854.

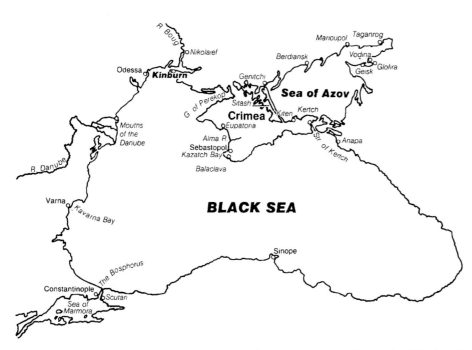

The Black Sea.

Little or no damage was caused and the *Edinburgh* closed to 480yds, firing a further 250 rounds. A small breach was made in an area of badly constructed masonry and more considerable damage was caused to embrasures and other portions of the work. No breach was large enough to permit an assault to have taken place, even though 640 shot and shell weighing 40,000lb had hit a relatively small area. The Lancaster guns demonstrated their inaccuracy and all shells, with either percussion or time fuses, burst on impact doing little damage.

The fleet left the Baltic during September and on returning to Britain, Admiral Napier was somewhat ungraciously dismissed, even though he had done all or more than required by his instructions; he had, however, lost the confidence of both his men and his masters.

The Black Sea 1854

The allied fleet moved into the Black Sea in January 1854 with instructions to prevent any further Russian attacks on Turkish ships. The frigate *Retribution* was sent under flag of truce to Sevastopol to warn the Russians of the fleet's new instructions and, arriving in fog, entered the harbour without being detected. Dundas and the French Admiral Hamelin soon decided that the Black Sea was too dangerous for sustained operations by sailing ships so early in the year and withdrew them, leaving the task to the steamships. In April the paddle frigate *Furious* visited Odessa to take off the British Consul and to give notice of a formal blockade of the port. Her flag of truce was fired on and, after failing to obtain an apology, the admirals decided to bombard military installations in the town.

A squadron of five British and three French steam frigates, together with the sailing frigate *Arethusa*, opened fire at dawn on 22 April; it was the last major action in which a sailing ship of the Royal Navy took part. Initially, the ships fired at a range of about 2,000yds while steaming in circles. Little damage was caused on shore, but *Vauban* was set on fire by red-hot shot, an old weapon but still seemingly more effective than shells. The squadron then anchored and the firing became more effective, setting fire to storehouses and ships. During the confusion, several allied merchant ships escaped from the harbour.

During May there were a number of minor operations, mainly at the eastern end of the sea, and the

The bombardment of Odessa, 22 April 1854. (© National Maritime Museum PU5899)

paddle frigate *Tiger* was destroyed by shore guns after it ran aground in a fog.

Invasion

By May, the fleet was based at Kavarna, in what is now Bulgaria. Captain Mends was given the task of planning the invasion of the Crimea; working with his French colleagues, this took until August. The size of the force to be transported was formidable.

Table 12.7 **The Invasion Force**

	British	*French*
Infantry	22,000	25,000
Cavalry	1,000	–
Engineers, etc	3,000	2,800
Guns	60	68

The British used fifty-two sailing transports and twenty-seven steamers with 350 boats while the French had 200 small sailing craft, three steamers and put 1,800–2,000 men in each of their battleships. Since ships so overcrowded could not use their guns, this left the Russian fleet of fourteen liners and seven frigates temporarily superior to the British squadron of ten liners and two frigates. Two of the liners were steamships, *Agamemnon* and *Sans Pareil*, though the engines of the latter were chronically unreliable.

Allied preparations were also affected by a cholera epidemic, particularly in the French ships. The military risk was perceived, correctly, as the difficulty in maintaining a large army on an inhospitable coast without proper ports and in bad weather. However, the generals were confident that the war would be over before the autumn gales.

The French began to embark on 31 August, taking three days to load their ships, while the British were not ready until 7 September. Earlier fears – and still more, later fears – of an overnight French invasion of England were shown to be unrealistic. The transports, with 52,000 troops, sailed in six divisions with each steamer towing two sailing vessels. The escort force was three liners, two frigates and eleven steamers.

When the fleet sailed, it was intended to land at the mouth of the Katcha, but the generals thought this was too risky and chose to land close to Eupatoria, despite its distance from Sevastopol. Disembarkation started on 15 September, with about 28,000 troops getting ashore that day. By the 19th all had been landed. The armies, after a victory at the battle of the Alma, marched round Sevastopol, investing the town from the south. The British supplies had to be landed at the narrow inlet of Balaclava while the French had the better anchorages at Kamiesh and Kazach.

The Russian admiral, Kornilov, wanted to attack the allied force, but got little support from his captains and at a council on 21 September it was decided to scuttle seven of the largest ships to block the entrance to the

harbour and free their crews to fight on shore. The remaining ships were drawn up in a line where their guns could command the north side of the harbour.

The allies planned a grand assault on Sevastopol on 17 October and the fleets were asked to attack the coastal forts as a diversion. The original plan was to attack on the move, at fairly close range, but at General

Table 12.8 **Sevastopol Forts**

Fort	*Guns (total)*	*Facing the fleet*
Alexander	56	17
Constantine	94	23
Quarantine	58	33
Wasp	12	3
Telegraph	17	6

The boats of the fleet going to the assistance of the French steamer *Vauban*, set on fire by red hot shot during the bombardment of Odessa. *(© National Maritime Museum PU9640)*

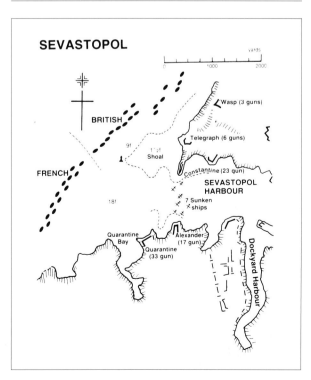

The attack on Sevastopol.

Canrobert's insistence it was agreed to anchor and engage at 1,500–2,000yds range. British boats found a deep water channel some 750yds from Fort Constantine and neighbouring batteries and a small inshore squadron was planned. Two Turkish ships joined the attacking fleet. Accounts vary concerning the strength of the forts facing the fleet, but the figures given here are of the right order.

Both fleets had landed many men and guns to fight on shore and there had been considerable losses from disease. Full crews were available for one broadside only, and in some ships the upper deck guns were not manned, which must have helped to reduce casualties. Firing began ashore at 0630hrs and continued until 0900hrs, when the main French magazine blew up; the attack was called off soon after.

Not knowing this, the fleets began to engage at about 1230hrs with the French ships attacking the southern forts and the British, commencing a little later, those to the north. The inshore squadron of the two steam liners and sailing ships, pulled into place by steamers lashed alongside, engaged Fort Constantine and the batteries known as the Telegraph and Wasp.

Actual damage to the forts was negligible, though Fort Constantine had all but five of its guns put out of action, mainly as a result of a magazine explosion caused by a shell from *Terrible*.[12] The fort then fell silent as the remaining gunners took cover. A reporter steaming past at close range the next day said that every fort was 'perfectly covered from base to summit with shot marks'. Except where *Agamemnon* had been firing at close range, the amount of damage 'is literally nothing'.

It is not surprising that the damage was so small since even the closest ships were 750yds offshore and most even further out. Douglas[13] makes some interesting points about the gunnery of the flagship *Britannia*. She fired at a range of 2,000yds, too great for any projectile available to cause damage. Fired closer, and with a full charge, 710 32lb shot from her 56cwt guns could have had an effect. The 785 shot fired with reduced charge (6lb or 8lb) and the 320 hollow shot, including a few shells, could never have made any impression.

Damage to the ships

This was one of the very few actions in which wooden ships were exposed to shell fire and is of interest on that account. Apart from trials, the only evidence from before the Crimean War was from the battle of Eckenfjorde on 5 April 1849 (see Appendix 11), where the Danish *Christian VIII* was in action with Prussian shore batteries whose fire was rather ineffective when using shell, but later destroyed her with red-hot shot. At Sevastopol the only British ship to receive serious damage was *Albion*. She was hit close to the waterline by four shells from Fort Constantine, of which three burst in the cockpit. She was on fire twice and had to cease fire when the magazine was closed as a precaution against the fire reaching it. She had eleven men killed and had to be towed out of action by *Firebrand*.

The frigate *Arethusa* was also damaged. One shell burst on the gun deck and knocked over the crew of two guns, another destroyed the partitions of three cabins

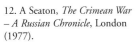

12. A Seaton, *The Crimean War – A Russian Chronicle*, London (1977).
13. Douglas (1860).

The attack on Sevastopol, general view. The sailing liners were manoeuvred into position by steamers lashed alongside. (© *National Maritime Museum C0715*)

The end of the action off
Sevastopol. To the left
Bellerophon, with *Cyclops*
lashed alongside is being
towed out; *Spitfire* (centre) is
performing the same duty for
Rodney beyond; *Agamemnon*
is to the far right. (© *National
Maritime Museum PX9167*)

The damaged *Albion* under
tow after the action of
17 October 1854. Note the
patches covering shot holes
below the lower deck ports.
(© *National Maritime
Museum* X2045)

and set fire to a bed (close to a shell room containing 300 shells). A third blew in seven planks just above the waterline, and a fourth burst in the thickness of the waterline timbers. If there had been a sea running she would have been in some danger, but it must be remembered that she was a frigate and not intended to fight forts. These two ships were the only ones not fit for action the next day, but they were able to make their own way to Constantinople for temporary repairs before sailing to Malta for full repair.

Agamemnon and *Sans Pareil* suffered heavily aloft. *Agamemnon* was hit 214 times, including three shells and a rocket. One of the shells burst on the deck and the other two on the masts, one starting a fire on the main yard, quickly extinguished. Coles says that there was hardly a rope left uncut and that the upper deck was covered in splinters.[14] Luckily, the upper deck guns were those usually manned by the Marines, who were ashore with the Naval Brigade, and these guns were unmanned. The rocket hit 6ft below the waterline and caused a violent concussion but little damage. A diver found the case of the rocket sticking out of the hull. *Agamemnon* had four killed and twenty-five wounded.

London was hit in the hull by both shot and shell

from the Telegraph and was on fire three times in two hours. *Queen* was forced to withdraw after a fire started by red-hot shot and *Rodney* suffered some superficial damage aloft after she ran aground. *Ville de Paris* was the only French ship to receive serious damage. She was hit under the poop by a shell, probably from a mortar, which caused extensive damage and killed or wounded many of her crew. In all, she was hit by forty-one shot or shell in the hull, and by almost as many again in the masts and rigging. Her crew were able to repair the damage overnight and she was reported fit for action the next day.

The Russian gunners found the visibility much obstructed by smoke, and at times could fire only at the gun flashes. The British inshore squadron was in the blind arcs of many guns; some batteries had to fire across the bay at extreme range in order to sight a target. The damage inflicted on the ships was a not very impressive return for the expenditure of 16,000 rounds and 138 casualties.[15]

After the battle, Admiral Hamelin summed up the rival claims of *Agamemnon* and *Napoleon* by saying, '*L'*Agamemnon *et le* Napoléon *étaient superbes tous les deux – oui, superbes c'est le mot.*'[16]

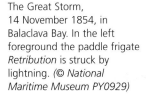

The Great Storm, 14 November 1854, in Balaclava Bay. In the left foreground the paddle frigate *Retribution* is struck by lightning. (© *National Maritime Museum PY0929*)

Arrow, the first of the new screw gun vessels, trying the range off Sevastopol, October 1854. (© National Maritime Museum X2046)

The Great Storm

The activities of the Naval Brigade ashore were truly heroic but fall outside the scope of this book. Some five thousand sailors and marines with 140 large guns were landed; a notable feature was that they suffered much less from sickness and disease than did the army. During October and November there were a number of small bombardments, but the Navy's chief task was to keep open the sea lanes.

On 14 November 1854 the anticipated disaster occurred. The morning was clear with a calm sea, a light wind and the barometer reading 29½in. No special precautions were in force either at Balaclava or at Katcha, where part of the fleet was moored. By 1000hrs a tremendous gale was blowing from the southwest. Off Balaclava, thirty-two transports were lost, including the *Prince*, a big ship carrying winter clothing for the army. HMS *Vesuvius* and *Ardent* were severely damaged in the storm, which only lasted two hours and moderated after lunch.

Fourteen more transports were lost off Katcha. One of these fouled HMS *Sampson*, breaking both her masts, and the *London* was also severely damaged. At Eupatoria the French First Rate sailing liner *Henri IV* dragged or snapped all four anchors and was lost, as was *Pluton*. At least four more British transports were lost. The investigation into the losses suggested that many

were due to poor quality wrought-iron anchor chains, and as a result standards of manufacture and testing were improved.

The problems of transporting men and stores to the Crimea had a major effect on the development of the steamship in commercial service. The government was willing to pay a high charter rate for steamships and the building cost could be paid off in twelve months. Alfred Holt wrote, 'This naturally increased investment in steamships'.[17]

Dundas hauled down his flag on 22 December, handing over to the popular and highly respected Sir Edmund Lyons.[18]

The gun boat programme

Even before war was declared, it was realised that the Navy needed a considerable number of fast, shallow-draught, heavily armed steamers. Such ships were needed to enforce the blockade, carry out raids and bombardments of coastal targets, to carry despatches and for survey work. Heavy guns would be needed to attack the great fortresses of Sevastopol, Sveaborg and Kronstadt.

None of the ships in service was suitable since they had too deep a draught, to a large extent as a result of Symonds's obsession with a high rise of floor. Their arma-

14. G P Bidder, 'The national defences', *Trans Institute of Civil Engineers* (1860). Contribution by Captain C P Coles.

15. Seaton, op cit.

16. *Life and Letters of Sir James Graham.*

17. A Holt, 'Review of the progress of steam shipping during the last quarter of a century', *Trans Inst Civil Engineers*, London (1877).

18. B S Mends, *Life of Admiral B R Mends*, London (1899). Note: there is a persistent story, confirmed by Mends, who was there, that a 'mistake' was made in the farewell signal from Lyons to the unpopular Dundas. Instead of saying 'Happiness attends you', it read 'Hanging attends you'.

A Naval Brigade 68pdr Lancaster RML (rifled muzzle loader) during the siege of Sevastopol, 15 December 1854. The gun had been landed from the Sixth Rate *Diamond*. This type of gun proved highly accurate when mounted ashore, but was less effective when chosen as the main armament for the small and lively gun boats. (© *National Maritime Museum BHC0643*)

19. G A Osbon, 'The Crimean gunboats, parts I and I*F*, *Mariner's Mirror*, vol 51 (1965); see also A Preston and J Major, *Send a Gunboat!*, London (1967).

As fitted profile draught of the *Clown* class gun boats *Janus* and *Drake*. (© *National Maritime Museum DR11185*)

ment consisted of a number of medium-calibre guns, rather than the very large weapons needed to attack forts. Shortage of small ships seems almost inevitable at the start of a major war. During peacetime stringency, it is right and proper to spend available funds on the big ships which take so long to build, and hope that there will be enough grace to build the 'small fry' quickly.

The Board acted fast and in March 1854 they invited tenders from eight Thames yards for six gun vessels. The builders were given only nine days in which to respond and on 11 April Mare's tender for four and Green's for two were accepted. These six ships were first described as 'despatch steam gun vessels', later abbreviated to gun vessel. They were always independent commands, first under a lieutenant and later a commander, in contrast to the later gun boats which were administered as tenders to bigger ships.

Table 12.9 *Arrow* Class

Displacement	550–600 tons
Dimensions	160ft x 24ft 4in x 10ft (forward), 11ft 8in (aft)
Armament	Two 68dpr/95cwt RML Lancaster, four 12pdr howitzer

The machinery fit and trial speed varied considerably, but in service they were good for about 9 knots and were used mainly to carry messages, often without their 68pdrs. Problems with the heavy guns were soon evident when *Arrow* demonstrated her capability to Queen Victoria at the Needles on 24 August 1854. *Arrow* was at anchor in fairly rough weather, 4,000yds from an old lighthouse used as the target. The first two shells burst on leaving the muzzle and the next three

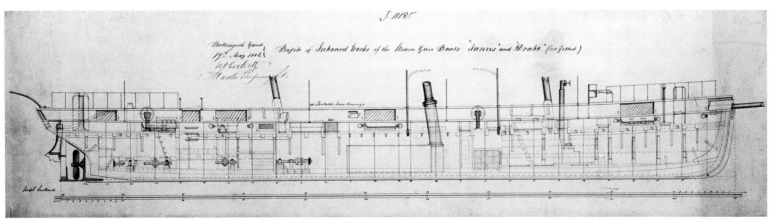

went right over the promontory on which the light-house stood. The last round hit one of the Needles. Though the Lancaster gun, mounted on shore, had shown impressive accuracy up to 5,000yds, this could not be repeated from a small ship rolling and pitching in a seaway (see Chapter 6).

All six had steamed to war by September, *Wrangler* to the Baltic and the rest to the Black Sea. The guns were landed from *Arrow* and *Beagle* on arrival and used by the Naval Brigade; three out of four guns had burst by the end of October. There was fairly acrimonious correspondence between Dundas and the Board, who were not prepared to accept the view that the motion of the ship in a seaway made the big guns ineffective. *Wrangler* was also disarmed as a despatch vessel in the Baltic.

These six ships were a step in the right direction, but many more were needed, with even less draught. As an interim measure, two paddle gun boats (*Recruit* and *Weser*), building by Scott Russell for Prussia, were purchased. They had iron hulls and were double ended with 4–8in, 65cwt guns mounted each side of the paddle boxes. It was noted that the forward rudder was ineffective. With a draught of 7ft, they were well-liked, *Recruit* becoming a prominent member of the Azov squadron. Two diminutives, with a draught of 4ft and two 8in guns, were ordered in November 1855 at a cost of £11,400 each. These four paddlers were the only iron seagoing ships ordered for the Navy for many years. Some attempts were made to hire merchant ships for use as gun boats, but without success, since few such ships had shallow draught and these were too flimsy to carry heavy guns.

The full solution was not long in coming. By June 1854, W H Walker, a constructor in the Surveyor's department, had designed the *Gleaner* class with a draught of 6ft and six had been ordered. By October these were followed by the first twenty of the improved *Dapper* class of which ninety-eight more were ordered in 1858. Walker later designed the *Cheerful* and *Clown* classes with even less draught.

Design

The characteristics of all four classes were generally similar.[19] All had a flat bottom with a false keel projecting 2–3in. They had a full bow and stern joined by a long parallel body, with vertical sides rising from a tight turn of bilge to which heavy bilge keels were fixed. The stem was slightly cut away, without a knee, while the stern was rounded in the two smaller classes with a square transom in the others.

The upper deck was flat except for a slight sheer forward. At the stern, the officers' heads projected above the 4ft high bulwarks, while the crew made do with a plank over the side forward.

Below deck, the boiler and engine room, flanked by the coal bunkers containing 25 tons of coal, took up the midships half of the ship. The shell room was forward of the machinery and the magazine aft, both given some protection by water tanks outboard. The remaining

Table 12.10 **British Gun Boats**

Class	Number built	Tons (bm)	Dimensions	Armament	NHP
Gleaner	6	216	100ft x 22ft x 7ft	Two 68pdr	60
Dapper	118	233	106ft x 22ft x 6ft 9in	Two 68pdr	60
Cheerful	20	212	100ft x 22ft 10in x 4ft 6in	Two 32pdr	20
Clown	12	233	110ft x 21ft 10in x 4ft	One 68pdr, one 32pdr	40

space forward accommodated the crew, with a stove serving both to keep them warm and as a galley. The officers lived aft and were allowed the luxury of a wash basin.

During the war, gun boats nominally acted as tenders to larger ships, which meant that the complement and armament could be altered to suit a specific operation.

Recruit, an iron paddle gun boat designed by Scott Russell.

Plan of *Beacon* (*Albacore*) class. *(Drawing by the author)*

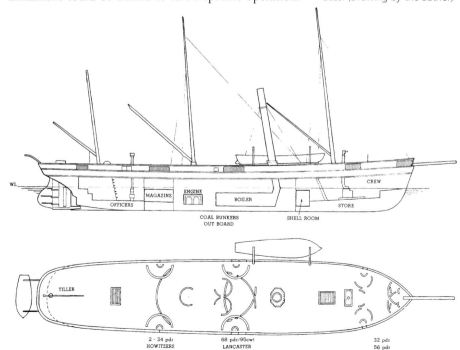

Ruby, a *Gleaner* class gun boat, seen attacking Fredrickshamm in September 1855. Behind is the paddle frigate *Magicienne* (note her twin funnels), the *Amphion* and the corvette *Cossack*. The *Cossack* was built for Russia by Pitcher as the *Witjas* and seized for the Royal Navy before she could be delivered. Note the rocket launching tubes in the ship's boat.

Albacore class gun boats at Devonport after the Crimean War. (© *National Maritime Museum N05384*)

the front of the slide engaged in the socket of the port required. The broadside ports allowed 56 degrees training each way and there was also a bow port. A 68pdr gun with its carriage weighed some 6 tons and when both guns were on the same side there was a considerable list (about six degrees, reducing the possible elevation and range). There was stowage for twenty-five Lancaster shells (costing £20 each) or 68lb shot. The choice of armament must have been difficult. For fighting Russian gun boats, particularly in a seaway where the heavy guns could not be worked effectively, a greater number of smaller guns would have been better. The heavy guns were essential for attacking forts, and not unreasonably it was thought that such actions would usually be in sheltered waters.

Machinery

The contracts for all the machinery sets were divided between two builders only, John Penn of Greenwich and Maudslay, Son and Field of Lambeth. The designs were unusual for the day in their use of 'high pressure steam', a working pressure of 35lb/sq in, with the safety valve set a little higher. The boilers were similar to those used on locomotives, though working at only half the 70lb/sq in of the railways since they had to work with salt water. There were several reports of trouble with these boilers, due to rapid burning of the tube plates. Douglas, no lover of the gun boats, says, 'So great is this evil in the gun boats that in the mere trials of the engine the boiler becomes so bad as to require extensive repairs'.[20] The boilers were cylindrical, with fire tubes leading to a funnel at the aft end in the *Gleaner*s and *Cheerful*s and forward in the others. The '60hp' boats had three boilers

Typically, the crew would be thirty to thirty-six, with two officers. The *Gleaner*'s armament was varied considerably. *Pincher*, as tender to *Blenheim*, carried three 68pdrs, while a common fit in both this class and the *Dapper*s was one 68pdr, one 32pdr and two 24pdr howitzers (brass). The 24pdrs were truck-mounted and the larger guns were carried on an iron slide which could be pivoted and trained over curved training races let into the deck.

The heavy guns were carried on the centre line, forward and aft of the funnel. They would then be turned about the rear pivot, until the 'fighting bolt' at

with two in the others.

The engine builders each received orders for ten sets in October 1854, followed by another order for forty-nine sets the following year. It seems that much of the work was subcontracted; for example, the Thames Iron Works forged many, if not all, of Penn's crankshafts.[21]

Table 12.11 **Machinery Particulars**

NHP	ihp	Number of cylinders	Bore (in)	Stroke (in)	Rpm	Speed (knots)
20	92	1	15	12	225	6¾
40	145	1	21	12	220	8
60	270	2 (Penn)	21	12	190	7½
		(Maudslay)	15½	18	190	7½

Note: the Penn engines for the 20NHP and 40NHP boats were single piston rod design and not his usual trunk engine. Altogether Penn built 97 sets of engines.[22]

The engines drove a single, two-bladed propeller, non-hoisting, of 4ft diameter in the smaller classes and 6ft in the bigger ships. The high rotational speed of the engines led to some lubrication problems, which in turn caused rapid wear and overheated bearings.

Production

The truly remarkable feature of the gun boat programme was the speed with which ships were ordered and put into service (see Table 12.12).

All but ten dockyard-built craft were built by contractors, many of whom had never seen a warship before. The contractor was responsible for a bare hull; the engines would be installed by the machinery contractor which would not take long; Penn installed *Arrow's* engines in fifty-four hours, raised steam on the third day after launch and carried out trials the next day. The new gun boat would then steam to a dockyard to be coppered, rigged and armed. In a great many cases this work was handled at the purpose-built Gunboat Yard, Haslar (near

Above: *Magnet*, an *Albacore* class gun boat. (© *National Maritime Museum neg 5385*)

Left: Orders for gun boats.

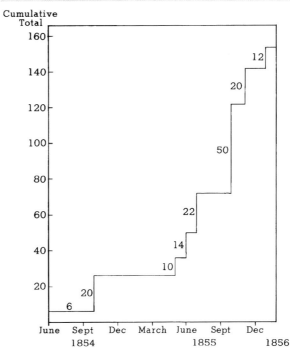

20. Douglas (1855).
21. Special Committee on Iron.
22. Committee on Marine Engines, 1859.

Sectional model of a horizontal marine steam engine as fitted to RN warships by Maudslay, Son & Field, 1860. (© *National Maritime Museum L2287-002*)

Gosport), where the boat would be hauled up a slipway, onto a travelling carriage designed by Brunel, and moved into one of several large sheds. Altered, but still recognisable, these sheds still stand (1989).

Payment was made in instalments, the first when the framing was complete, the second after launch and the balance on delivery. For the *Dappers* the instalments were £1,600 each. The programme soon caused problems for the shipbuilders, as the war led to rapid inflation in prices of materials and in wage rates, particularly on the Thames where labour was scarce. By moving from yard to yard, strikes, 'go slow', etc, the workers forced the pay up from 7 shillings an hour to 9, 12 and eventually 15 shillings. The new men taken on helped to speed the degradation of discipline of the workforce. Meal times, usually spent in the nearest pub, extended by ten to twenty minutes and some men were not fit for work afterwards.[23]

Below: The 68pdr Lancaster RML pivot mounting on the gun vessel *Snake* off the Crimea in 1855. (© *National Maritime Museum PW6072*)

Bottom, left: The gun boat sheds at Haslar. The steam transporter on the right was designed by Isambard Brunel.

Bottom, right: Maudslay's return connecting rod engines for *Wanderer* (gun vessel, *Vigilant* class).

Table 12.12 **Production**

Order date	Number ordered	Class	Average cost
Jun 1854	6	*Gleaner*	£8,200
Oct	20	*Dapper*	£9,500–£10,000
May 1855	10	*Dapper*	
Jun	14	*Dapper*	
Jul	24	*Dapper*	
Oct	50	*Dapper*	
Nov	20	*Cheerful*	£7,000
Jan 1856	12	*Clown*	£9,500–£10,000
Total	156		

(Listed by builders in Appendix 12.)

Theft was common; there were all too many cases in which only the head of a brass bolt was in place, the shank having been cut off and sold for its scrap value. In an attempt to meet the strict contract dates, night shifts were worked throughout the severe winters of 1854–5 and 1855–6. With only oil lamps and no protection from the bitter cold, the task would have been difficult even for a better motivated workforce.

There was also a shortage of seasoned timber. The specification called for:

Keel	Oak or elm
Stem and stern	Oak
Side planking	Oak, 3–5in thick
Deck	Fir

Standards inevitably had to be relaxed and with the shortage of overseers some green timber was worked into the structure. Within a few years thirty-two ships had rotted beyond repair without ever having entered service. On the other hand, many gun boats remained in service for many years of peacetime operation.

The engines of the gun boats which rotted were reused in the twin-screw *Beacon*-class gun vessels (1867–8), the original engine builder refurbishing the machinery and installing it with two sets in each new hull.

The result of the wage and price explosion was disastrous for some firms. Pitchers, with fifty-four orders, were in receivership in 1857, as was Mare with six. Fletchers do not seem to have built any more ships and other companies were in difficulty. This financial storm was the main cause of Scott Russell's problems with the *Great Eastern* and marked the beginning of the end for the Thames shipbuilding industry.[24] The Admiralty, largely due to Baldwin Walker's concern, made ex gratia payments to some yards, an unprecedented step. J T Fields said, 'It was insufficient, but we knew it was an addition to our contract, gratuitously given; we had no legal claim.'[25] Another shipbuilder remarked:

> The reminiscence of the Russian war, to those who built the gun boats, is an exceedingly painful one. Ruin befell one or two of these builders, and all sustained heavy pecuniary loss. The only relieving light it has is the indelible impression which the urbanity and sympathy of Sir Baldwin Walker evinced and the appropriateness and beauty of form of the vessels which his immediate assistants designed.

The design of these vessels won universal praise. Captain Dahlgren called them 'well adapted – far better than any other', while Edward Reed wrote, 'No one, however, who has seen the contemporary vessels, designed by the French, and who understands *all* the difficulties of combining speed, lightness, sea worthiness and a powerful armament will question them'. All the ships ordered in 1854 were available for operations the next year, but few of the 1855 orders saw action. Most were complete for the Victory Review in 1856, and for many this was their only service.

Gun boat operations and the Black Sea 1855

Naval activity in the Black Sea resumed in February with a series of operations at the eastern end around Anapa. From April onwards there were many single-ship bombardments of Sevastopol by night, which must have had considerable nuisance value. During one such raid, the frigate *Valorous* was hit on a paddle wheel and, despite heavy vibration, was able to complete the operation (cf French experience with the *Fulton*, discussed earlier.)

Kertch and the Azov expedition

The Russian armies in the Crimea depended for their food supplies on the rich farms surrounding the Sea of Azov. It is said that 1,500 waggons of stores left Kertch every day.[26] The naval commanders had pressed for an attack on this area in 1854, but troops could not be made available. By April 1855 the Turkish and Sardinian reinforcements in the Crimea made it possible to spare

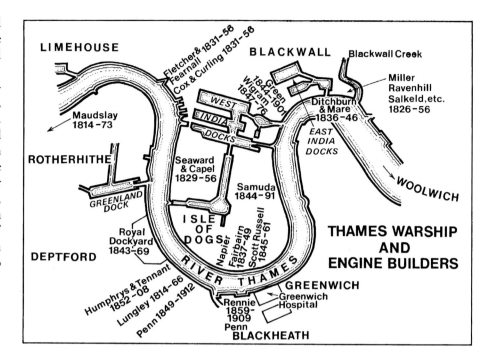

The warship building yards on the Thames.

men for Kertch. Winter gales had cleared the obstructions placed by the enemy to block the straits, but the water depth was only 18ft, making it essential to use shallow-draught ships such as the new gun boats.

The expedition sailed on 3 May 1855 with 11,000 men, mainly French, in forty ships, but it was recalled by the emperor, using the newly completed cable – the first such telegraphic interference with operations by a home government. The delay was, however, brief and a new expedition sailed on 22 May with 7,000 French troops, 5,000 Turkish and 3,500 British and Sardinian. They landed on the 24th near Kertch, which surrendered, as did Yenikale a few days later, giving the allies 100 guns and 12,000 tons of invaluable coal.

As Williams wrote:

> The doorway of the Sea of Azov was now open to us and fourteen British steamers, aided by four or five French vessels, poured eagerly into the almost unknown sea. It was like bursting into a large treasure house crammed with wealth of inestimable value. For miles along its shores stretched the countless storehouses packed with the accumulated harvests of the great corn provinces of Russia. From them the Russian armies in the field were fed; from them the beleaguered population of Sevastopol looked for preservation from the famine which already pressed hard upon them.

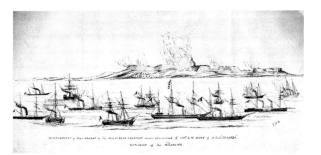

23. Select Committee on Gun and Mortar boats, 1860.
24. L T C Rolt, *I K Brunel*, London (1970).
25. Select Committee on Gun and Mortar boats, 1860.
26. H Williams, *Britain's Naval Power*, London (1898).

Sea of Azov expedition. Eyewitness sketch of the squadron under Captain Edmund Moubray Lyons in the screw sloop *Miranda* bombarding Fort Arabat on 28 May 1855. (© *National Maritime Museum PU9034*)

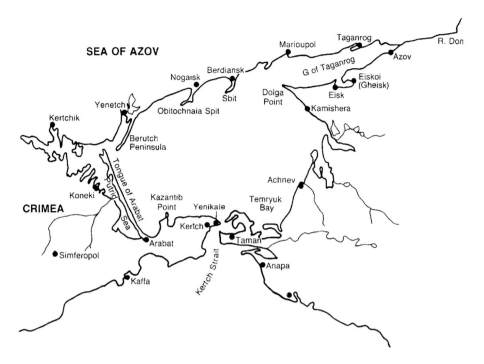

commander of the squadron, Captain Lyons (son of the admiral), halted the work of destruction which continued under Captain Osborn. Only when the Sea of Azov began to freeze on 24 November 1855 did the squadron withdraw.

The fighting at Sevastopol came to an end in September 1855. There was a three-day bombardment starting on the 5th, which set fire to one of the surviving Russian two-deckers that evening; on the 7th another caught fire. At 1200hrs on the 8th the French army stormed the Malakov, the key to the defences. Even though the British failed to take the Redan, the Russians withdrew from the south side of Sevastopol, destroying magazines, batteries and sinking the last six warships and seven other ships. Altogether the Russians lost at Sevastopol:

Five 120-gun ships	Four 60-gun ships
Eight 84-gun ships	Three 20-gun ships
One 80-gun ship	Two 18-gun ships
Six large steamers and six small	

The Azov expedition. All the coastal towns shown were attacked by the gun boat force, some several times. The expedition disrupted supplies to the Russian Army in the Crimea.

All the towns shown on the map and many others were attacked; storehouses were burnt and batteries destroyed. Like Sherman's march through Georgia, it destroyed the economic heart of the enemy.[27]

After a month, six of the *Dapper*s joined the squadron. *Jasper* was the only one to be lost during the expedition when her only officer, worn out by days of continual operations, fell asleep, leaving ambiguous orders. She ran ashore on the Crooked Spit, near Taganrog, and was beset by Cossack cavalry. *Swallow* came up and took off the crew while the ship was burnt. Neither this nor the death of the original

Because of a strong northwest gale, the Navy had played little part in the final assault, but *Odin* and some mortar vessels stationed in Streletska Bay did join in the firing.

Sevastopol Dockyard was a surprise to the officers who inspected it. There was a big cradle on a slip, designed by Upton, a British engineer, and a foundry. Docks were arranged like a canal, with the upper end 20ft above sea level. There were three docks abreast at the top, then a large basin, three more docks and then a flight of locks to the sea, each one some 270ft x 60ft. It was said to have cost £20 million.

The range of docks at Sevastopol that so impressed British naval officers after its capture. (From *Russian Warships in the Age of Sail* by Tredrea and Sozaev)

The Baltic 1855

Mortar vessels, armoured batteries and mines

The British fleet, all steamships, assembled in the Downs at the end of March and joined the French fleet near Reval in early May. The admirals inspected Sveaborg from Sulivan's new survey ship, *Merlin*, on 11 May, noting that sixty new guns had been mounted in earthworks. By the end of May, the fleets were off Kronstadt where the defences had also been strengthened.

Mines

During the war between Prussia and Denmark there was some use of controlled mines, exploded from an observation chamber on shore. Similar mines were occasionally used during the war with Russia, but during 1854 rumours gained ground of a different sort of Russian 'infernal machine', exploded by contact.

No such mines were encountered in 1854, but on 9 July 1855 *Merlin*, with *Firefly* and *Dragon* and the French corvette, *d'Assas*, were surveying to the northeast of Kronstadt when the *Merlin* was fired on by a distant Russian gun boat. In chase, the *Merlin* was lured to within about two and a half miles of the island when:

Suddenly the vessel received a heavy shock, which shook her more than any running ashore and in a different manner. I thought some large part of the engines or boilers had broken, and ran to the engine room. Seeing them working well, I stopped her and as we were still going fast, and still had five fathoms of water I knew that she could not have struck the ground. Some said it was an explosion and that we had struck an infernal machine. When stopped and going astern slightly, Erskine called to me from the port paddle box that he could see a stone. I crossed over and saw just under the paddle box what appeared to be the head of a large pile three feet under water. We were just watching for it to come under the leadsman, who had still five fathoms of water, when a second and much sharper explosion took place just before the starboard paddle box. The second threw a mass of water three feet above our hammock nettings and gave us a terrible shake; the vessel seemed jerked on one side, and heeled over a little, the masts shaking so that some ran from under them. A strong smell of sulphur left no doubt it was a veritable infernal machine.[28]

The only leak came from a fractured drain pipe to the engineers' bath, 'but the blow had driven her side in for the moment over an extent of many feet each way, and everything in contact suffered'. A tallow tank weighing 1,200lb was torn from its seat and all the engineers' mess traps and food jars were smashed. A large wooden diagonal intersected an iron girder at the point of explosion, which broke the wood and bent the iron. The shelf piece split and broke. The bulkheads were pulled away from the side and her copper was torn off. The pitch in the seams of the lower deck was forced out. This description

27. Seaton, op cit.
28. Sulivan, op cit.

Merlin and *Firefly*, the first ships to be mined, on 9 June 1855, a notable date in naval warfare. (© *National Maritime Museum PU6154*)

provides a clear preview of the damage which would be caused by the non-contact mines of both world wars. *Firefly* was also mined without serious damage.

The Russians used two types of mine: one, an electrically-operated, remote-control mine was designed by Jacobi, a German living in Russia; the other, a contact mine, by the Nobel family.[29] The Nobel mines were used more extensively and were more effective. They consisted of a cone of zinc about 2ft deep and 15in wide at the top. The pointed bottom held about 8lb of powder, increased to 35lb in later mines, and the upper part provided buoyancy. A pair of spring loaded rods (AA in accompanying drawing) ran across the top connected to a tube (DD) running down to the powder chamber inside an outer tube (BB), to which it was pivoted at mid-length. If the rods were disturbed, the pivoted lever would move, breaking a phial of sulphuric acid which fell onto a small quantity of potassium chlorate, causing a violent reaction exploding the main powder charge.

They were tricky things to handle as both the Royal and Russian navies discovered. The Russians lost seventeen men killed by explosions while laying and in

consequence many mines were laid with their safety caps still on.

Vulcan hit a mine off Sveaborg on 20 June without damage, and sweeping began the next day. The mines were close to the surface and could usually be seen and recovered with grapnel lines. In seventy-two hours of this, the world's first minesweeping operation, thirty-three infernal machines were recovered. One of these was 'played with' by Rear Admiral Seymour and Captain King-Hall in their gig. They then took it to the flagship and played with it again on the quarterdeck where it exploded, knocking everyone down. No one was killed and all recovered, though Seymour lost the sight of one eye.

Mines had no great influence on this war, but their introduction marked a turning point in naval warfare, probably more significant than the introduction of armour. The devices were ingenious and practical, spoilt only by the use of such an inadequate amount of explosive. Brief mention must be made of a development whose effect was even further in the future. Both Britain and Russia worked on the design of submarines and the Russian boat began trials during the war.

In November 1853 Prince Albert persuaded the German inventor, Wilhelm Bauer, to come to England to build a submarine at Admiralty expense. It was started at Scott Russell's yard but does not seem to have been completed. Scott Russell was working on a submersible of his own design and Bauer was afraid that his ideas were being stolen and that the contract did not give him a fair return. Details of the Scott Russell design are unclear, but essentially it was a diving bell which could be walked along the bottom by its crew of two, and trials were carried out under Sir Astley Cooper Key.

Bauer left England and went to St Petersburg where he completed a submarine in November 1855. The *Seeteufel* was 16.3m x 3.45m with a 13mm skin and intended to dive to 47m. She began trials off Kronstadt in May 1856 and by October had dived 134 times. A series of minor problems then led to her sinking, without loss of life, and, though raised, she did not re-enter service.

Mortar vessels

After various minor attacks and blockade work, it was decided to carry out a major attack on Sveaborg. The motives for the attack were mixed; Dundas was under pressure from the government to do something, while Sulivan seems to have urged the attack as a rehearsal for his proposed attack on Kronstadt, discussed later. The principal feature of the attack was to be the destruction of the dockyard buildings and barracks using shells fired from mortars. To carry the mortars, yet another specialised assault craft was devised and built.[30]

Bomb vessels had been used in earlier wars and some remained in service after 1815. Because of their strong construction, they proved useful for polar explorations and by 1854 there were none left. In March 1841 trials were carried out with a 13in mortar in the 10-gun brig

1 THE INFERNAL MACHINE SIDE AND END
2 CAP OR COVER
3 TUBE DISSECTED
4 THE MACHINE AS IT FLOATS THREE FEET BELOW THE SURFACE OF THE WATER
5 TUBE PUT TOGETHER

Nobel's contact mine. Initially it had only an 8lb charge which caused little damage. It was not very safe to lay and caused several injuries to Russian crews.

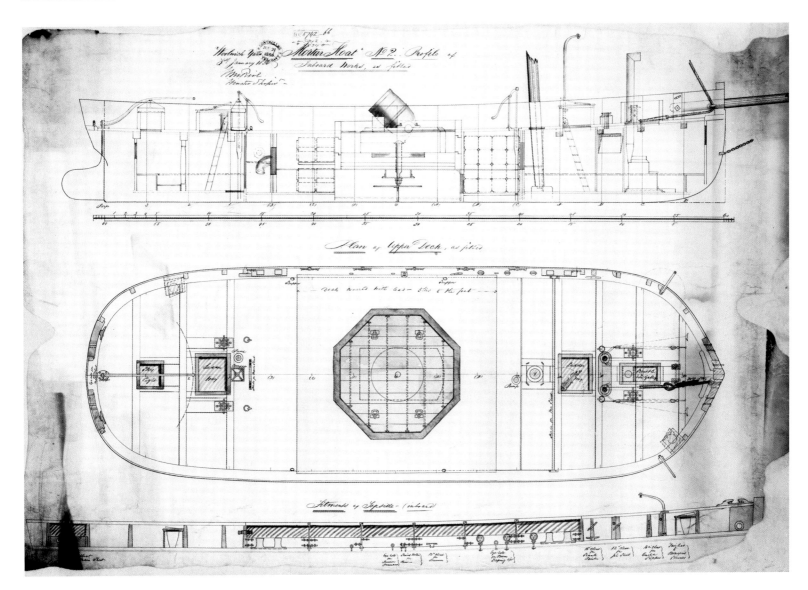

Admiralty draught for an iron mortar float. None was completed in time to see service during the war. (© National Maritime Museum DR08042)

Curlew, but they do not seem to have been successful. In October 1854, it was decided to convert two twenty-year-old dockyard lighters to carry mortars. At the same time, ten specially built craft were ordered, followed by forty-four more between October and December. In addition, fifty mortar floats, generally similar but with an iron hull, were ordered in November 1855. The first twenty-two mortar vessels received names which were in use at Sveaborg, but changed to numbers only in October 1855. Later vessels and the floats never received names.

The new construction craft resembled lighters and, indeed, many were used as such after the war. They all had a flat bottom, vertical sides and almost square bilges. The parallel section amidships extended for three-quarters of the length with a bluff, rounded bow and stern, almost indistinguishable. The single mortar rested on circular iron races amidships, set in an octagonal well about 4ft 6in deep, while the decking surrounding the mortar was covered with sheet lead as a precaution against fire. The space below the mortar was filled in with solid baulks of timber to absorb the recoil forces. The shell room was beneath the mortar with the

magazine just aft. There were two handling rooms, one just forward of the mortar and one just aft. The crew lived forward.

There were no engines and the craft were usually towed. There was a mast stepped on the keel forward of the mortar and a lighter mizzen in a tabernacle, well aft. Hawse holes were arranged on each side, right forward and aft, with a capstan forward of the mast for warping on the anchor cables.

Table 12.13 **Mortar Vessels and Floats**

Group	Number of ships	Tons (bm)	Length	Beam	Draught	Depth
I	2	109	60ft	21ft	5ft	–
II	10	117	65ft	20ft 10in	–	7ft
III	10	155	70ft	23ft 4in	8ft 6in	9ft 4in
IV	34	166	75ft	23ft 4in	–	9ft 4in
Floats	50	100	60ft	20ft	5ft 8in	6ft 6in

The 13in mortar fired at a fixed elevation of 45 degrees, range being altered by varying the charge. The mortars

29. Greenhill & Giffard, op cit.
30. G A Osbon, unpublished notes, now with the World Ship Society.

The mortar vessels in action during the bombardment of Sveaborg in August 1855. The nearest vessel is *Pickle*. Note the 13in mortar amidships, the sail yards lashed to the side and the lee boards. The bombs, trailing smoke, were clearly visible in flight. *(© National Maritime Museum PX9261)*

weighed 5.05 tons and fired a shell of 196lb containing 6¾lb of powder with a maximum charge of 20lb.

Table 12.14 **13in Mortar**

Charge (lb)	Range (yds)	Time of flight (sec)	Length of fuse (in)
2	690	13	2.7
8	2,575	24¾	5.09
12	3,500	29	6.02
20	4,200	31	6.44

Firing tests on shore showed such weapons to be very accurate; at maximum range some 50 per cent of shells would fall within a square of side 50yds. From a lighter, even in calm weather, accuracy would be much less.

Among the war's novelties was the Mallock mortar, built in sections with a 32in bore. It was originally built for use on land against Sevastopol, but use at sea was intended. The surviving mortar can be seen at the Woolwich Arsenal Mess and shells (empty) are to be seen at Tilbury Fort.

During the war it was decided to convert the original four frigate blockships, together with the *Fox*, into

mortar frigates. Although they all received engines and ran trials, only *Horatio* seems to have been armed. Accounts vary, but the likely outfit was:

Upper deck	Two 68pdr/95cwt
Main deck	Two 13in mortars, eight 32pdr/42cwt.

Fox completed as a transport.

Sveaborg

The fortress of Sveaborg, close to modern Helsinki, consisted of five islands separated by narrow channels and armed with about 800 guns. Some of the channels were blocked, and others dominated by the guns of four liners and some smaller ships. Captain Sulivan carried out a meticulous survey in August 1855 and marked the positions for the bombarding ships.[31] The main fire was to come from thirteen British vessels and five French craft with two 12in mortars each, together with a French battery of four 10in mortars on the Abraham Holm rock. Initially, the mortar vessels formed up at a range of 3,900yds from the batteries and then closed in to 3,600yds. Four steam frigates acted as supply ships for the mortars.

A force of gun boats, with additional heavy guns,

One of the gun boats in action during the bombardment of Sveaborg, at the moment of an explosion ashore. (© *National Maritime Museum PU5906*)

strengthened the bombarding force. Early on 9 August 1855 the mortar vessels moved into place and opened fire just after 0700hrs. Two gun boats with Lancaster rifled guns fired on a battleship, the *Russia*, off Gustavsvard and hit her several times with 68pdr shells.[32] Her survival again demonstrates the limited power of shells against wooden ships with well-trained crews. Firing on both sides was intense, with little apparent effect until 1000hrs when a heavy explosion occurred on Vagen, followed by another on Gustavsvard an hour later as magazines blew up. Fires gradually consumed the storehouses, particularly on Vagen.

The gun boats withdrew at sunset and were replaced by thirty ships' boats firing rockets in a three-hour bombardment, causing new fires. On the 10th, the mortar attack was resumed with daylight and continued through the next night. The bombardment was called off before dawn on the 12th, as many of the mortars had cracked or burst. It is claimed that the British ships used 100 tons of powder and fired 1,000 tons of projectiles. (This seems unlikely, as it implies about 13,000 projectiles or 1,000 per vessel. Other reports suggest 200 rounds per mortar.) The French fired 2,828 mortar shells, together with 1,322 from other ships.

The extent of the damage caused remains uncertain. General Borg says that all dockyard buildings, workshops and stores on Great East Svarto were destroyed and lesser damage done elsewhere.[33] No forts or guns were put out of action but they were not the target. Russian losses were fifty-five killed and 199 wounded, though other accounts, from Helsinki, suggest much higher figures. Seen in the context of a war for limited

objectives, the attack was damaging to the enemy and provided useful lessons to the allies.

Sveaborg marked the end of the war in the Baltic. Winter, with its storms and ice, was approaching and it was time to go home. A little-known feature of the Baltic war was the extensive use of colliers and store

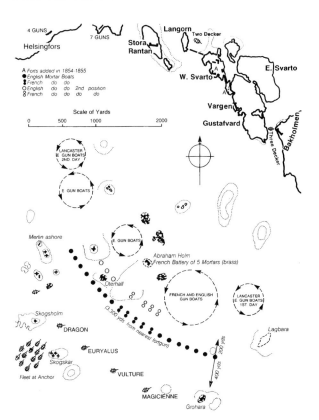

31. Sulivan, op cit.

32. *The Russian War 1855, Baltic*, Naval Records Society.

33. Borg (General), *Helsingfors Times*, 29 Aug 1855.

The attack on Sveaborg.

Replenishment at sea during the Crimean War. Left to right: *Holyrood* (merchant ship), *Monarch*, *Cumberland*, *Boscawen* and *Imperieuse*. (© National Maritime Museum PY8343)

ships to resupply the fleet at sea. Today's replenishment under way was not attempted; supply ships and warships anchored in a quiet bay for the transfer of the best Welsh coal, etc.

Armoured batteries

After Sinope, the Emperor Napoleon had initiated the design of armoured, steam-propelled batteries for the French navy. The original intention was to protect them using boxes of cannonballs along the side but, on a visit to Paris, Thomas Lloyd suggested the use of plate armour instead. Tests showed that this proposal was much more effective and was adopted. The emperor wanted ten such ships for the start of the 1855 campaign, but found that French iron founders and shipyards could manage to build only five and Britain was asked to build another five.

The project was delayed by Sir James Graham, First Lord. He had memories of problems with the iron-hulled, unarmoured frigates of the previous decade and confused these with the proposed wood-hulled, armoured batteries. Despite the Surveyor's assurance and the results of tests at Vincennes, Graham insisted on more tests at Portsmouth in September 1856. A target 9ft square was built from seven 4½in plates, backed by 4in of fir planks and well supported.

In the first trial the target was hit by ten 32pdr shot

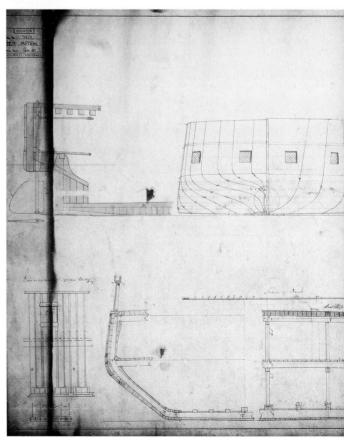

fired at 300yds with a 10lb charge and no significant damage was caused. The target then resisted two 68lb shot fired at long range, though one plate cracked. Two more 68lb shot at 400yds seriously damaged the target and a further seven rounds drove bits of plate through the backing. Thinner plates were also tested; ½in plate would break hollow shot and ⅝in would stop shell. These tests, demanded by Graham, confirmed the *Vincennes* results and ensured that the British ships would be too late for the war.

Five British ships were ordered on 4 October 1854.[34] They had wooden hulls, straight vertical sides and a flat bottom with a very bluff bow and stern. Their armour plates, nominally 4in but in many cases rolled ¼–½in under thickness, were locked together with tongue and groove joints. In *Erebus*, and possibly others, only the waterline strake was 4in, the rest being 3½in. The upper deck was of wood but 9in thick to give some protection. There were two conning towers protected with ⅝in plate. Their fourteen 68pdrs fired through ports 34in x 40in, whose size must be seen as a weak point (see picture of *Thunder* in the Introduction.)

Of these first five ships one, *Aetna*, was destroyed by fire at Scott Russell's yard before launch. A replacement, to a slightly different design, was built in Chatham Dockyard.

In December 1855 three more ships were ordered with iron hulls, and these were the first iron-hulled, armoured ships to be built. They differed in appearance from the earlier vessels as they had a 30 degree tumble-home to improve the resistance of their armour to shot,

giving an upper deck only 35ft 3in wide (waterline 48ft 6in).

Meteor reached 5.7 knots on trial with a single propeller 6ft in diameter and 12ft 6in in pitch, absorbing 530ihp at 139rpm with the safety valve set at 60lb/sq in. Only twelve days later a second trial was run, by which time she had been altered to a three-shaft ship with wing propellers of the same 6ft diameter, but with a pitch of 7ft 6in. At 113rpm she developed 498ihp and reached 5.25 knots. It is possible that a three-shaft arrangement had always been seen as an option; the method of driving the wing shafts is unknown, but in view of the timescale it is most likely that belts were used, which was common practice at the time.

The French ships had problems, too. They had

Table 12.15 **Armoured Batteries**

	Glatton	British *Aetna* (ii)	*Erebus*	French *Lave*	Confederate *Virginia*
Length	172ft 6in	157ft 10in	186ft	170ft	279ft 4in
Beam	45ft 2½in	44ft	48ft 6in	38ft	39ft
Draught	8ft 8in	6ft	8ft 10in	8ft 6in	22ft 4in
Depth	14ft 7in	16ft	15ft 6in	–	–
Armament	Fourteen 68pdrs*	Fourteen 68pdrs	Sixteen 68pdrs	Sixteen 50pdrs	Two 7in, RML Six 6.4in, RML Six 9in, SB (smooth bore)
Armour	4in	4in	4in	4in	4in
Speed	4½–5½ knots		5½ knots	3½ knots	5 knots

*Reduced from sixteen to keep draught below 8ft 8in.

34. G A Osbon, notes.

Admiralty draught for the armoured battery *Meteor*. The section shows the wooden hull construction. (© *National Maritime Museum DR7279*)

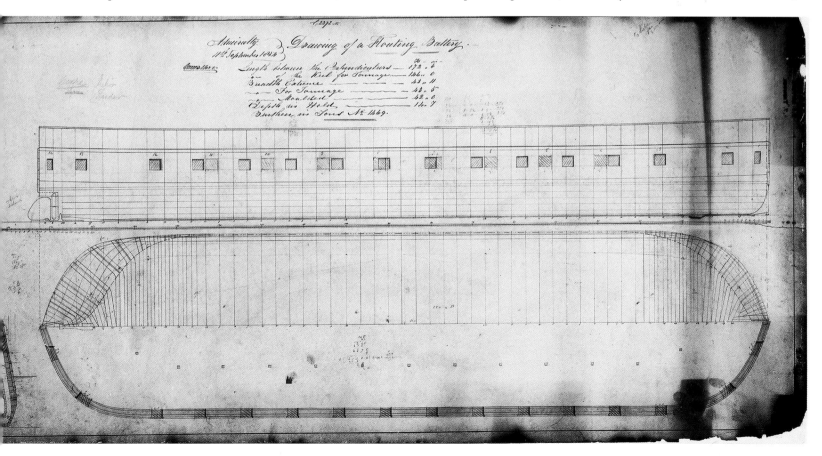

The remains of the *Aetna* after the fire at Scott Russell's yard. *(© National Maritime Museum PZ7968)*

The *Terror* seen in later life as a guard ship at Bermuda. This class were the first iron hulled, armoured ships to go to sea. *(© National Maritime Museum A7534-16)*

expected a speed of about 6 knots using Schneider high pressure engines of 150hp. On trial, they were found to be hot and ill-ventilated, hard to steer and with speeds of 3–4 knots. After various trials, they were given three rudders and two lee boards. Propulsion and steering of very bluff forms present a range of difficult problems even today and it is not surprising that mid-nineteenth-century designers, without the help of model testing, did not get it quite right.[35]

These armoured batteries were among the most revolutionary ships ever built and provided British and French designers with the germ of the battleship. The table below compares them with the much more famous, but inferior, Confederate ship *Virginia*, ex-*Merrimac*.

Of the British ships only *Glatton* and *Meteor* were ready in 1855, reaching the Black Sea too late for action. They were laid up for the winter and, in the spring, when peace was signed, returned home for the great review.

Kinburn

The French ships made their mark in the attack on Kinburn, which stands on the western extremity of the spit forming the southern end of the basin known as the Liman of Dneiper. Control of the channel between Kinburn and Fort Otchakof to the north would close the Dneiper and Bug to Russian shipping and threaten the rear of their armies.

The fort was of masonry with an earth parapet and mounted sixty guns in casemates and about twenty more in barbettes. There were also two powerful open batteries. The allied fleet consisted of the three French armoured batteries, ten liners, seventeen frigates and sloops, three corvettes, four despatch vessels, twenty-two gun boats, eleven mortar vessels and ten transports under Admirals Lyons and Bruat. They reached Kinburn on 14 October 1855 and at dusk nine gun boats ran past the batteries and anchored inside the spit. Because of heavy swell there was no attack the next day, though towards evening the mortars fired some ranging shots.

At 0800hrs on the 17th the sea was still with a light northerly breeze when the three batteries, *Devastation*, *Lave* and *Tonnant* steamed into position between 900 and 1,000yds from the fort. At 1200hrs the Russian fire

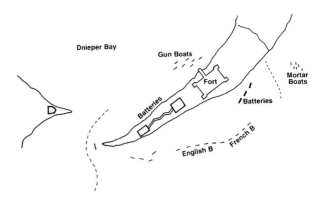

The attack on Kinburn.

slackened and nine more allied ships steamed through the channel to attack from the inside. The battleships fired heavily, but probably ineffectively, at a range of 1,600yds. The Russians surrendered at 1325hrs having lost forty-five killed and 130 wounded; the British had two men slightly hurt.

It is not clear what damage was done to the fort, nor is it possible to say whether it was the close-range fire from inside the spit, the firing of the batteries or the shower of shot from the liners which led to the surrender. Once again, heavy firing from the sea forced the surrender of a fort with little damage.

The success of the armour was abundantly clear. *Devastation*'s armour was hit by twenty-nine shot, probably 24pdrs, and thirty-five more ploughed furrows in her deck. One shell entered the battery through the main hatch and two shot came in through the ports, killing two and wounding thirteen. The *Lave* had no casualties and the *Tonnant* nine wounded from fragments of shot through the ports. She was hit fifty-five times on the armour, with ten hits on the deck and one on the rudder. Technically, the resistance of 4in of armour to 24lb shot at 1,000yds proved nothing; symbolically, it was the start of a new era.

The Victory Review

The signing of the peace treaty was marked by a big naval review at Spithead in 1856, when Queen Victoria

35. P de Geoffrey, 'La guerre du Crimêe et la France – les batteries flottantes aux garde-côtes', *Marine et Technique aux XIXe siècle*, Paris (1987).

The *Dapper* class gun boat *Cracker* passing within 600 yards of the Kinburn shore on the morning of 15 October 1855. (© *National Maritime Museum PW4907*)

The victory review on 23 April 1856. A feature of the review was a dummy attack on Southsea Castle by the massed gun boat force, as seen in the centre right of this aerial view. It was the only service for most of the gun boats. (© *National Maritime Museum PY8273*)

Lessons of the war

Mobility

It was demonstrated, without any remaining doubt, that the steamship could be relied on to be at a given place at the stated time. This consistent mobility made strategic planning more certain than it could be for a sailing fleet: eg, Nelson's chase to the West Indies and back was at an average speed of 4 knots. The steamship proved far more capable of safe operation in bad weather than the sailing ship.

These lessons could be read across to the merchant navy and the reliable timing of arrival of the steamship earned for them higher charter rates than those for sailing ships. In turn, this caused a rapid expansion of the commercial steam fleet.

Industry

Penn and Maudslay learnt the benefits of mass production, though the postwar orders were too few to benefit from such skills. The other lesson was a sad one: the consequences of taking fixed price contracts during a period of inflation caused several yards to close, hastening what was probably the inevitable end of the Thames shipbuilding industry. Shipbuilding relies on cheap labour to this day and the activity will migrate to cheap areas.

Coastal attack

It had long been accepted that ships cannot successfully attack forts, but this war went far to contradict this proposition. Bomarsund and Kinburn had surrendered, as had defences at the entrance to the Sea of Azov. Sveaborg had been heavily hit with little damage to the bombardment force. Sevastopol can perhaps be seen as a draw, with little damage of consequence on either side, but this was early in the war when specialised attack craft were not available. The plans for an attack on Kronstadt

inspected 240 ships, mainly built during the war:

Steam line-of-battle ships	24
Screw frigates and corvettes	19
Paddle frigates and corvettes	18
Sailing frigate	1
Armoured batteries	4
Gun vessels and boats	120
Mortar vessels and floats	50
Ammunition ships	2
Hospital ships	1
Floating foundry	1
Total	240

It was an imposing force, technically advanced, strong in its steam battle line and superbly equipped to attack coastal fortifications. Within a very few years they would all be outdated.

The Austrian wooden battleship *Kaiser* after the battle of Lissa in 1866. She was hit 60 times, including by one 300lb shell, and had rammed an Italian ironclad but, despite 100 casualties, was seaworthy and ready to fight the next day. The unarmoured wooden battleship was not as vulnerable as was believed.

One of the few battleships launched during the war, the *Royal Albert* at Woolwich, 13 May 1854. The ships in the foreground have not been identified but probably include *Alban*, *Black Eagle* and *Monkey*. (© National Maritime Museum PY0960)

(Appendix 13) in 1856 show that modern technology in purpose-built, shallow-draught vessels gave ships a very good chance of defeating a fort.

The reasons for this ability of fragile ships to defeat stone forts are not entirely clear; in both Kinburn and Bomarsund morale was destroyed and comparatively undamaged forts surrendered. Such surrenders happened, too, a few years later in the American civil war. Both sides fought with great bravery in the field, but forts quite commonly gave up under the sudden and somewhat unexpected hail of fire from a fleet. Earlier in the century, Exmouth's attack on Algiers and the bombardment of St Jean d'Acre showed the value of careful planning and accurate, rapid gunnery in defeating fortifications.

The vulnerability of ships

Contemporary writers saw the main lesson as the appalling vulnerability of wooden ships to shells. This was probably the normal reaction to being hit after a long period of peace (one might compare the impact of the Exocet missile in the Falklands conflict of 1982 where the loss of *Sheffield* is remembered, but not the survival, fit to fight, of *Glamorgan*). In fact, the survival, with light casualties, of *Albion*, *Arethusa*, *Ville de Paris*, *Russia* and others shows that the shell of the mid-1850s was not a very effective anti-ship weapon. This lesson was reinforced at Lissa in 1866 when the Austrian wooden screw

battleship *Kaiser* was heavily hit, including one from a 300lb shell, but was ready for action within twenty-four hours. On the other hand, the old-fashioned red-hot shot was still a very effective anti-ship weapon.

The damage to *Valorous*'s paddle wheel supported the evidence from the *Fulton* at the Parana that even severe damage to the wheel would not be likely to immobilise the ship.

Gun range was about 4,000yds, but lacking any control system and very slow to train or elevate, the chances of hitting at over 1,500yds, even in calm weather, was remote. To some extent, Cole's development of the turret with power operation can be seen as an appropriate but partial response to this problem.

The future

The value of armour was well appreciated, and perhaps over-publicised, but its application to a seagoing battleship, already burdened with heavy machinery, was not easy. The threat from mines and other underwater attacks does not seem to have been recognised, though it must be said that this threat was not a serious one for some years.

By and large, the fleet which went to war was a good one, short only in shallow-draught vessels. The fleet of 1856 was a very fine fighting machine, embodying a considerable, though not universal, will to use new technology.

Thirteen | The Last Wooden Ships

ONCE THE CRIMEAN WAR was over, the age-old suspicion and hostility between Britain and France was resumed, leading to a classic arms race in which both countries believed, and perhaps even encouraged, exaggerated reports of the other's potential. During the 1850s both Britain and France built large fleets of wooden screw battleships, frigates and smaller ships, all soon to be regarded as obsolete.

In wartime the Royal Dockyards had been forced to concentrate on fitting out gun boats and other small craft, though a considerable number of steam liners were built or converted. As a result, by 1856 it seemed possible that an energetic French building programme would enable them to equal or surpass the strength of the Royal Navy.

Table 13.1 shows the actual building rate in the two countries. In both, there was a mixture of new construction and conversions, and while the new ships were well designed and built, the quality of the conversions varied considerably. Some, extensively modified on the slip, were virtually the equal of new construction, while in other more limited conversions, in both countries,

Duke of Wellington. Lengthened and given engines during building. (© National Maritime Museum neg 6819)

Table 13.1 **British and French Liner Programme**

| Year | Built (or converted) in the year | | Cumulative total | |
	Britain	France	Britain	France
1850	– + (4)[a]	1	0	1
1851	1	1	1	2
1852	2	1	3	3
1853	7	2	10	5
1854	8	4[c]	18	9
1855	6 + (5)[a]	4	24	13
1856	–	5	24	18
1857	4	6	28	24
1858	6	4	34	28
1859	11	2	45	30
1860	8	4 + (3)[d]	53	34
1861	5	–	57[b] + (9)[a]	34 + (3)[d]

Notes: a Blockships; b *Conqueror* sunk; c *Dugueslin* sunk; d Three liners converted to troopships.

engines were dropped into existing, sometimes aged, hulls with less satisfactory results. The size and arma-

Table 13.2 **Contemporary Comparison of Forces**

Category	Britain Complete	Building	France Complete	Building
STEAM				
Liners	29	21	29	11
Blockships	9	–	–	–
Screw frigates	17	8	15	12
Paddle frigates	9	–	19	–
Screw corvettes, sloops	38	9	9	4
Paddle corvettes, sloops	35	–	9	–
Gun vessels, screw	29	–	17	10
Gun vessels, paddle	24	–	66	–
Batteries	8	–	5	–
Gun boats	161	1	28	–
Miscellaneous	62	–	22	4
SAIL				
Liners	38	–	10	–
Frigates	70	–	28	–
Corvettes, sloops	43	–	11	–
Miscellaneous	125	–	61	–

ment of the ships also varied from eighty to 130 guns. Account must also be taken of what was believed, erroneously, to be the balance of forces. A Treasury committee[1] was given figures for 1858 as they appeared to the Royal Navy (Table 13.2).

These figures cannot be reconciled with those now known to be correct, but they were probably an honest attempt at the time. Other contemporary writers, eg Hans Busk,[2] were more alarmist.

Table 13.3 compares the rival fleets in terms of mode of build and number of guns.

The distribution of age between the two navies is worth a more detailed examination (for converted ships from laying down – Table 13.4).

Table 13.4 **Distribution of Age (in years)**

	Less than 10	10–20	20–30	30–40	Over 40
British	2	22	8	8	1
French	–	5	8	11	4

These two tables make it clear that the Royal Navy had a higher proportion of new construction and of major conversions and that they carried many more guns. There is a marked difference between the two navies in the proportion of older ships, a difference which would have had a major effect on maintenance costs and on availability had not all these ships become obsolete so quickly. The NHP of the French engines tended to be greater but, as discussed in the context of *Agamemnon* and *Napoleon,* this is not a good guide. Despite the British concept of engines as an auxiliary, in practice there was little or nothing between the actual power installed. With only one or two exceptions the British engines were very reliable.

Table 13.3 **Screw Battleships**

	Britain		France	
New construction	18	(average age 5.8 years) Two 121-gun Three 101-gun Twelve 91-gun One 88-gun	9	(average age 10.2 years) One 130-gun Eight 90-gun
Lengthened on slip	22	(average age 24.4 years) Five 131-gun Fourteen 89/91-gun Two 86-gun One 81-gun	4	(average age 15.8 years) Four 90-gun
Engines added	18	(average age 18.3 years) Two 120-gun One 102-gun Four 90/91-gun Eleven 80/81-gun	25	(average age 34.1 years) Four 114-gun Eleven 90-gun Nine 80-gun One 70-gun
Blockships	9	(average age 50.2 years) Nine 60-gun		

Overall, the bare statistics in Table 13.3 probably underestimate the British superiority. Other than France, only a few countries built steam liners.

Table 13.5 **Steam Liners (Other Navies)**

Country	Number of ships, guns
Russia	One 111, two 135, four 86, two 74
Turkey	One 110, one 94, one 90
Sweden	One 68, one 86
Austria	One 91
Denmark	One 64
Italy	One 66

Frigates

It is even more difficult to make a reliable comparison of the numbers and power of screw frigates. Table 13.7 presents the British building and conversion programme and both this and the French totals agree fairly well with the 1858 Committee report. Note that the seven smaller second-class frigates derived from *Cyclops* were then classed as sloops, leaving six first-class and three second-class paddle frigates. The four mortar frigates were of little fighting value.

Looking back, the inadequate number of screw frigates should have been a greater cause for concern than the balance in battleships. Britain was far more dependent on

1. Committee appointed by the Treasury to inquire into the Navy Estimates, 1852–8.

2. H Busk, *The Navies of the World,* London (1859; reprint 1871).

Table 13.6 **Merchant Ships 1858**

	Britain			France		
	Number	Number over 800 tons	Tonnage	Number	Number over 800 tons	Tonnage
Sail	24,406	763	4,075,245	14,845		980,465
Steam	1,813	119	416,132	330	30	72,070

Table 13.7 **British Screw Frigates**

Year	Ordered to build or convert	Completed within year	Cumulative total
1844	2	–	–
1845	3 + 4 block + 4 iron	–	–
1846	1+1 iron	1	1
1847	–	–	1
1848	–	1	2
1849	–	–	2
1850	3	–	2
1851	2	–	2
1852	2	2	4
1853	4	2	6
1854	3	2	8
1855	2	–	8
1856	6	1	9
1857	1	2	11
1858	4	1	12
1859	3	8	20
1860	3	6	26
1861	5	31	
1862	2	33	
1863	1	34	
1864	–	34	
1865	1	35	
1866	1	36	

Two more were completed in 1870 and one in 1874.

Table 13.8 **Distribution**

	Ships	
Area	1852	1858
East Indies, China, Australia	20	49
Cape of Good Hope	8	8
West Africa	20	18
Brazil	8	9
Pacific	8	12
North America & West Indies	16	21
Mediterranean	18	22
Total	98	139
Home ports	34	45
Coast Guard	–	26
Channel	8	7
Particular service, etc	63	58
Total	203	267

Table 13.9 **Annual Pay Bill**

	1852		1858
Britannia	£26,643	*Marlborough*	£35,248
Arethusa	£14,585	*Shannon*	£19,241

The ships

The development of the wooden screw battleship has been covered by Lambert in a comprehensive account which needs only to be summarised here.[4] The majority of the new construction ships were derivatives of *Agamemnon*. The first five were almost identical and five more were ordered, but four of these were lengthened by about 15ft and given 800NHP engines, forming the *Renown* class. With over 3,000ihp, they were only about half a knot faster than the *Agamemnon* and carried the same 91-gun armament. (*Defiance* was generally similar.)

The *Duncan* class were modified *Renown*s with more beam and 101 guns. Only two completed to the original design, seven more became armoured ships and five were broken up on the slip.

The armament of these ships varied only slightly:

Gun deck	Thirty-four 8in/65cwt
Main deck	Thirty-four 32pdr/56cwt
Upper deck	One 68pdr/95cwt, twenty-two 32pdr/45cwt

They cost between £135,000 and £176,000.

The steady development of this group of ships (of which at least twenty-four were planned) shows how sound was Edye's original design. Three slightly longer variants of *Agamemnon* were ordered in 1851–5 and carried 101 guns.

There were two new design three-deckers, *Victoria* and *Howe,* designed by Watts in 1854 (approved January 1855). In December 1857 Walker decided that they should have finer lines and they were lengthened by 15ft forward while on the slip. Their size, length and 1,000NHP (*c*4,500ihp) gave them a speed of about 12½

overseas trade than was France and had a much more widespread empire. Britain's merchant fleet, freed from the Navigation Acts in the 1830s and encouraged by subsidies in the war, had grown rapidly. (Table 13.6).

The lack of steam frigates was partially offset by some seventy steam corvettes and sloops, half screw, half paddle, and by over fifty gun vessels, some of substantial size and firepower. The majority of these ships carried a more powerful armament than could readily be mounted in a converted merchant ship.

Admiral Milne, as a junior naval lord, sent a memorandum to the minister on trade protection in 1858 but nothing came of it.[3] Even when he became First Sea Lord, he was unable to obtain resources to increase the level of trade protection, a neglected aspect of naval policy at least until 1917.

Numbers of ships alone do not reveal the full size of the increased commitment. In several foreign stations, frigates were replaced by battleships, particularly as flagships. The cost went up even more; able seamen's pay went up from 16d to 19d per day and the newer ships needed more men. The total number of officers and men increased from 40,761 to 55,500 between 1852 and 1858.

The combined effect on the pay bill was considerable. This was just one of the factors which led the Treasury to set up its Committee on the Navy Estimates to see why the total had gone from £5.835 million to £8.851 million between 1852 and 1858.

3. B Ranft, 'The protection of British seaborne trade 1860–1906', from *Technical Change and British Naval Policy*, London (1977).
4. A Lambert, *Battleships in Transition*, London (1984).

Opposite, top: *Trafalgar* with her sister *Neptune* astern. Two of five sailing First Rates of this class were lengthened and cut down to 89-gun two-deckers when they were converted to steam. (© *National Maritime Museum D2164*)

Opposite, bottom: Although she was laid down as a sailing ship, the conversion of *Marlborough* began so early that she was widened as well as lengthened. (© *National Maritime Museum L2614-002*)

Galatea was approved as a fast corvette but completed as a frigate with a heavier armament and less powerful engines. The screw corvette *Challenger* is behind. (Allan C Green, via the State Library of Victoria)

knots, making them the fastest of the wooden battle-ships.

With their two funnels lowered, to the untutored eye they did not look very different from Nelson's *Victory* and this still gives rise to ill-informed comments on lack of progress. Table 13.10 shows that displacement had doubled, as had the weight of a broadside. *Victoria*'s manoeuvrability under steam and her heavy guns, able to fire shells, made her even more formidable than is indicated by the figures.

Boulton and Watt built two sets of machinery, both unsatisfactory. The rest came from Maudslay (nine) and Penn (seven).

The *Agamemnon* was good for about 11 knots at sea with an endurance under steam, in moderate weather, of about two thousand miles. She had fifty days' water and eighty days' provisions for a crew of about 850; later ships were similar in these respects. Reports were universally favourable – except for the Watts engines – as would be expected from the repeated orders. They were well-built, durable ships, several lasting well into this century as training ships.

Major conversions

These ships, all lengthened, usually on the slip, were very effective and were ranked almost as highly as new construction. In many cases there can have been little of the original design left, for, as an example, *Marlborough* was widened by a foot as well as being lengthened by 40ft. The *Duke of Wellington* was cut in two places and given an extra 23ft amidships and 8ft in the run.

Table 13.10 **Victory** to **Victoria**

	Victory	Victoria
Displacement (tons)	3,500	6,959
Length (ft)	186	260
Guns (as designed)	Thirty 42pdr	Thirty-two 8in
	Twenty-eight 24pdr	Eighty-eight 32pdr
	Thirty 12pdr	One 68pdr
	Twelve 6pdr	
Weight of broadside (tons)	1.182	2.372

Topaze. A wooden screw
frigate completed in 1859
and broken up in 1884.
*(© National Maritime
Museum D2178)*

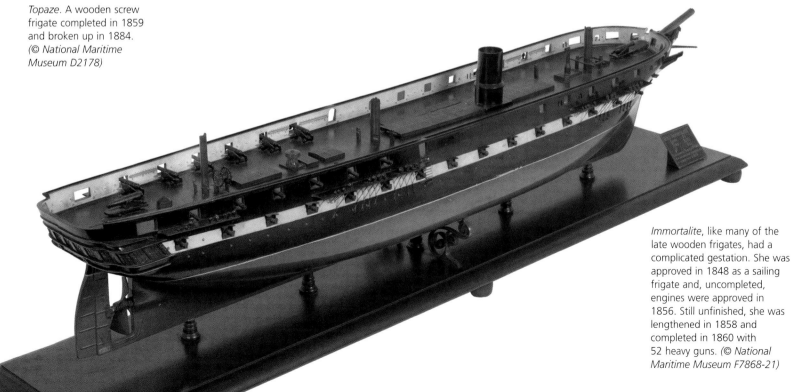

Immortalite, like many of the
late wooden frigates, had a
complicated gestation. She was
approved in 1848 as a sailing
frigate and, uncompleted,
engines were approved in
1856. Still unfinished, she was
lengthened in 1858 and
completed in 1860 with
52 heavy guns. *(© National
Maritime Museum F7868-21)*

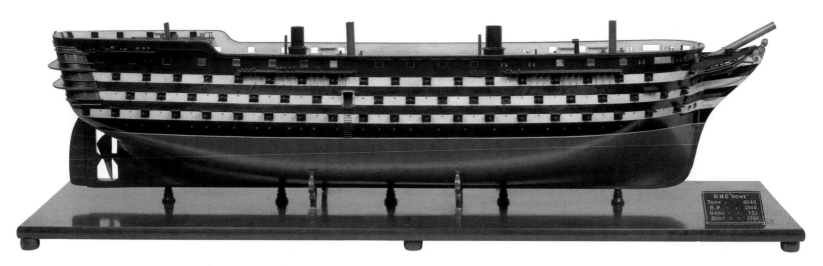

Howe, designed by Isaac Watts, was one of the biggest wooden ships ever built. This model shows her two funnels, ports for a total of 121 guns and her screw. (© *National Maritime Museum F7867-001*)

5. D K Brown, 'Speed of sailing warships', *Empires at Peace and War*, conference, Portsmouth (1988).

There were problems with the machinery installation in the 90-gun *Algiers* class due to their Symondite hull form, perhaps contributing to their unreliability. On the other hand, the smaller 80-gun *Orion*, also a Symondite, was very successful, though since she was in frame when the conversion began and was lengthened by 40ft, there cannot have been much of Symonds's form left.

It is clear that Walker and his staff believed that lengthening led directly to higher speed, but it does not now seem likely that even a 40ft increase in the length of these bluff forms would in itself add more than half a knot to the speed.[5] What it did do was to make space available for bigger and more powerful engines and the

men to steam them. The speeds achieved on trial seem to have varied more than in the new construction ships, but 10–10½ knots sea speed was typical, with endurance of the same order as the new ones.

Limited conversions

Dropping engines into an existing hull was a quick and easy way of increasing the number of steam battleships. They were not as effective as the full conversions, but it is wrong to think of them as simply 'cheap and nasty'. They were slower, typically 9¼ knots, due to their lower power engines, had a little less endurance and were much overcrowded.

Severn. Designed as a sailing frigate by Fincham – the last purely sailing warship to be completed for the Royal Navy – and converted to steam in 1860, she was one of a group of 50-gun frigates ordered to be converted in 1859-60. (© *National Maritime Museum N05333*)

Renown was the lead ship of the second batch of *Agamemnon* derivatives. (© *National Maritime Museum neg 3838*)

Victoria, sister of *Howe*, was another immensely powerful wooden three-decker. (© *National Maritime Museum A4197*)

Parity or better with the French navy could not have been achieved without these ships and many of the French ships were inferior to them.

To convert or build?

One of the main tasks of the 1861 Commission[6] was to examine the programme of converting ships to take engines and to report on the efficiency of the work. Some of the evidence was surprisingly muddled: James Peake, master shipwright of Devonport, told the commission, 'I cannot say that I think it [conversion] has been economical; it may have saved time but I doubt the economy of it'. He went on, at length, to say that the money should have been spent on new construction, that the conversions, designed as sailing ships, would be inefficient, and that their life would be short. These were all quite sound points, but spoilt by his last comment, that timber supplies were inadequate for new construction.

Table 13.11 **Building of Steam Liners**

Dockyard	Number built	Cancelled
Devonport	5	1
Pembroke	5	1
Chatham	3	2
Woolwich	3	–
Portsmouth	2	1

The building of these ships was reasonably distributed round the dockyards though Portsmouth was a late starter.

The conversion programme was intended to produce steam battleships quickly, to save money and timber and to economise in shipwright labour. The figures given to the commission confirm that these objects were achieved.

Time

The average time for a conversion was twelve to sixteen

Table 13.12 **Conversions**

Converted		Engines	
Devonport	12	Penn	13
Chatham	9	Maudslay	11
Portsmouth	9	Ravenhill & Salkeld	8
Pembroke	4	Napier	2
Sheerness	4	Humphrys & Tennant	2
Woolwich	1	Fairbairn	1
Deptford	1	Scott, Sinclair	1
		Rennie	1
		Watt	

months, with surprisingly little difference between full conversion and the simpler alterations. New construction ships took two or three years to build.

The figures from the report of the commission (Table 13.13) compare the cost of full and limited conversions with that of a hypothetical new ship. Such comparisons are always difficult; there is a suspicious similarity in the ratio of cost between new build and conversion. It should also be noted that the costs exclude the cost of the engines in all cases. Like many 'official' figures they represent truth, but not necessarily the whole truth. However, it is clear that the conversions were considerably cheaper.

Timber

The table also gives the difference in timber required and there can be no doubt that there was a very substantial saving. Good seasoned timber was hard to obtain and expensive. It is fairly certain that sufficient timber for a much increased new construction programme could not have been found. The cost of timber was rising rapidly as it became scarce. African oak had gone up from £11 in 1852 to £12.4s in 1858 while English oak had gone up about 10 per cent (as had many other shipbuilding materials).

6. Committee appointed by the Treasury to inquire into the Navy Estimates, 1852–8.

This cutaway drawing gives an idea both of the size and complexity of the last wooden liners. (© *National Maritime Museum neg 9351*)

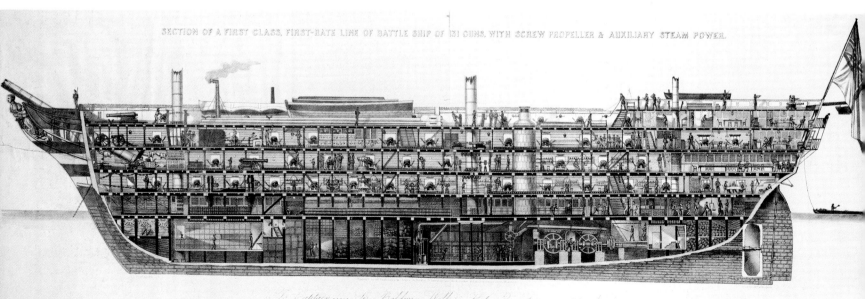

SECTION OF A FIRST CLASS, FIRST-RATE LINE OF BATTLE SHIP OF 131 GUNS, WITH SCREW PROPELLER & AUXILIARY STEAM POWER.

Shipwrights

A full conversion needed about five-eighths of the man-hours needed for new construction.[7] It is likely that there was no real shortage of skilled men, but a limit on numbers permitted.

Conclusion

Overall, the conversion programme was essential to match the perceived threat from France. Timber resources, too, dictated a conversion programme. There was also a saving in cost, though this might have been a little less than the commission believed. Had the ships not been overtaken by the iron ship revolution and had, in most cases, a fairly short active life, any such savings would have been offset by a high running cost.

The threat from France was such that it was thought necessary to convert any and every more or less sound ship into which engines could be squeezed. The Committee on Marine Engines noted that Symonds's *Queen* had 1,300cu ft less in her hold than the *Nile*. The value of some of the older and smaller ships was questionable but they were as good as, or better than, many similar French ships.

Table 13.13 **Costs**

	If they had been built new		Conversions		Ratio of	
	£	Loads timber	£	Loads timber	£	Loads timber
Limited Conversion						
Royal George	78,480	3,800	23,716	247	.3	.065
Colossus	77,700	3,750	23,743	280	.3	.075
Full Conversion						
Royal Albert	111,780	4,140	57,343	960	.51	.23
Prince Regent	93,870	4,500	38,981	525	.42	.117
Nile	78,660	3,800	23,903	593	.3	.16

There seems to have been little or no discussion at the time of armoured conversions. There were numerous proposals for armoured ships, including several from Scott Russell, but they were all rejected on the usual basis that it was not for Britain to initiate change.

Both the building and conversion programmes depended on the Royal Dockyards and on a small number of marine engineering companies and they were well managed and equipped for the task.

7. J Scott Russell, *A Modern System of Naval Architecture*, London (1865).

St George. She was converted and lengthened before completion. (© *National Maritime Museum neg 6152*)

The Halifax station about 1862. The principal warships are all 91-gun screw two-deckers, but their genesis varied: *Nile* was converted without being lengthened; *Agamemnon* and *Edgar* were purpose-built; *Hero* was an improved *Agamemnon*. (© National Maritime Museum A7854-019)

Developments in the Royal Dockyards

The full story of developments in the Royal Dockyards would need a book in itself, but since it is so much a part of innovation in the Navy, some outline must be given here. Despite the low level of funding for all Navy Votes in the first half of the century (post-war), the Admiralty accomplished a great deal in modernising and extending the dockyards. New slips were built and old ones covered, new docks were constructed and, most important, facilities for refitting and, very occasionally, building machinery – steam factories as they were known – had been brought into operation.

Wooden ships needed to season if early rot was to be avoided. The best way was for the ship to lie in frame, under cover, for a long time. Ships in this condition could be completed for sea in a short time. Table 13.14 shows that the French navy was far better off for slips, mainly covered, than was the Royal Navy. Britain had enough slips for the peacetime building programme, making it difficult for the Board to argue a case for more.

The surviving covered slips of this era are remarkable buildings, with some of the widest unsupported wooden roofs ever built. The Admiralty, perhaps regrettably, was a pioneer in the use of corrugated iron and from 1840 slips were iron framed and clad. Coad has shown[8] that the Admiralty was in the van of building methods, the boat shed at Sheerness, completed in 1861, being one of the first multi-storey, iron-framed buildings. Great attention was paid to making buildings fire-resistant, as

8. J Coad, *Historic Architecture of the Royal Navy*, London (1983).
9. G Dicker, *A Short History of Devonport Royal Dockyard*, Devonport Yard Museum (1980).
10. R C Riley, *The Evolution of the Docks and Industrial Buildings in Portsmouth Royal Dockyard*, Portsmouth City Council (1985).

Table 13.14 **Dockyards in 1858**

Yard	Area (acres)	Number of slips	Number of docks	Docks building
Portsmouth	115	5	9	2
Devonport	71	6	5	
Keyham	73	–	3	
Chatham	95	8	4	
Sheerness	57	1	5	
Woolwich	56	6	3	
Deptford	38	5	2	
Pembroke	77	13	1	
Total	866	44	32	2
Total French*	865	73	17	7

*Cherbourg, Brest, Lorient, Rochefort, Toulon.

the vast quantities of inflammable materials – rope, paint, tallow and timber – made fire an ever-present risk. Even so, big fires did break out, such as that which destroyed a considerable area of Devonport, together with the *Talavera* (74) and *Imogene* (28) on 27 September 1840.[9] The cast iron fire station in Portsmouth is another expression both of concern over fire and of the intelligent use of new materials.

The railway also began to make its mark, rather slowly, in the yards. Portsmouth had a tramway in operation by 1828, which was further extended by 1835 to carry masts to the Sheer jetty.[10] A true railway formed part of the steam basin extension and this was linked to the main line in 1849. Only then could steam engines enter the yard, but only to a reception area since the internal system used turntables at right-angle intersections of the roadways. It was sometimes claimed that the Board spent too much on fine buildings when corrugated iron huts would have done. There is some truth in this but, overall, the capital investment was a wise move for the future – and left some very fine buildings for posterity.

Labour

Warships grew rapidly in size and complexity and the labour force matched these developments with increasing numbers and skill. The accompanying figures show that the labour force doubled in number between 1838 and 1859. There were large increases in the traditional trades but, in addition, the steam factories employed over 2,000 craftsmen (Table 13.15).

Men were organised into gangs of about twenty under a leading hand. Periodically, the gangs would be 'shoalled', when foremen chose men in turn, to avoid the position reached in earlier years when the more senior foremen chose all the best men for their gangs and, no doubt, then complained of the poor output from the gangs of their junior colleagues. Even so there was a pecking order, the best gangs working on the after end of the ship. The system was over-rigid, but bred a fine loyalty.

An inspector would supervise the work of three leading hands and, in Portsmouth, there would be eight inspectors working for three foremen and the assistant

Table 13.15 **Dockyard and Factory Labour**

Date	Officers	Permanent workmen	Temporary	Convict men	Factory	Total
1840	384	6,301	680	1,100	–	8,469
1850	445	9,630	2,498	876	1,856	15,305
1859	475	10,850	1,365	1,279	2,360	16,334

master shipwright. The master shipwright was the managing director with the master smith, millwright, etc, independent, but co-ordinated by him.

Table 13.16 **Pay (c1860)**

	£ pa		£ pa
Master shipwright	500–750	Inspector	150
Assistant master shipwright	400	Leading hand	120
Foreman	250		

These were quite high salaries for the day and the master shipwright would often be a colonel in the militia. Craftsmen on day rates, as most of them were, earned 5s 6d a day. ('Task and job' 5s 9d average.) Working overtime could increase that to 12 shillings, but such earnings were unusual in peacetime. Convicts were paid 6d a day and were mainly used on building work. Working hours were not excessive; Pembroke worked 0740hrs to 1200hrs and 1315hrs to 1645hrs. Compared with outside earnings these were on the low side, but a good workman could earn 'established status' with a considerable measure of job security. Table 13.17

A mid-nineteenth century view of Devonport, including the new Keyham and Royal William yards. (© *National Maritime Museum neg 4955*)

shows the variety of trades involved and the distribution of numbers.

Table 13.18 shows the distribution of shipwrights between the various activities of the yards. In 1860, roughly two-thirds were in new construction or on converting sailing ships to steam. Barry, a contemporary journalist, in a frequently quoted book,[11] suggests that the dockyards used skilled men when cheaper, unskilled men were adequate and also claimed that the yards would use a whole squad when only a few men were needed. Since there were repeated Parliamentary enquiries into the dockyards during the century, with

Table 13.17 **The Distribution and Variety of Dockyard Trades c1840**

Description	Deptford	Woolwich	Chatham	Sheerness	Portsmouth	Devonport	Pembroke	Total
Blockmakers	–	1	1	2	3	3	–	10
Boys, House	–	–	20	–	20	20	–	60
Ocham	–	3	6	3	8	8	2	30
Wheel	–	–	–	–	–	12	–	12
Braziers, tinmen and apprentices	2	4	6	4	8	8	–	32
Bricklayers and apprentices	–	6	8	6	12	12	–	44
Labourers	–	2	3	3	4	4	–	16
Calkers and apprentices	–	16	30	40	50	50	14	200
Coopers	1	1	1	4	1	1	–	9
Engine repairers	–	3	–	–	–	–	–	3
Founders	–	–	–	–	2	–	–	2
Hemp-dressers	–	–	–	–	–	16	–	16
Joiners and apprentices	–	44	80	43	106	100	40	413
Key-bearers (ropery)	–	–	1	–	1	1	–	3
Labourers, storehouse	19	11	14	10	14	14	3	85
Yard	4	40	80	40	100	100	40	404
As boatmen								
Line and twine spinners	–	–	–	–	–	14	–	4
Locksmiths and apprentices	–	1	2	1	2	2	–	8
Masons and apprentices	–	–	2	2	10	10	10	34
Messengers	2	4	5	4	6	6	2	29
Millwrights	–	2	2	2	–	2	–	8
Plumbers and apprentices	1	2	4	2	4	4	–	17
Painters, glaziers and apprentices Grinders Labourers	1	6	14	16	20	20	4	81
Pitch heaters	–	1	1	1	1	1	1	6
Riggers	–	20	20	40	50	50	–	180
Labourers	–	6	6	12	13	13	–	50
Sailmakers and apprentices	20	1	36	1	36	36	1	131
Sawyers	–	60	80	60	100	100	60	460
Scavelmen	1	10	10	10	20	20	–	71
Shipwrights and apprentices	3	200	500	300	650	650	200	2,503
2 as house carpenters								
Smiths and apprentices	1	50	80	50	110	120	50	461
Spinners and apprentices	–	–	136	–	136	136	–	408
Warders	3	10	13	18	20	20	6	90
Wheelwrights	–	1	2	1	2	2	1	10
Workmen at Wood mills	–	–	–	–	20	–	–	20
Metal mills	–	–	–	–	40	–	–	40
Millwright's shop	–	–	–	–	40	–	–	40
Total	58	505	1,163	675	1,610	1,555	434	6,000

only minor complaints resulting, it is likely that Barry had exaggerated a few minor incidents.[12]

The workforce was a well-educated one, as in 1843 the Board had set up dockyard schools in each yard, under a board of governors comprising the admiral, master shipwright and the chaplain.[13] All apprentices attended for the first two years, working three evenings and two afternoons a week, half in working hours and half in the boys' own time. The brightest boys could continue for four years, receiving an engineering education, which in the twentieth century was almost the equivalent of a pass degree. A pass in the qualifying

11. P Barry, *Dockyard Economy and Naval Power*, London (1863).

12. Ibid.

13. G Dyson, 'Development of Instruction in Naval Architecture in 19th Century England', MA thesis, University of Kent (1978); A W Johns, 'Dockyard Schools and the 2nd School of Naval Architecture', *Engineering*, (Jan–June 1929).

The screw frigate *Liffey* was originally approved as a sailing ship but completed as a steamer. (© *National Maritime Museum F8988)5*

Table 13.18 **Distribution of Dockyard Labour 1860–1**

	Deptford	*Woolwich*	*Chatham*	*Sheerness*	*Portsmouth*	*Devonport*	*Pembroke*	*Total*
New construction								
Battleships	–	143	137	–	186	202	214	882
Frigates	87	138	131	–	287	154	125	921
Corvettes	22	111	108	87	–	–	–	326
Sloops	154	18	45	–	70	84	80	457
Gun vessels & boats	45	–	–	–	20	–	55	120
Conversions								
Battleships			117	128	178	178		601
Frigates			160	160	160	160		640
Total build & conversions	308	410	696	375	901	778	474	3,946
Repairs & fitting	33	119	44	182	299	404	7	1,088
Mast house		20	40	36	65	40		201
Boat house		20	30	8	45	40	1	144
Capstan house		3	5	6	20	20	2	56
Miscellaneous	39	45	95	63	120	118	36	519
Total	380	620	910	670	1,450	1,400	520	5,950
Established	300	500	550	450	1,900	900	400	4,000
Hired	80	120	360	220	550	500	120	1,950

Melpomene was a sailing frigate converted for screw propulsion during construction. This was an elaborate process that involved cutting the hull in half and inserting a new 52ft section to accommodate the 600NHP engines. (© *National Maritime Museum N05334*)

examination was a prerequisite for promotion to draughtsman or inspector. The dockyard schools were extremely competitive and, with few vacancies in the yards for promotion, many apprentices left to market their skills elsewhere.

For the very best, in 1848 the Admiralty opened the Central School of Mathematics and Naval Construction (frequently known as the 'Second School of Naval Architecture'). This school had much in common with the first school – long hours, very hard work and a distinguished list of graduates who would lead the Admiralty and related industry into the next generation of technology. Like the earlier school, this one too was closed by Sir James Graham in 1851. It was alleged that the graduates were not as skilled as their contemporaries with their tools. Graham had few doubts over his actions; he told the 1861 Committee, 'I am not sure, looking back, whether, if it were to be done again I would advise it [closure] … if you only go into the market when you want an article, and pay

for it, you will find a supply' – still a fallacy today.

Machinery made slow inroads into the traditional work. By 1850 Peake, master shipwright at Devonport, listed the following machines:

3 frame saws	1 curvilinear saw
2 circular saws	50–60 traditional saw pits.

The three-decker *Queen* dry-docked at Keyham, the first ship to dock in the new yard. *(© National Maritime Museum P39667)*

Another view of *Queen* at Keyham in 1853.

There were also two steam cranes and a steam engine for hauling timber.

Planning

Careful records had been kept for many years on the man-days required for specific tasks and these were put into a standard form by Seppings in 1830. A typical example is shown in Table 13.19.

Table 13.19 **Man-days for a 3-deck ship, 204ft long**

Work item	Man-days
Lay and secure blocks	60
Trim, scarph and secure temporary keel	78
Trim, scarph, bolt, get in place and secure stem	164
Trim, etc, partially fasten fore and aft dead wood and midships rising wood	179
Trim half floors and cross piece, coak and bolt	560
Trim and bolt the first futtock, fay and coak their heels	512
Score the dead and rising woods and floors, level and shore	67

For the first seven days there would be about twenty shipwrights working, increasing to thirty. After thirty days, progress would be checked to ensure that the work completed corresponded with instalment payments.

Figures are also quoted for the time required to build and outfit a ship.[14]

Table 13.20 **Building Time**

Guns	120	80	74	46
Loads of timber	5,880	4,339	3,600	2,372
Men to build hull in 12 months	200	153	122	92
Time (hours) for 20 men to fit rigging and blocks	300	285	250	

There were differences in the way in which various yards developed; a summary is given in Appendix 14.

Machinery

In 1860, Parliament set up yet another committee, to report on marine engines.[15] The chairman was Rear Admiral W Ramsay and he was assisted by James Nasmyth and John Ward (assistant chief engineer at Keyham). Their terms of reference were extremely lengthy but can be summarised as expressing concern on two issues:

Cadmus at Sheerness in May 1868. A 21-gun screw corvette, she was about as powerful as the smaller frigates and well able to tackle any converted merchant ship. (© *National Maritime Museum C2438*)

a. that warship engines were different in design from those of commercial ships and hence more expensive;
b. that almost all the orders went to Thames factories and most to the two firms of Maudslay and Penn.

Their report is lengthy and muddled, concentrating on a few early and not very serious failures, but also including some sensible views.

They set out the requirements for naval machinery as:

a. All the machinery must be below the waterline.
b. The engines must be simple in construction, at least as simple as is consistent with efficiency.
c. All parts of the engine must be readily and easily accessible so as to be easily removed and replaced when they require repair.

The first of these clearly applied to warships alone, but the committee saw the other two requirements as being more stringent for warships, since they were away from the yards for such long periods.

They criticised the choice of some early direct-action paddle engines, without noting that it was the Admiralty's Steam Department which forced the pace in getting rid of the obsolete side-lever engine. They found the oscillating engine (designed by Penn), and the double cylinder engine (Maudslay) to be the most satisfactory for paddlers.

For screw ships, the committee recommended three designs of engine. At the lower powers, the single piston rod engine, as adapted by Humphrys, Tennant and Dyke, was superior and they noted that both Penn and Maudslay used this type in the later, lower-powered gun boats. At the highest power, the Penn trunk engine has 'answered extremely well'. In these conclusions they vindicated the choice of the Steam Department, though its keeping of accounts was criticised; warship engines really did need to be different, and limiting the number of firms invited to tender was sound practice.

Thomas Lloyd's evidence was, as might be expected, interesting. Contracts were not open to all firms, but only to those whose work had given greatest satisfaction. It was not the custom, nor was it desirable, to enforce the use of a particular style of engine; each builder used his own design with which he was familiar. He was quite satisfied with the way that contractors performed their work and that the engines supplied to the Navy 'are generally superior to those supplied to the merchant service'.

The frigates *Orlando* and her sister *Mersey* were the longest wooden hulls ever built for the Royal Navy, but structural problems simply underlined the argument for iron construction. By the time these ships entered service the decision to build the *Warrior* of iron had already been taken. (© *National Maritime Museum neg 9077*)

14. G Harvey, *Naval Architecture*, London (1849).

15. Committee on Marine Engines, 1860.

The boiler works of Penn & Sons, about 1863. (© *National Maritime Museum H4782*)

Baldwin Walker also made a good point, saying:

> It is important to look at the capabilities of a firm, and the circumstances connected with it at the time when the question of entrusting it with an order is under consideration … It is essential also to know that at this particular time the mechanical management remains in the same hands or has been entrusted to some competent person.

The committee added, 'Now if the above remark is of importance as respects private firms … it is doubly important as respects the professional advisers of the Admiralty'.

Lloyd continued, pointing out the number of aspects in which the Admiralty were the first to adopt improvements in marine engineering. For example:

a. The change from flue to tubular boilers.
b. The direct action engine in place of the beam engine.
c. The screw in place of the paddle.
d. Quick working engines in lieu of engines using gearing.

'The majority of proposals for improving engines,

boilers, etc, are of little value.' All boilers were tubular with the areas of heating and fire surface specified in the contract (grate area 0.68sq ft/NHP, heating 18sq ft/NHP). Pressure was kept to 20lb/sq in; the high-pressure boilers of the gun boats, using salt water, had given a good deal of trouble.

Replacement boilers were made in the dockyards, which could cope with the most major repair to the engines. Lloyd thought that dockyards should also build a few sets of engines, on a regular basis, to ensure continuity of work.

It is perhaps not surprising that the favoured contractors agreed with their customer, but even the less successful found little with which to disagree in Lloyd's remarks.

All engine builders were unanimous that tubular boilers were the only choice for warships, though there was some difference of opinion as to the use of brass, iron or steel tubes. The limit for salt water feed was about 20lb/sq in; a higher pressure could be used with fresh water and a condenser, but trials had not yet proved successful. The Admiralty specified more copper parts than commercial operators, which improved reliability but increased cost. The contracts also called for a spare propeller.

The committee does not seem to have considered the problems of vibration in screw ships, particularly those with two blades behind a thick dead wood. The fluctuating thrust and torque loading probably accounted for the breaking of *Arrogant*'s propeller shaft on 30 October 1855.[16] Vibration also contributed to the rapid wear of the brass stern tube bearing. In a trial in *Malacca*, the brass wore at the rate of 3½oz an hour; Penn and Pettit Smith then tried a lignum vitae bearing, which after 15,000 hours showed no sign of wear. The real cure was a strong iron hull, which also permitted finer stern lines combined with more blades; this was not possible on a hoisting propeller.

The problems of vibration and of bearing wear are good examples of how an apparently trivial detail can have major consequences. In 1856 the battleship *Royal Albert* had to be beached to prevent her sinking from

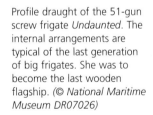

Profile draught of the 51-gun screw frigate *Undaunted*. The internal arrangements are typical of the last generation of big frigates. She was to become the last wooden flagship. (© *National Maritime Museum DR07026*)

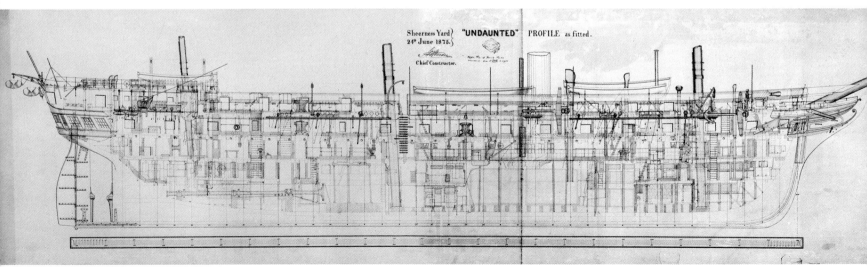

flooding through a worn bearing. Lambert lists several other liners disabled by rudder or stern post problems or by leaks in this area.[17]

It is indeed unfortunate that there is no comprehensive history of marine engineering or of the industry (see sources). The Navy is even more indebted to Maudslay and Penn than mere figures suggest, since several of the founders of other firms learned their skills from these two companies. Both were family concerns; Maudslay and Field had their houses within the factory precincts and Penn lived close to his works. Both firms died in the collapse of Thames shipbuilding at the end of the century.

Guns

The bigger ships carried guns of three calibres: the 68pdr/95cwt as a pivot at the bow and, usually, the stern; the 8in/95cwt shell-firing gun, usually on the lower gun deck; and 32pdrs of 58cwt and 45cwt on other decks. All were formidable weapons which could pierce the side of any unarmoured vessel at any range at which hitting was practicable.

It was claimed that a rate of one round per minute was achieved, but this was a freak performance under ideal conditions. A more practical rate, at least for sustained fire, was one round every two and a half

minutes. The percussion lock was introduced from 1842 which, because the moment of firing was predictable, also improved accuracy.

The wooden steam battleship was introduced in 1846 and within a decade had rendered the sailing fleet obsolete. The steam liner was 'Queen of the Seas' for a very short time indeed. The completion of the *Warrior* in 1861 marked the beginning of the end.

The engine works of Penn & Sons, about 1863. (© *National Maritime Museum H0642*)

16. *The Russian War*, Naval Records Society.
17. Lambert, op cit.

The forward pivot gun of *Immortalite*, a 68pdr, 95cwt gun. Note the ports either side of the bow and the 'racers' (tracks on which it is trained). By this date gun mountings were already far more complicated than in Nelson's day. (© *National Maritime Museum PV6162*)

Fourteen | *Warrior*

IN 1857, DUPUY DE LÔME was appointed '*Directeur du Matériel*' of the French navy and began the design of a seagoing ironclad, the *Gloire*. As discussed earlier, de Lôme was a keen advocate of iron ships, but French industry was not then able to build such a large ship in iron and *Gloire* had a wooden hull, though with much iron stiffening.[1]

Table 14.1 *Gloire*

Displacement	5,630 tons
Dimensions	255ft 6in (wl) x 55ft 9in x 27ft 10in max
Machinery	1 shaft, 2500ihp = 12.5 knots
Armour	Belt, 4.7–4.3in
Armament	Thirty-six 6.4in RML

She was laid down in March 1858, launched on 24 November 1859 and completed in August 1860.

News of her order caused alarm in Britain and provoked a rapid response. In March 1858 Baldwin Walker called on Isaac Watts for the design of an armoured corvette of 5,600 tons to carry twenty-six large guns. In the same month there was a change of government and in June the Surveyor wrote to the First Lord, Pakington, using the passage quoted in the Introduction which, because of its significance, bears repetition:

Although I have frequently stated that it is not in the interests of Great Britain – possessing as she does so large a navy – to adopt any important change in the construction of ships of war which might have the effect of rendering necessary the introduction of a new class of very costly vessels, until such a course is forced upon her by the adoption by foreign powers of formidable ships of a novel character requiring similar ships to cope with them, yet it then becomes a matter not only of expediency, but of absolute necessity … This time has arrived.[2]

Conception

In July 1858 the Board set aside funds for the building of an armoured screw frigate. On 27 November, the Surveyor was directed to prepare a design for 'a wooden steam man of war to be cased in wrought iron 4½ inches thick'. Provision was made in the 1859 estimates for the sum of £252,000 for the building of two such ships by contract.[3]

Even though the Board minute specified a wooden hull, it does not appear that the Surveyor's department ever considered this material. Isaac Watts's first proposal was for an iron-hulled ship, but with thick timber backing for its armour. There is no clear evidence on who made the decision in favour of an iron hull, but all concerned would have been aware that the longer and

'A Design for building an Iron Frigate of 36 Guns & 1250 HP, having 214 feet of its length covered on the outside with Armour Plates of 4½ inches in thickness.' Design draught, dated 1 March 1859, for the ship that became *Warrior*. (© National Maritime Museum J8608)

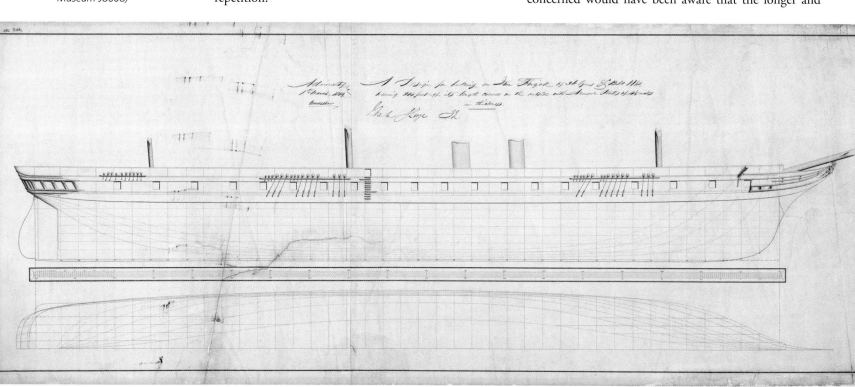

Warrior soon after completion when her funnels had been raised. Note that she flies the Red Ensign. (© *National Maritime Museum N00298*)

more powerful wooden ships were showing signs of weakness, and that a stronger hull was needed to take the weight and forces of *Warrior*'s machinery and armour.

The Board received Watts's design in January 1859 and decided to circulate it to eight private firms skilled in iron shipbuilding and to the master shipwrights, inviting them to propose alternatives to Watts's design. They were asked to propose a warship with 4½in armour capable of carrying a specified load which included thirty-six guns mounted at least 9ft above the waterline and 12ft apart (later increased to 15ft). The speed was to be at least 13½ knots with coal for seven days at full power; stability was to be adequate both fully laden and with all the coal and stores used up.

Iron hulls were to be preferred, but proposals for wooden ships would be considered. In this case the armour belt was to be complete from end to end, while for iron hulls it was suggested that the belt should cover the battery amidships and be terminated by armour bulkheads, provided that the ends were well subdivided and that the bow was strong enough for ramming. The required load was made up as follows:

Payload required	Tons
Water	124
Provisions and slops	119
Officers, men and effects (total 550)	75
Masts, rigging and sails	189
Anchors and cables	121
Armament	388
Stores, spares, etc	145
Total	1,161

Coals were to be provided on the basis of 10lb/NHP/hr. The tender was to state:

a. Weight of hull
b. Weight of armour
c. Weight of engines, boilers, spare gear, etc.

Fifteen proposals were submitted and these were forwarded to the Board in April 1859, together with Watts's detailed comments. He thought that none of them was as good as his original design and the supporting arguments convinced the Board. Watts's objections were quite specific, and appear fully justified in the light of today's knowledge. One or two were too big, some had underestimated the hull weight, stability was insufficient and power estimates were inadequate.[4] It was a very professional review, and made it clear that Watts and his assistant, Large (1st SNA), together with Lloyd, knew precisely what was necessary to meet the Board requirements.

Scott Russell claims that he was co-designer of the *Warrior*.[5] This claim is based on a design which he submitted to Baldwin Walker in 1855 for an iron-hulled, armoured ship[6] and on his response to the 1859 competition. Watts saw his later design as lacking in strength and having stern lines that were too full for good flow into the propeller. Scott Russell deserves great credit for his persistent campaign for the armoured battleship, but *Warrior* was not his design. His claim was formally rejected by the Admiralty in a letter dated 17 June 1859. The contribution of Large is less clear. Most of the design drawings were signed by him rather than by Watts, a very unusual feature. It may merely reflect a

1. J Chantriot, 'La Frégate Cuirasse la *Gloire*', *Marine et Technique au XIXe siècle*, Paris (1987).
2. Select Committee 1861.
3. J P Baxter, *The Introduction of the Ironclad Warship*, Harvard (1933; reprint Archon 1968).
4. Select Committee 1861.
5. J Scott Russell, *A Modern System of Naval Architecture*, London (1865), p652.
6. G S Emerson, *John Scott Russell*, London (1977).

temporary illness of Watts, but it may mean that Large played a major role in the design. Large was the last graduate from the first school and an early vice president of the new Institution of Naval Architects.

Isaac Watts

Isaac Watts, Chief Constructor of the Navy, responsible for the design of the *Warrior*, is a little-known character. He was born at the end of the eighteenth century and entered the School of Naval Architecture in 1814. He became a foreman at Portsmouth in 1833 and probably stayed there until promotion to master shipwright at Sheerness in May 1847. Twelve months later, he became Assistant Surveyor and later Chief Constructor.

Watts described his method of working to the Parliamentary Commission of 1861[7] as follows:

> When a drawing is prepared, and in fact, during the progress of the drawing being prepared, I have frequent communications with the Controller on the subject. I consult with him many times during the course of its construction, and also consult with my fellow constructor [Large] and occasionally with the Chief Engineer [Lloyd] if it is a question out of the ordinary course; for instance, in the building of the iron cased frigate *Warrior* we had communication repeatedly with regards to the arrangements to be made.

Watts seems to have been an autocrat – as are most successful designers. He told the commission that there was not much advantage in consulting 'practical men' and little value in outside advice. Evidence to the same commission from the master shipwrights, many of them fellow students of the school, made it clear that they would not consider offering criticism or suggesting alterations to a design by Watts – he would not like it!

Thomas Lloyd said of the plans for a new ship, 'They would be drawn up by the Chief Constructor and probably after consultation with myself, but the Controller, of course, would be consulted throughout, and the information would be sent to the Board by him.' Of his contacts with Watts he said, 'We meet daily, and consult about every matter which requires consultation'.

Watts and Large developed their design, which was approved by the Board on 29 April 1859. There were some last-minute worries over what was regarded as the excessive cost of the new ships, but orders were placed for two ships on 6 May. The contractors were the companies which were judged to have submitted the two best entries in the design competition, Thames Iron Works and Napiers.

Watts made it plain that the length was determined by the armament requirements and was not aimed at speed. The gun ports were to be 9ft above the waterline and 15ft apart for ease of working, nineteen ports on the main deck, the battery would be 285ft long. The ends of

Warrior, simplified profile, upper and gun decks.

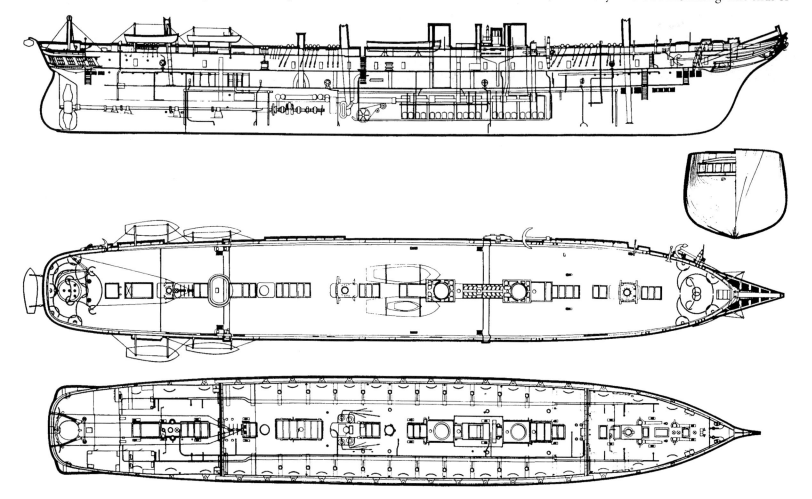

the battery were not armoured, as it was believed that heavy weights near the bow and stern would cause heavy pitching. The idea was sound in principle, but the weight involved would have made no noticeable difference. The armoured battery was closed by 4½in bulkheads and the side belt extended a little beyond them, covering 213ft of the hull from 6ft below the waterline to 21ft above. Two guns each side, forward and aft of the belt, were unprotected, as were two other big guns and the 40pdrs on the upper deck; a strange decision in the light of contemporary views of the danger of unarmoured iron hulls.

The unarmoured ends were well subdivided, with four transverse bulkheads ahead of the armour and two abaft. Flooding of the two ends would have admitted 1,070 tons of water and increased the draught by 26in (a later calculation says 43in, with a remaining metacentric height of 2.6ft).[8] Such flooding would not have seriously reduced her fighting capability, though the lack of protection to the steering gear was a weak feature. The armour covered the two boiler rooms, shell room and engine room, and the two magazines at each end of the machinery were further protected by water tanks.

Warrior had a partial double bottom and watertight

Table 14.2 *Warrior*

Displacement	9,180 tons
Dimensions	420ft (oa), 380ft (pp) x 58ft x 26ft 4in forward, 26ft 10in aft
Machinery	1 shaft. Penn trunk. 10 boilers. 5,270ihp = 14.0 knots at 50rpm. Coal 853 tons
Armament	Design: Forty 68pdr, SB
	As completed: Ten 110pdr, RBL Twenty-six 68pdr, SB Four 40pdr, RBL
Complement	705

wing bulkheads which should have given her added protection against underwater damage, though there were a number of watertight doors, low down, which seriously reduced the effectiveness of this subdivision.

Developing the armour for *Warrior*

Warrior was the culmination of the trends discussed in earlier chapters with screw propulsion, an iron hull and armour. Of these the most novel was the armour.[9] Since

Gloire, as completed in 1860 with a light fore-and-aft rig. The wooden two-decker *Donawerth* astern is included to point up the radical nature of the *Gloire*. (© *National Maritime Museum PY0973*)

7. Select Committee 1861.

8. Sir W E Smith, Manuscript Work Books, National Maritime Museum.

9. D K Brown, 'Developing the armour for HMS *Warrior*', *Warship* 40 (1986).

the end of the Crimean War there had been a number of tests of the use of armour to resist shot and shell, both on ships and for use in fortifications. In 1856 and 1857 tests were carried out at Woolwich against plates from different manufacturers to see if there was any difference in their power of resistance.[10] The gun used throughout these tests was a 68pdr/95cwt with a full charge of 16lb fired at 400yd and 600yd ranges. Both cast and wrought iron shot were used and there was one example of Martin's shell filled with molten iron. The 1856 series tested plates made by Bowling Iron, Parkhead Forge, Mare and Beale.

After twenty-two hits the whole 30 tons of target had been forced back by 3–4½ft. The cast iron shot were all broken into fragments which flew 100–150yds sideways and about 50yds to the rear. The wrought iron shot did not break and bounced back a few yards. The plates cracked and pieces were driven into the thick timber backing but there was no penetration of the target.

Iron plates by Swanfield, Beale and Chatham Dockyard were tried the next year, together with a steel plate by Begbie, which was only half the thickness (2in) of the iron plates. After thirty-eight hits by 68lb shot the target was a complete wreck and had been moved back 14in. One wrought iron shot had penetrated the target; there were other holes, but these were caused by several shots hitting the same spot. The contemporary report put the relative effectiveness of wrought to cast iron shot at 3 to 1. All the iron plates kept cast iron shot out at 600yds but were broken at 400yds.

The report also says, 'The experiments clearly show that Mr Begbie's steel plate is much inferior, offering no effectual resistance, the shot going clean through it and the backing'. On the face of it this comment is most unfair, since this plate was only half the thickness of the iron plates and was hit only once.

In October 1858 there were some test firings by the gun boat *Snapper* against a 4in iron plate fastened to the side of the old battleship *Alfred*. These tests showed that a single hit by a 68pdr would do as much damage to the plate, and much more to the planking and frames of the ship, than would five 32lb shot striking close together. Six 32lb shot hit an area 32in x 33in causing very little damage, while a single 68lb shot broke the plate, penetrated 2ft into the timbers and damaged a frame. The report put it more dramatically: 'It is not so much in the penetration that this difference is shown, as in the general shaking and bursting in of the ship's side.'

Finally, *Snapper* was brought within 20yds of the ship's side and hit with a 32lb, 68lb and 72lb shot, the first two being of cast and the last of wrought iron. The cast iron shot did not penetrate even at this close range,

10. Special Committee on Iron 1862.

Official midship section drawing of *Warrior* as built. (© National Maritime Museum J8629)

while the wrought iron shot went right through the ship's side, carrying with it a shower of splinters which hit the opposite side of the ship. It was concluded that a well-backed 4in plate would stop most practicable projectiles at fighting range.

The next trials, in October and November 1858, involved firing against the armour of two of the floating batteries, *Erebus* with an iron hull and *Meteor* with a wooden hull, and was intended to compare the effectiveness of the different materials in resisting the impact of shot. The *Erebus* had iron armour of 4in nominal thickness (probably rolled too thinly) over 5½in of oak. Its effectiveness was enhanced by sloping the side at 30 degrees to the vertical. Behind this was a ⅝in iron plate supported on iron frames. (From the drawings, these were 4½in deep, probably angle bars with 3in x 3in backing angle in a 'Z' shape.) The firing ship was again the *Snapper*, at 400yds, in the '1,200yd' creek at Fareham. The aiming point was in line with the main mast, between the ports and 2ft above the waterline.

The first hit was from a 32lb shot with a 10lb charge, which caused a dent and a few small cracks. A 68lb shot with a 16lb charge broke out a piece 11in x 12in, but did not penetrate. The side was bulged in over an area 3½ft x 3ft to a depth of 1¼ in. The second 68lb shot broke the lower corner of the plate, then broke up, and the fragment pierced the side. The inner skin was torn over an area of 2ft x 14in, a beam knee was broken and driven in 2ft and two frames were cracked. Many rivets and bolts were broken and 700 pieces of iron were picked up on the gun deck.

The *Meteor* fared much better. She also had a nominal 4in of iron backed by 6in oak. Behind this, the timbers were 10in deep, 4in apart, and filled in solid with another layer of oak behind this, 9in thick at the top, thinning to 4in at the bottom. The armour was attached by bolts with their heads countersunk into the armour and passing right through the side and lining, fastened by washers and nuts inside. *Snapper*'s first shot was from a 32pdr causing no significant damage. Three 68lb shot, one of which was of wrought iron, caused some cracking and a few pieces of armour were broken off. The shots themselves were broken but nothing penetrated the side. Two or three bolts were 'started', but did not break. The next day began with two 32lb shot which caused little damage. Two 68lb shot caused more extensive cracking of the armour and broke a bolt. The shots broke up and did not penetrate. Finally, a sand-filled shell was fired from the 68pdr with a 12lb charge at a range of 300yds, which did no harm.

The report says:

From the foregoing experiments, the advantage of the *Meteor* class of battery over the *Erebus* has been fully established. Throughout the experiments with the former, it does not appear that the damage inboard would at any time have proved seriously inconvenient to the men fighting the guns; whereas with the latter vessel, not only did the shot on one occasion penetrate her side,

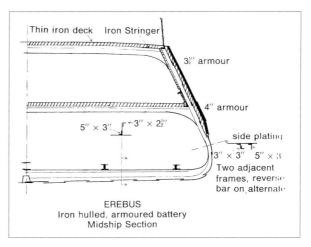

Midship section of *Erebus*, used for tests of armour protection.

scattering the fragments over the gun deck, but every hit, not penetrating, caused bolt heads and nuts to be scattered about the deck, doing apparently as much damage as a volley of grapeshot.

The value of a thick timber backing was apparent and due account was taken in the final design of *Warrior*'s armour system. Between 1858 and 1861 there were further tests of armour for ships and forts. In October 1858 a Whitworth 68lb, hexagonal bore, rifled gun was tested against another 4in wrought iron plate attached to the side of the *Alfred*. Both cast and wrought iron shot were used; the former broke up with little damage while the latter passed through both the plate and the 6–7in side planking. This trial was terminated when the gun 'burst with great violence' on the seventh round.

A Whitworth 80pdr was tried from *Stork* in January 1861 against a 4½in wrought iron plate attached to the side of the frigate *Sirius*. The plate was made by the Thames Iron Works and was identical to those made for *Warrior*. Three rounds were fired, of which only one hit the target plate, which was cracked by the blow, and the intact shot bounced back. This trial, too, was stopped as the gun was cracked.

There were still more trials with plates attached to the side of the frigate *Undaunted*. A more novel approach was the 'Jones' angular butt' in which 3½in and 4½in plates were arranged at an angle of 52 degrees to the vertical on the side of an old ship. The idea was to ensure that the shot would strike a glancing blow and be less able to penetrate. This is a feature of modern armour systems and the tests at Portsmouth confirmed the principle. Wrought iron plates resisted penetration but the steel plates failed. The damage to the supporting woodwork was much the same as with conventional plate armour. More tests at Shoeburyness in 1859–60 and against the sides of the battery *Trusty* confirmed that thin plates would break up shell, but 4¼in plate would stop all shot.

Special Committee on Iron

In January 1861 the War Office set up the Special Committee on Iron for both forts and ships. Its members were Captain Dalrymple Hays RN, chairman; Major Jervois RE; Brevet Colonel W Henderson RA; Dr Percy, Museum of Geology; W Fairbairn, shipbuilder; and Dr W Pole, a well-known civil engineer.

They were asked to carry out experiments to 'ascertain the thickness, size and weight of iron plates of a specified composition and manufacture that will resist shot of given shape, weight and material at given velocities, striking both directly and at given angles'. They were to study manufacture, chemical and physical properties, study previous tests and initiate new ones, interview witnesses, etc. They planned and carried through a very comprehensive research programme and, over a hundred years later, one can find nothing wrong, and very few omissions, in their work.

The committee began their work by measuring the physical properties of samples from many manufacturers. Tensile and compressive strength was measured both along and across the plate, as well as the energy to break a bar by sudden impact. The chemical composition was also determined. Witnesses were questioned,

Half mid-section model of *Warrior*'s structure and armour. (© *National Maritime Museum L0290-002*)

but these had either been involved in previous trials or had little to contribute, a clear indication that the earlier, less-organised trials were still comprehensive. It was generally accepted that there were no magic solutions in either material or configuration and that tough, soft iron plates, either hammered or rolled, were the best protection available.

The committee then set up a series of large-scale trials, the first aimed at fortifications but the later ones testing arrangements for ships. All four were possible arrangements for *Warrior*. The tests on the unsuccessful ones will be outlined before considering the final arrangement in a little more depth (for fuller detail of the other tests see the author's article quoted in footnote 9).

Roberts

This used plates 2ft wide set in adjoining Vs, was equivalent in weight to 5in conventional plate and was described as very expensive. The iron was of good quality and rarely cracked but *the supports broke* and the plates detached.

Fairbairn No 1

Fairbairn was not convinced of the need for wood backing and designed two targets without timber. The first was of 5in plates with tongue and grooved joints. It was hit by some thirteen shot with weights up to 200lb, 1,024lb in all, with little damage to the plates, frames or the skin behind. However, almost all *the securing bolts broke* and the target collapsed.

Fairbairn No 2

This was built from four plates, 4in thick, the larger plates being held on by fifteen 2in bolts and the smaller ones by eight similar bolts. Altogether, the target was hit by eighteen shot of up to 20lb, a total of 1,958lb. Only one shot penetrated, from an Armstrong 100pdr, but once again all the *bolts failed* and the target was useless.

The *Warrior* target

This was an exact replica in both material and construction of the side of the *Warrior* and was tested at Shoeburyness in October 1861. It was 20ft long and 10ft high, with a gun port in the middle built from plates by the Thames Iron Works made as for *Warrior*. They were manufactured from a mixture of two-thirds good, clean scrap iron bought in London and one-third newly puddled Yorkshire iron. The scrap was cleaned and the paint burnt off before being rolled into iron bars about 5in square. These bars were arranged with the new bars laid crossways before being forged into a plate about 12ft x 3ft. These plates were then forged together into larger plates and then hammered down into a plate 4½in thick under a Nasmyth steam hammer with a 4-ton blow.

These plates were bolted to two layers of 9in square teak beams arranged crossways. Behind this was the iron skin, ⅝in thick, and frames filled solid with more teak. The bolts were 1½ in in diameter with countersunk heads

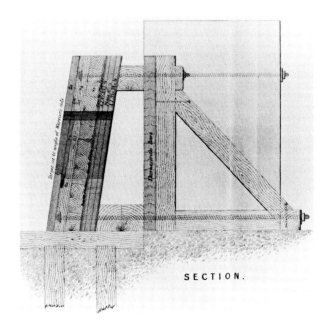

SECTION.

Table 14.3 Hits on the *Warrior* Target

Gun	Shot (lb)		Charge (lb)	No of hits
120pdr RML (Shunt)	140	Solid	20	2
100pdr Armstrong BL	110	Solid	14	6
100pdr Armstrong BL	104	Shell	12	6*
100pdr Armstrong BL	200	Solid	10	6
100pdr Armstrong BL	109	Solid steel	16	1
68pdr SB 95cwt & 112cwt	66¼	Solid	16	4
68pdr SB 95cwt & 112cwt	49½	Shell	16	4

*3 sand filled, 3 live

plished ... It was and will remain a remarkable illustration of the ability which is brought to bear in this country upon even the most novel and difficult mechanical problem as soon as the solution is felt to be necessary.[11]

The replica of *Warrior's* protection system as used in tests.

and two nuts on the inside, spaced about 15–18in apart.

A total of 3,229lb of shot and shell hit this target. The severity of the test was further increased by using three 100pdr guns which twice fired a salvo, the three 200lb solid shot impacting close together. Not one of these projectiles penetrated the target, the twenty-ninth and last coming nearest; a 109lb steel shot hit a spot which had been previously hit by three 200lb shot, three 100lb shot, three 100lb shells and two 49½lb shells – all in a space 3ft x 1½ft. This 109lb shot damaged a bolt and drove it back; the plate was dented by 3.3in but not pierced.

The committee report said:

Without at present expressing an opinion as to the absolute merits of this mode of construction, we must observe that this target has sustained a greater amount of firing with less injury than any other we have tried. The tongueing and grooving is, however, as we have previously stated, objectionable.

The committee's objections to tongue and groove joints was that an impact on one plate could damage the next one and that replacement of damaged plates would be very difficult. Many years later, Dr Pole summed up the work of the committee as follows:

And when it is considered how little knowledge there was when they began their work, and that when they finished they had left the system of armour both for sea and land defences fully and successfully proven ...

Rarely can a committee have done so well.

Sir Edward Reed said in 1866 that the *Warrior* scheme of protection was not a 'haphazard collection of parts', but was, on the contrary:

a highly skilful and scientific construction carefully designed in view of the object which had to be accom-

The strength of the *Warrior* scheme was fully proved but, with hindsight, there are a few things which could have been better. It was thought that the numerous trials had shown the need for thick wood backing and yet within a few years much thinner backing was found to be perfectly satisfactory. The real problem was in the method used to bolt the plates to the hull and the clue should have been apparent from the passages italicised in the reports of the earlier tests and, indeed, from the trial of *Erebus*, where bolt heads were lying around at the end.

The same problem occurred in the use of powerful steam pile drivers. If a bolt or a pile receives a sudden blow on one end, this will pass down the metal as a shock wave, compressing it. When the shock wave hits the free end, it will be reflected back up the bolt, but this time the metal is in tension. It is this reflected pull which breaks the bolt. The wooden backing merely gave some damping to the bolt, reducing the strength of the shock

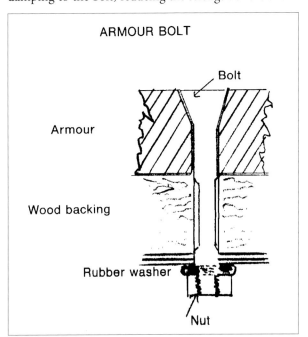

ARMOUR BOLT

Bolt

Armour

Wood backing

Rubber washer

Nut

11. Sir E J Reed, 'The *Bellerophon, Lord Warden* and *Hercules* targets', *Trans INA*, vol 7, London (1866).

A detail of the bolts used to hold the armour in place. It was failure of the bolts that was the weak point of many early armour arrangements.

wave. The French had identified this problem rather earlier and attached *Gloire*'s armour with wooden screws into the timber hull. The better solution was to fit tapped bolts into the back of the armour with no head exposed to the shock and once this was done, backing could be much reduced.

The other problem which was not discovered was the temperature effect, mentioned in Chapter 8, which makes wrought iron brittle under sudden loads at low temperatures (see also Appendix 9). The effect of temperature on brittle characteristics of metals was not really appreciated until the end of the Second World War, so one can hardly blame the committee for missing this point. *Warrior*'s armour was well able to do the job but it was unnecessarily heavy and costly.

Armament

The original intention was to fit a uniform armament of smooth bore 68pdrs, the best guns available, even though the tests showed that they would not have been able to penetrate *Gloire*'s armour. During construction the 110pdr Armstrong breech loader became available and seemed more powerful. They were fitted in place of the upper-deck 68pdrs and four more replaced six of the main deck battery. Later tests showed that the penetration of the Armstrong was inferior to that of the 68pdr.

Warrior abounded in novelty. Forced ventilation using steam-driven fans kept the pressure in the battery slightly higher than atmospheric in order to drive the smoke outboard. In the boiler room there was a small blast furnace making molten iron to fill Martin's shell. The shell was a hollow, cast iron sphere, lined with horsehair. Once filled with molten iron it was hoisted up the ventilation shaft to the gun deck and had to be fired within four minutes of filling, though tests at *Excellent* showed it remained as effective as a red-hot shot for an hour. Martin's shell was tested by the gun boat *Stork* against the old frigate *Undaunted* and proved very successful; indeed, Scott Russell and others were to say

A 110pdr Armstrong breech loader, as carried on *Warrior*'s upper deck. *(© National Maritime Museum A7087-019)*

that it was the Martin shell which caused the end of the wooden battleship. The furnace could fill thirty 8in shells an hour with 26lb of molten iron. (Fillings were 16lb for a 32pdr and 45lb for a 10in.)[12]

Machinery

Warrior had a two-cylinder Penn trunk engine which the Committee on Marine Engines regarded as the best engine available for larger powers. There was a jet condenser for each cylinder and double-acting air pumps worked off the pistons. The ten boilers were all of the box tubular type with the safety valve set at 22lb. Each boiler held 17 tons of sea water, had a fire grate of 900sq ft and a heating surface of 22,000sq ft. The engine room temperature would be 85–90°F and that of the stokehold, 100–115°F.

Table 14.4 **Machinery Particulars**

Cylinder, bore/stroke	112/48in
Max rpm, piston speed	54¼rpm, 434ft/sec
ihp	5,469
NHP	1,250
Endurance	1,420 miles at 12½ knots
	2,100 miles at 11 knots

Fuel consumption was about 3¾–5lb of coal per horsepower per hour. (Also given as 1¼ tons/hr cruising in a Force 6 wind.)

The funnels and waste steam pipes were telescopic and could be lowered for sailing. The draught was insufficient as completed and the funnels were increased in height by 6ft. (As reconstructed the ship has the original, low funnels.)

Sailing

With such a heavy consumption of coal, sails were essential for ocean voyages and *Warrior* was given 21,400sq ft of plain sail (48,400 with studding sails). This was thought inadequate for such a big ship, and the Controller asked for four or five masts, but in service *Warrior* proved fast under sail; trials in 1868 placed her fastest of the ironclads under plain sail on a wind, and she is said to have logged 13 knots under sail alone. Her great length made her slow in tacking and wearing.

When sailing, her funnels were lowered and the screw, which was connected to the shaft through a dog clutch, was hoisted. Her two-bladed, 26-ton Griffiths propeller was the largest hoisting screw ever made and needed six hundred men on a fourfold purchase to raise it.

Hull form, power and seakeeping

Watts, like most designers of the day, was influenced by Scott Russell's wave line theory. Though fallacious, this theory led to the use of fine ends which were, in fact, appropriate to *Warrior*'s speed and length. It is likely that Watts estimated the power required using the Admiralty

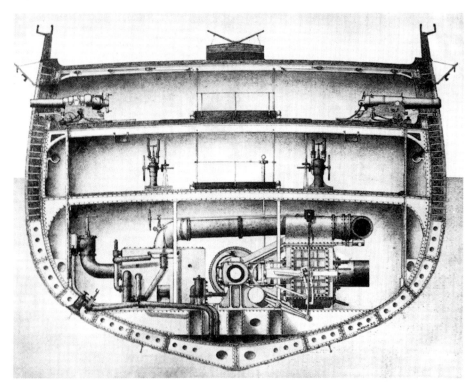

coefficient, with an appropriate value derived from similar ships with the same type of machinery. This approach was developed in the Steam Department at about the time *Warrior* was designed. While there is no evidence, it may well be that the Admiralty coefficient was developed for the novel *Warrior* and probably by Lloyd.

Section through *Warrior*'s engine room. Note the details of her trunk engine, the closely spaced bolts for the armour and the guns with a 68pdr on one side and, incorrectly, a 110pdr breech loader on the other. *(Science Museum)*

Despite early requests for four or more masts, *Warrior* was completed with the conventional rig of a three-masted ship and performed well under sail. *(© National Maritime Museum PU6222)*

$$\text{Admiralty coefficient} = \frac{(\text{displacement})^{2/3} \times (\text{speed})^3}{\text{ihp}}$$

Study of values of the coefficient for frigates with Penn trunk engines suggests a value of about 200 for *Warrior* at 13 knots, leading to a requirement for 5,200ihp. The

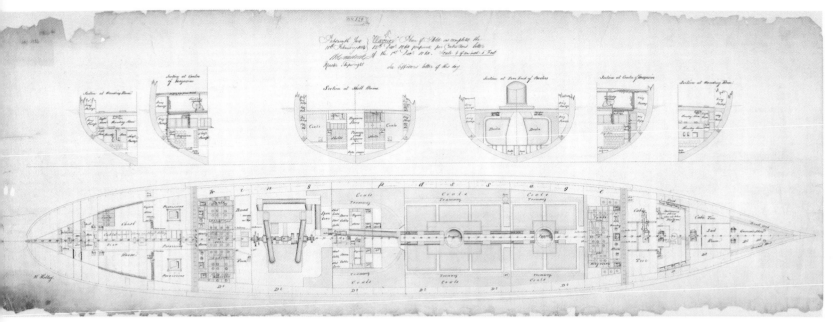

Plan of the hold, as fitted 1863, showing the layout of boilers and engines.
(© *National Maritime Museum J8595*)

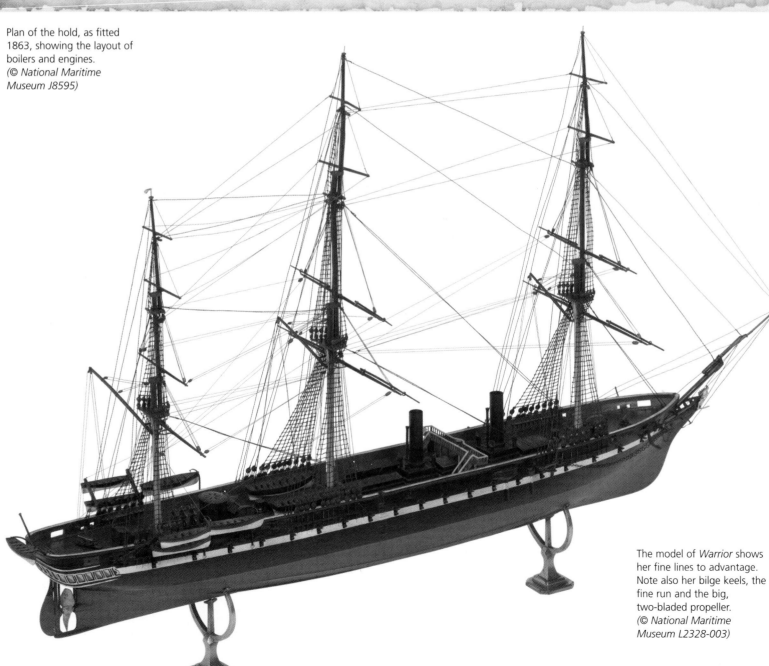

The model of *Warrior* shows her fine lines to advantage. Note also her bilge keels, the fine run and the big, two-bladed propeller.
(© *National Maritime Museum L2328-003*)

achieved speed of 14 knots seems to have been a bonus from a good hull form.

Seakeeping estimates have been made using a modern computer[13] and these show a performance in pitch and heave somewhat worse than that of a modern ship of the same length, possibly due to the very fine bow. Contemporary accounts describe her as lacking in buoyancy forward and say that she was a wet ship. In part, this must be due to the old-fashioned knee bow, close to the water and generating spray. She had small bilge keels which seem to have been effective as there were no complaints about rolling.

Warrior was a long and fairly deep ship with a rather small rudder; about half the area which would be provided in a modern ship of that size. The rudder was hand worked and took one and a half minutes to turn to its maximum angle of 25 degrees and in bad weather forty men were needed on the relieving tackles. The turning circle was about 1,000yds.

Structural design

Warrior's structure was typical of good iron shipbuilding practice using a mixture of longitudinal and transverse framing.[14] She was second in size only to the *Great Eastern* and by far the largest armoured ship. Novel in overall concept, Watts was rightly cautious in detail. Using modern methods, one may estimate a maximum stress of about 3½ tons/sq in in the upper deck and a factor of four against buckling. Since wrought iron was a somewhat variable material – most samples examined during the reconstruction had many small cracks formed when the plates were made – and there was no real evidence on the loading to be expected on such a long ship, these seem very reasonable figures.

Fairbairn's work on buckling in connection with the Britannia bridge had made engineers aware of the problem, but as yet there was no way to calculate the strength needed. Watts's lack of familiarity with iron construction is shown in the use of diagonal tie plates on the upper deck. These had been used to give rigidity (shear strength) to the decks of the big wooden ships, but were quite unnecessary on the rigid iron deck of *Warrior*.

Comparisons show that *Warrior*'s hull was heavy in relation to her dimensions and later ships improved in this aspect. However, most modern designers would commend Watts's caution in such a novel ship.

Accommodation

By the standards of previous ships, *Warrior* was extremely spacious. The men messed on the gun deck with a 7ft headroom and 15ft between each gun to give room for the mess table. The vast, uncluttered upper deck provided space for recreation in calm weather. She had what was probably the first laundry in a warship (with hand-cranked washing machines), still an unusual feature in Second World War British ships. Visitors to the ship today will see for themselves that considerable thought was given to the well-being of the crew and wonder how this care was reconciled with the continued use of flogging as a punishment.[15, 16]

The officers, too, were well catered for in the *Warrior* with spacious, though ill-lit, cabins and wardroom.

Building

The Thames Iron Works were paid £31 per ton for the hull, a total of £190,255, and Penn received £74,409 for making and installing the machinery. Payment was in five instalments and the contract included penalties if the ship was late. These penalties seem to have been waived when it was found that the task of building the great ship was more difficult than expected.

She was laid down at Blackwall on 25 May 1859 and launched on 29 December 1860, eight months behind the contract date. The engines were installed across the river in the Victoria docks and she was rigged in Chatham Dockyard. On 8 August she moved down the river, under her own power for the first time, and arrived at Portsmouth on 21 September. She was docked and given a fresh coat of Hay's anti-fouling paint before trials at Stokes Bay. The trials can be compared with later model tests carried out at the Admiralty Experiment Works in 1883, which confirm that she was a good

13. D K Brown and J G Wells, 'HMS *Warrior* – the design aspects', *Trans RINA*, vol 128, London (1986).

14. Ibid.

15. J G Wells, *The Immortal Warrior*, Emsworth (1987); A Lambert, *Warrior*, London (1987).

16. A Lambert, *Warrior* (1987).

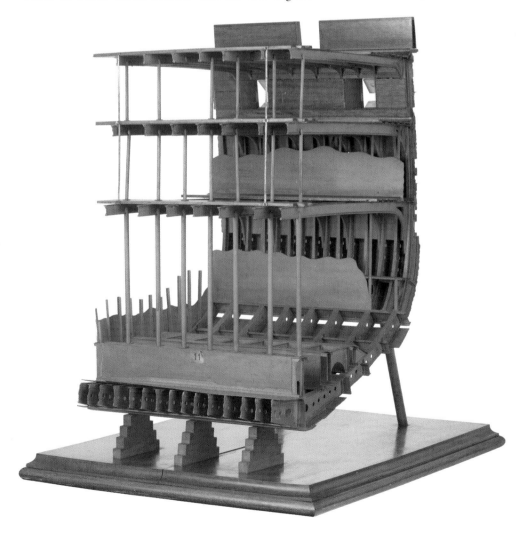

Warrior's structure was typical of the best practice of the day. Note the deep longitudinals within the double bottom. (© *National Maritime Museum L0417-002*)

Warrior returning to Portsmouth in June 1987. She brought together the main themes of this book: steam, screw, iron hull and armour and, in her designers, Watts and Lloyd, the final justification of the School of Naval Architecture. *(William Mowll)*

conventional design with no surprises. It can be deduced that the drag of the masts, spars and rigging amounted to about 15 per cent of the total resistance of the ship when steaming on a windless day, a figure consistent with that quoted earlier for the loss of speed due to masts, etc.[17]

Apotheosis

Warrior was a revolutionary ship, but she was also the end of the evolution described in this book. Iron hulls, the screw propeller and armour had at last come together in a comprehensive and effective ship design. Her guns were bigger by far than those commonly used in the wars of 1793–1815 and could fire a variety of projectiles. Her very novelty condemned her to a short active life as new technical changes, triggered by her success, soon made her obsolete. By 1872 she was largely confined to harbour service until a century later, in 1979, the generosity of the Manifold Trust made it possible to restore her to the days of her glory, a monument to the sailors, politicians and engineers who had made the Navy's industrial revolution possible.

The Admiralty, naval and civilian, was far from the reactionary organisation so often portrayed. The work of Seppings, developed by Lang and Edye, enabled the wooden ship to double in size. It made possible Edye's *Agamemnon* class, one of the great designs of all time, and the even bigger *Victoria*, designed by Watts, who also designed some very big wooden frigates before turning to iron for *Warrior*. Steam propulsion was developed in commercial service, but the Admiralty was an interested and careful observer, and as soon as the

weights of machinery and coal were reduced sufficiently, they started to build steamships.

Commanders-in-chief were enthusiastic about their new paddle ships, which were developed into effective warships. As Lloyd pointed out, the Admiralty actively nurtured many of the improvements in machinery and auxiliaries. This policy of encouraging developments was applied to Pettit Smith's screw propulsion, though not to Ericsson, who spoke to the wrong man.

Iron hulls became possible because the Admiralty solved the problem of correcting the magnetic compass for the effects of the iron. Unarmoured iron ships were adopted somewhat over-enthusiastically by the Navy until tests showed the real problems of wrought iron plates. These and later tests were thoughtfully planned and carefully carried out, eventually leading to the armoured ship.

The big building programme of the Crimean War and the postwar steam battleship programme was efficiently and economically managed. It is too often forgotten that the Navy was short of money and other resources throughout this period, except during the war. Of course, there were a few mistakes and a few individuals who were obstructive, but an organisation which could move from the fleet of 1815 to *Warrior* in 1860 was one which must have been basically sound, capable and enthusiastic.

In particular, one can regard *Warrior* as marking the overdue vindication of the School of Naval Architecture. Her designers, Watts and Large, and the Chief Engineer, Lloyd, were graduates of the school, while others held the majority of master shipwright posts, and some had achieved success outside the Admiralty.

16. A Lambert, *Warrior* (1987).
17. Brown & Wells, op cit.

Appendices

Horsepower

Power is the rate at which work is done. A man who weighs 200lb climbing 10ft does 2,000ft-lb of work. If he takes 5 seconds, the power exerted is 2,000 divided by 5 = 400ft-lb/sec. James Watt claimed that the power which a draught horse could exert was 550ft-lb/sec (about twenty times the sustained power of a man). Other engine builders had different definitions but, by 1815, Watt's version was generally accepted. His horse seems to have been a weakling, but the low figure used for the power of the horse helped to make the steam engine more impressive.

Nominal Horsepower

In the early nineteenth century it was not easy to measure the actual power of a steam engine and as a result a nominal horsepower (NHP) was defined, based on the geometry of the engine. The formula for NHP used in ships was:

$$NHP = \frac{7 \times \text{area of piston} \times \text{equivalent piston speed}}{33,000}$$

For paddle ships the piston speed was taken as:

$$129.7 \times (\text{stroke})^{1/3.35}$$

This leads to the following relationship between stroke and piston speed:

Stroke (ft)	Piston speed (ft/sec)
3	180
4	196
5	210
6	221
7	231
8	240
9	248

For the nominal power to equal the actual power it would be necessary for the mean steam pressure in the cylinder during the stroke to be 7lb/sq in and for the piston speed to be that given in the table. In the earliest days, the formula was reasonably accurate, but as engines improved and, in particular, ran faster, the real power departed more and more from the nominal power. Nominal horsepower, being derived from the size of the engine, proved to be a good guide to price.

Indicated horsepower

Early in the nineteenth century an instrument was developed, called an 'indicator', which could draw a graph of pressure against piston movement during one stroke of the engine. From this, the power available in the steam could be calculated from the area of the graph. This power in the steam is called the indicated horsepower (ihp). (Modern practice is to use lower case letters for horsepower, eg ihp, shp. In the nineteenth century capitals were used and this convention is used here for NHP to distinguish it from real power.)

Shaft horsepower

Shaft horsepower (shp) is that actually transmitted to the propeller by the shaft and is much less than the indicated power. The power of the steam has to overcome friction inside the engine and drive the engine's own auxiliaries such as the air pump. Froude[1] and White[2] both divide friction into 'dead load friction', constant at all speeds due to the weight of the moving parts, tightness of the piston packing, friction of the shaft bearings, etc, and the 'working friction', varying with the thrust developed and with the speeds of engine and ship.

Froude, writing in 1876, suggests that each component was about 14.3 per cent of the shp. White in 1900, based on more trials of later and more efficient ships, suggested that dead load friction was 5–9 per cent of the ihp (*Iris* dead load 8 per cent at 18 knots, 30 per cent at 9 knots). White had no direct information on working friction and accepts Froude's assumption that it was of the same order as dead load at full speed.

Overall, White suggests that in the later ships, shp is about 80–85 per cent of ihp, but he does not include the power needed to drive the air pump. For *Warrior*, with Penn trunk engines, it seems that shp was about 75 per cent of the ihp. As suggested in the next section, this may be too high a percentage for earlier, less efficient engines.

Thrust horsepower

This is the power put out by the propeller and differs from the shaft power by the hydrodynamic losses of the propeller and the effects of the interaction of flow between hull and propeller.

The relationship between ihp and NHP

Figures for the early ships are hard to find and those which are available show no consistent trend.

1. W Froude, 'On the ratio of indicated to effective horsepower as indicated by Mr Denny's measured mile trials at varied speeds', *Trans INA*, vol 17 (1876).

2. W H White, *Manual of Naval Architecture*, London (1900).

Table A1.1 **Power of Early Steamships**

Ship	Engine builder	NHP	ihp	ihp/NHP
Dee	Maudslay	200	272	1.36
Rhadamanthus	Maudslay	220	400	1.82
Locust	Maudslay	100	157	1.57
Porcupine	Maudslay	132	285	2.16
Jackall	Napier	150	455	3.03
Harpy	Penn	200	520	2.6
Spitfire	Butterly	140	380	2.7

Too much should not be read into the apparently low ratio for Maudslay's engines; in general they relate to an earlier generation of engine and reflect Maudslay's earlier use of the indicator.

There are more data available for early screw ships, as the Admiralty frequently published tables of speed trial results. For a large number of Penn trunk engines the ratio ihp to NHP is 3.8 (standard deviation 0.45). The high pressure engines of the Crimea gun boats are excluded as they were four-cylinder engines. Some of the first trunk engines had very low ratios and these too have been omitted. There is a slight increase in the ratio for the very largest engines, most noticeable between 400–800NHP. The gun boat engines had ratios of about 4 to 5.

For thirty-four Maudslay engines of the same era, the value of ihp to NHP had a mean of 3.8 (standard deviation 0.67). Sufficient data from other builders are not available for a full analysis, but what there is suggests results of the same order as that of Maudslay and Penn. The Admiralty's claim to the 1859 Committee on Marine Engines that there was little to choose in performance between the leading builders seems well justified.

Note: The French navy used the same definition of NHP as that used in Britain,[3] but it seems likely that their earlier engines, at least up to *Napoleon,* produced less shaft power than British engines of the same NHP.

3. Dupuy de Lôme, unpublished report of his visit to Britain in 1855. My thanks are due to M R Estienne for giving me a copy.

Appendix 2
The Work of Colonel Beaufoy

Colonel Beaufoy was sponsored by the Society for the Improvement of Naval Architecture to carry out a long series of model tests, which it was hoped would lead to an understanding of the nature of ship resistance and the development of a form of minimum resistance. He had previously conducted some small-scale experiments on the resistance of bodies of various shapes. In 1793 William Wills, a member of the society, made the Greenland Dock at Deptford available for very much larger-scale tests (see map in Chapter 12). Initially, the length of run was 300ft, reduced in a later series to 160ft, while the models were 30–42ft long. The models were pulled by a tow rope from a falling weight which applied a constant force. The steady speed was measured by an ingenious automatic apparatus.

There were some 173 runs in 1793–4, which Beaufoy discarded as unreliable. Up to November 1795 he carried out a further 776 successful runs. After a break in testing, there were 895 more successful runs between September 1796 and October 1798. The results were published by the society in 1800 and republished by Beaufoy in Thomson's *Annals of Philosophy* in 1814. A very full account was published in 1834, after Beaufoy's death, by his son.

A recent re-examination of Beaufoy's work by Dr Tom Wright (Science Museum) has shown that his experimental techniques were excellent, and that his measurements of frictional drag were in close agreement with those made by Froude seventy years later. Beaufoy's numerical analysis was based on work by Charles Hutton, and appears to be sound. His breakdown of resistance is that proposed by the Earl of Stanhope in 1795 who suggested the following components:

a. Friction due to water rubbing along the surface of the ship.
b. The algebraic sum of the added pressure at the bow and that at the stern.

While this division is reasonably sound, it does not bring out explicitly the changes of pressure associated with the generation of waves. Beaufoy was aware of this component, but in his later tests attempted to eliminate it by running his models submerged. There is no indication that Beaufoy had any clear idea of how to use his data to estimate the resistance of a full-size ship. For this reason his work must be seen as a fascinating dead end, as were the earlier, and less satisfactory, experiments of d'Alembert, Condorcet and Bussut in 1775.

Beaufoy experimented further to verify Bouguer's work on stability at small angles and Attwood's large angle theories; the results were reported in 1816.

(This appendix is largely based on Dr Wright's PhD thesis and I am grateful to him for permission to use it.)

Appendix 3
Cost

Introduction

It is difficult, even today, to define the real cost of a warship with accuracy. Which components of cost are used? Do they include stores and ammunition? The value of money changes with time; we are used to inflation, but for most of the period of this book there was considerable deflation. The price index fell by nearly a half between 1810 and 1845. There was less awareness of this changing value of money than there is today, and many contemporary papers either confuse incompatible cost figures from different dates, or fail to attach a date to the figures they quote. Finally, there is the vexed question of overheads. How much of the total cost of running a dockyard and its storehouses should be added to the direct cost of building a ship?

Time and Cost

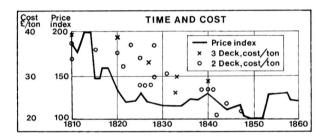

The accompanying graph shows as a solid line the way in which average prices varied in Britain between 1810 and 1860. Superimposed on this line are points marking the cost per ton of three- and two-deckers built during the period taken from the 1847 Select Committee report. It is clear that the cost of ships broadly follows the trend of general prices. There is an indication that three-deckers were a little more expensive per ton than the two-deckers, and a partial explanation will be given later. There is no sign that either Seppings's or Symonds's ships were more expensive than the normal trend, despite claims by their opponents. The terms used are not defined in the report, but comparison with other figures suggests that 'cost' is that of the hull alone and that the tons are weight and not builder's measurement.

Breakdown of ship costs

There are a few tables published in which the cost is broken down by the part of ship. An example from one such table is given in Table A3.1. It provides a nice warning on time variation. It was published by G Harvey in 1849[1] and might be thought to apply to the late 1840s, particularly as many of the tables are taken from the reports of the Chatham Committee. However, the figures were copied from a book by John Edye published in 1829[2] and were long out of date when Harvey used them.

Table A3.1 **Cost Breakdown 1829**

(Cost figures given in thousands of pounds.)

Number of guns	Labour	Material	(Total hull)	Masts/ Yards	Rig Blocks	'Furniture and sea stores'	Grand Total	Cost per gun
120	15.6	77.8	(93.4)	3.9	3.0	16.8	117.1	0.98
80	12.0	58.3	(65.3)	3.5	3.0	15.1	86.9	1.09
74	9.6	48.8	(58.4)	3.0	2.7	12.4	76.5	1.03
52	7.1	29.6	(36.7)	2.6	2.0	9.5	50.8	0.98
46	5.9	22.2	(28.1)	1.5	1.7	7.9	39.2	0.85
28	3.5	12.1	(15.6)	0.7	0.8	4.4	21.5	0.77

Table A3.2 **Screw Ship Cost Breakdown**

(Cost figures given in thousands of pounds.)

Ship	Hull	Spars & rig	Engines	Total	Annual running cost
Warrior	286	21	76	383	
Duke of Wellington	106	19	46	172	70
Agamemnon	91	16	37	144	58
Orlando	104	17	66	188	46
Euryalus	56	13	26	95	37

Note the very high cost of the giant frigates such as *Orlando* and the enormous jump to *Warrior*.

It is likely that the proportion of the costs did not vary greatly with time. There are further complications because the hull was often finished and laid up for many years before it was outfitted. The 'outfit' would then be supplied at a different price index from that for the hull. It seems that 'furniture and sea stores' includes the guns and their mounts, though this is not certain; whether it includes ammunition is unknown.

Some figures given by Scott Russell in the early 1860s show a somewhat similar breakdown for screw ships including the *Warrior*.[3]

Breakdown of dockyard costs

Table A3.3 **Hull Costs**

(Cost figures given in thousands of pounds.)

Type	Tons	Building Labour	Building Material	Outfit Labour	Outfit Material	Total
Liner	3,716	22.5	65.6	5.6	10.9	104.6
Steam frigate	3,353	21.5	53.5	5.4	8.9	89.3
Corvette	1,623	11.5	25.5	2.9	4.3	44.2

Costs reported by the dockyards were broken down into labour costs, the wages paid to the men working directly on the ship, and material costs of timber, etc, worked into the ship, including wastage. Scott Russell's book gives some figures for this breakdown of hull cost.

It was customary to take the wage rates paid per ton as varying with the rate of the ship. Some of Edye's 1829 figures illustrate the point:

1. G Harvey, *Naval Architecture*, Glasgow (1849).

2. J Edye, *A Constructor's Guide*, London (1829).

3. J Scott Russell, *Naval Architecture*, London (1862).

Table A3.4 **Wage Rates per Ton**

Number of guns	120	80	74	52	46
Rate per ton for:					
Shipwrights	4.67	4.13	4.36	4.00	5.55
Caulkers	0.25	0.20	0.20	0.17	0.19
Joiners	0.63	0.55	0.55	0.31	0.37
Smiths	0.37	0.33	0.32	0.32	0.38
Painters	0.09	0.08	0.08	0.07	0.08
Total	6.01	5.29	5.51	4.87	6.57

Overheads

Inevitably, there are a large number of costs incurred in building a ship which are not included in the breakdown into direct labour and materials. For dockyard-built ships, such costs were fully reported to Parliament, but under a different vote heading. While almost all ships were built in the dockyards it did not matter that these overhead costs were not attributed to individual ships, but the topic became important in comparing the cost of dockyard-built ships with those built in commercial yards. The issue was explored in 1867 in a correspondence between Mr Seely MP and the Admiralty.[5]

A longer selection of the costs making up these overheads is given in a note at the end of this appendix but, broadly, they include the pay of men not directly working on the ship, managers, storekeepers, those drawing sick pay, the cost of providing buildings and machinery, and the cost of providing services such as mooring. To this has to be added interest on the capital value of the yard. Seely took 1860–1 as an example and built up figures as follows:

Capital value	*£000*
Ships in hand	5,000
Plant and machinery	2,000
Ships building	3,516
Ships converting	772
Total	11,288

At 5 per cent, the interest on this is £564,000 pa. Other costs, taken from the published estimates were:

Overheads	*£000*
Interest	564
Wages of foremen, rent, cost of gas	328
Pensions	60
Cost of Admiralty officers	80
Moorings, cables, buoys	311
Total	1,343

Since the direct cost of the ships built was £2,966,000, the percentage overhead rate is 1,343 divided by 2,966, or 45 per cent. A modern accountant would look hard at depreciation rates, but his answer should be of the same order. Since the direct cost of the hulls of dockyard-built ships was £35 per ton, the full cost must have been about £50 per ton. Seely quotes £32 per ton for commercially-built warships, but his figures come from the early 1840s and should be increased to allow for the inflation of the Crimean War. Even so, it looks as though the dockyard ships were quite considerably more expensive. In part, this was because the yards had to keep a large war reserve of stores and of capacity.

It was also suggested by Barry, in a rather biased account, that the dockyards were inefficient.[5] He claimed that the yards used highly paid skilled men on jobs which could be done by unskilled labour, but this could be defended on the argument that the skilled men were part of the war reserve. Barry also claimed that the yards would keep a gang together and use twenty men when two or three could do the job. There were several searching enquiries into the yards in this period and, with a very few exceptions, Parliament was satisfied.

Summary

The make-up of cost, its variation with time and the way in which overheads were applied (or not) form many traps for the unwary. Comparisons are almost impossible to make, but it is clear that the full cost of a warship was some 50 per cent higher than the figures usually quoted.

Note on overheads
Cables, buoys, mooring hawsers
Opening dock gates
Landing and issuing stores
Collecting old timber
Preservation of timber
Cranes, workers' barrows
Fire engines
Chapel
Wages of boat crews, apprentices, police, men hurt, holiday pay
Sweeping chimneys
Stores, slipways, screws
Salaries

4. Correspondence – Seely – Admiralty, Parliament (1867).
5. P Barry, *Dockyard Economy and Naval Power*, London (1863).

Appendix 4
Building Programme, Sailing Ships

For each year, the line-of-battle ships launched that year are named below (number of guns in brackets) and the numbers of frigates and corvettes summarised. (Steamships are dealt with in the appropriate chapter.) This list should be used with caution, particularly in the later years. As far as possible, only ships completed without engines are given. No account is taken of conversion from one rate to another, eg the 74s razéed to frigates. (See *British Warships in the Age of Sail 1817–1863* by Rif Winfield for complete details.)

1815	*Howe* (120), *St Vincent* (120), *Cambridge* (80), *Defence* (74), *Hercules* (74), *Redoutable* (74), *Wellesley* (74), 1–52
1816	*Black Prince* (74), *Minotaur* (74), *Pitt* (74), *Wellington* (74), 2–46, 1–44,1–26
1817	*Agincourt* (74), *Melville* (74), 1–46, 1–26
1818	*Bellerophon* (80), *Malabar* (74), *Talavera* (74), 1–26
1819	*Belleisle* (74), 1–50, 4–46
1820	*Britannia* (120), *Camperdown* (106), *Hawke* (74), 1–52, 3–46, 1–28
1821	*Ganges* (82), 3–46, 1–28
1822	2–52, 2–46, 2–28
1823	*Prince Regent* (120), *Carnatic* (74), 1–52, 2–46, 3–28
1824	*Asia* (84), *Vengeance* (84), 1–46, 1–28
1825	*Formidable* (84), 1–44, 1–28
1826	*Powerful* (84), 1–44
1827	*Clarence* (84), 2–44
1828	*Royal Adelaide* (120), *Bombay* (84), 3–46
1829	1–52, 4–46
1830	4–46
1831	*Calcutta* (84), *Thunderer* (84), 1–28, 1–26
1832	*Neptune* (120), *Monarch* (84), 1–50, 1–36, 2–28
1833	*Royal William* (120), *Waterloo* (120), *Rodney* (82), 1–46, 1–26
1834	1–36
1835	*Vanguard* (80)
1836	1–36, 1–26
1837	1–28
1838	–
1839	*Queen* (100), *Nile* (92), *Indus* (80)
1840	*St George* (120), *London* (92), 1–46, 1–26
1841	*Trafalgar* (120), *Collingwood* (80), *Hindustan* (80), 1–36, 1–26
1842	*Albion* (90), *Goliath* (80), *Superb* (80), *Cumberland* (70)
1843	2–50,1–26
1844	*Centurion* (80), *Boscawen* (70), 1–36, 2–26
1845	1–50, 1–36, 2–26
1846	1–50, 1–36
1847	*Lion* (80), 1–36
1848	3–50
1849	2–50

Appendix 5
The Design of Wooden Warships

Introduction

The reports of the Chatham Committee, together with a few other references, form an excellent do-it-yourself guide to the design of a nineteenth-century wooden warship, though, with modern knowledge, it is possible to improve their procedures in some aspects. The collection and arrangement of accurate data is essential to design and in this task the graduates at the School of Naval Architecture excelled, as did John Edye.

Weight of the hull

The ship was normally launched as a bare and empty hull, with no masts, guns or equipment. If the draughts at which the hull floats after launch are measured, it is a fairly simple, if time-consuming, task to calculate the buoyancy of the immersed portion of the hull. Since the weight equals buoyancy, the weight of the bare hull is known. The Chatham naval architects scaled weights obtained in this way from several ships to the dimensions of the new design to estimate its hull weight.

They seem to have scaled on the basis of the product of the dimensions, ie:

$$W_H = \text{constant} \times L \times B \times D$$

where

W_H = weight of bare hull
L = length
B = beam
D = depth
T = draught

This gives satisfactory results only if the dimensions of the new ship are close to those whose weights are used. A rather better scaling factor, which might be used today, is given by:

$$W_H = \frac{L \times B + B \times D + L \times D}{a} + b$$

where a and b are constants. A considerable number of ships are plotted in this form on the accompanying graph and the values of the constants found.

For two-deckers, a = 8.7 and b = 100.
For frigates, a = 8.7 and b = 215.

Notes:
1. Fir-built frigates do not lie on the same line.
2. The data are insufficient for three-deckers but a = 8.7 and b = 446 seems possible.
3. The fact that the data fits (L x B + L x D + B x D) shows that the hulls were structurally inefficient.
4. The weights of ships designed by Seppings and Symonds do not stand out from others, despite allegations by their opponents.
5. Articles by Gardiner suggest that French ships were considerably lighter than British ships. Unfortunately, none of the classic French books on naval architecture gives weights, casting further doubt on their alleged scientific methods. Seppings says[1] that a French Third Rate would be 380 tons lighter than the corresponding British design. In a total weight of some 1,500 tons this is an enormous difference and seems unlikely.
6. For the statistician, the fractional error (error/true value) in the graph has a standard deviation of 0.05, ie the error is 5 per cent or less in two-thirds of the sample, a very good agreement.
7. Two-deckers, razéed to frigates, still lie on the 'two-decker line' if the new depth is used, reflecting their heavy scantlings.

1. R Seppings, letter to *United Services Journal*, 1830.
2. J Edye, *A Constructor's Guide*, London (1829).
3. G Harvey, *Naval Architecture*, Glasgow (1849).

Hull materials

The hull was mainly, but not entirely, timber. Edye (1829), gives the breakdown shown in Table A5.2.[2]

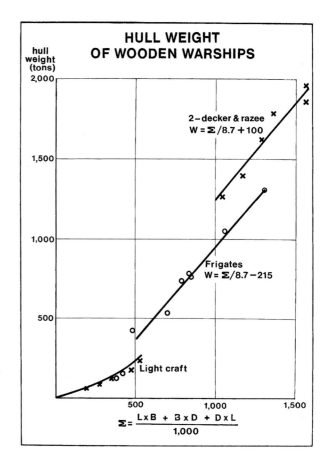

It is surprising that the hull weight was never calculated directly by working out the weight of each component and adding them together. This is a simple, though time-consuming, task and could have been carried out by one man in a few weeks. Table A5.1[3] gives the weights of different timbers.

Table A5.1 **Timber Weights**

Names of timber		Green (lb oz)		Seasoned (lb oz)	
English oak		71	10	43	8
Dantzic oak		49	14	36	0
African teak		63	12	60	10
Indian teak,	Malabar	–	–	52	15
green or seasoned,	Rangoon	–	–	26	4
about the same					
Indian mast peon		48	3	36	0
Cedar		32	0	28	4
Larch		45	0	34	4
Riga fir		48	12	35	8
New England fir		44	12	30	11
Elm		66	8	37	5
Beech		60	0	53	6
Ash		58	3	50	0

Armament weight

The armament was the heaviest and most important weight to be added after launch. The weight of the gun barrel formed part of its description, eg 32pdr/56cwt

Table A5.2 **Weight of the Various Articles Composed in the Hull of each Ship and Vessel**

Number of guns	120		80		74		Razée 50		52		46		Razée Corvette 26	
	(Tons	Cwt)	(Tons	Cwt)	(Tons	Cwt)	(Tons	Cwt)	(Tons	Cwt)	(Tons	Cwt)	(Tons	Cwt)
Weight of timber	2,197	10	1,653	11	1,406	2	1,255	10	904	0	690	13	615	6
iron	136	0	119	10	109	4	96	13	67	0	53	7	39	0
copper bolts	47	14	40	0	37	13	36	13	23	0	15	0	13	10
copper sheets	17	19	14	12	12	14	11	18	11	7	9	4	7	14
mixed metal nails	2	18	2	5	2	2	1	14	1	18	1	12	1	10
pintles and braces	2	11	2	3	1	15	1	15	1	15	1	9	1	0
lead of all sorts	9	0	8	9	8	0	7	10	7	2	5	4	4	9
oakum	16	1	13	10	11	10	9	7	6	10	4	18	4	1
barrels of pitch	5	7	4	6	4	12	3	18	3	17	2	18	1	17
barrels of tar	11	13	11	7	11	5	11	5	7	0	4	13	4	2
whiting and white lead	9	10	6	12	6	8	6	8	4	12	2	12	2	7
linseed oil	1	5	1	5	1	5	1	5	1	1	0	18	0	16
three coats of paint	9	10	4	16	4	5	4	2	3	10	2	15	2	8
Ship's weight when launched	2,466	18	1,882	6	1,616	15	1,447	18	1,042	12	795	3	698	0

Number of guns	28		Corvette 18		Brig 18		Brig 10		Schooner		Cutter	
	(Tons	Cwt)	(Tons	Cwt)	(Tons	Cwt)	(Tons	Cwt)	(Tons	Cwt)	(Tons	Cwt)
Weight of timber	358	14	238	0	175	4	132	18	89	10	68	12
iron	23	5	16	15	15	10	8	0	7	10½	5	1½
copper bolts	8	5	5	2	4	17	3	11	2	15	1	17
copper sheets	5	10	5	2	3	19	3	3	2	12	2	1
mixed metal nails	0	18	1	1	0	12½	0	10½	0	8¾	0	6¾
pintles and braces	0	11	0	11	4	0	54	0	0	4¾	0	4¼
lead of all sorts	4	10	4	7	4	2	3	0	2	3	1	2
oakum	4	0	3	12	3	0	2	0	1	12	1	8
barrels of pitch	1	5	1	3	1	4	0	15	0	15	0	11
barrels of tar	2	7	1	18	1	15	0	15	0	11¼	0	10¼
whiting and white lead	2	4	1	12	1	5	0	15	0	13	0	5
linseed oil	0	6	0	4½	0	3	0	2	0	1½	0	0¾
three coats of paint	2	2	1	15	1	13	0	13½	0	9¼	0	7½
Ship's weight when launched	413	17	281	3	213	10	156	8	109	6	82	7

(lcwt (hundredweight) = ¹⁄₂₀ ton) but a complete gun mounting, ready for use, weighed about 20 per cent more. For the 32pdr/56cwt the other items were:

Table A5.3 **Gun Mountings**

Item	Weight (lb)
Carriage, bed and quoins	923
Covers for lock	13
Locks, brass	2
Handspike, sponge, rammer	47
Rope & miscellaneous	151
Total	1,148

On top of this comes the ammunition. Some typical figures are given in Table A5.4.

For a First Rate one might add eighteen 8in grape and 180 32pdr grape.

Table A5.4 **Ammunition**

Ship	Guns	Powder	Number of projectiles 56lb hollow	32lb solid	8in shell	Weight
Queen	319	86	400	8,000	240	140
Rodney	291	80	400	6,560	400	119
Edinburgh	194	75	160	5,140	160	91
Portland	131	70	160	3,680	160	67
Belvidera	83	58	80	2,880	80	54
Curacoa	53	42	30			

Masts, sails and rig

In discussing the heavy and bulky steam engine, it is often forgotten how heavy was the rig of a sailing ship – some 180 tons in a First Rate.

Right at the end of the sailing era, constructor students at the Naval College were given the formulae below for sail area. It is unlikely that these were used in

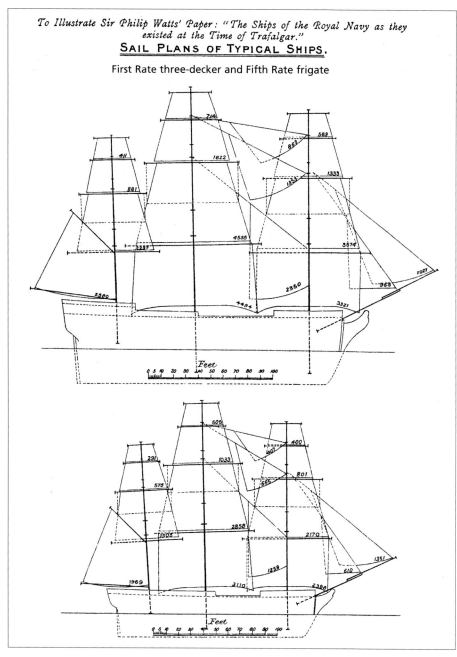

To Illustrate Sir Philip Watts' Paper: "The Ships of the Royal Navy as they existed at the Time of Trafalgar."

SAIL PLANS OF TYPICAL SHIPS.

First Rate three-decker and Fifth Rate frigate

this form as early as 1840, but experience would have given broadly similar figures:

Driving force $= A/(\text{displacement})^{2/3}$

Power to carry sail $= (\text{displacement} \times m)/(A \times h)$

where A = Sail area
h = Height of the centre of effort
m = Metacentric height

With recommended values as in Table A5.5.

Table A5.5 **Sail Power**

Class	A Mid section area	Driving force	Power to carry sail
Liner	30–35	100–120	20–30
Frigate	35–40	120–140	15–20
Brig	40–50	140–160	10–15

It will be noted that 'driving force' assumes that the force varies as sail area, which is a reasonable approximation, and that drag varies as the area of the midship section, which is not correct. It also implies that the force on the sails and the drag vary with speed in the same way, which is roughly correct up to about 10 knots but not at higher speeds.

The Chatham reports give very detailed lists of the dimensions of each sail, for each class of ship, of which a sample is given in Table A5.6.

A more useful table (A5.7) gives the area and the position of the centre of effort of each sail needed to calculate the value of 'h' in 'power to carry sail'. These figures are illustrated in Sir Phillip Watts's diagram, reproduced here.

Another table (A5.9) lists the dimensions of masts and yards.

Weights of sails, spars and their standing and rigging are given in the summary Table A5.9. Since the outfit of sails was matched to the tonnage (bm) of the ship, it is

Table A5.6 **The Dimensions of the Principal Sails**

Sails	First Rate Head (ft in)	Foot (ft in)	Depth (ft in)	80 Head (ft in)	Foot (ft in)	Depth (ft in)	70 Head (ft in)	Foot (ft in)	Depth (ft in)	Razée 50 Head (ft in)	Foot (ft in)	Depth (ft in)
Jib	– –	52 6	81 6	– –	51 0	78 0	– –	50	78 0	– –	50 0	82 0
Fore course	81 6	78 6	40 0	80 0	77 0	45 0	75 0	71 0	42 9	75 0	71 0	50 0
Top sail	51 6	82 0	53 6	51 2	82 0	54 3	50 3	77 6	50 6	50 3	77 6	50 6
Top gallant sail	38 6	54 9	28 8	34 8	54 9	27 0	35 9	51 3	26 4	35 9	51 3	26 4
Stay sail	– –	– –	– –	– –	– –	– –	– –	– –	– –	– –	– –	– –
Main course	93 10	97 0	45 6	92 9	96 7	52 0	86 0	90 6	48 9	86 0	90 6	56 0
Top sail	60 9	96 0	60 9	60 9	94 10	60 6	57 6	87 6	57 3	57 6	87 6	57 3
Top gallant sail	43 8	63 6	32 6	40 1	63 6	32 6	40 3	59 0	30 0	40 3	59 0	30 0
Gaff top sail	– –	– –	– –	– –	– –	– –	– –	– –	– –	– –	– –	– –
Mizen top sail	41 9	63 6	43 6	41 9	63 6	44 0	38 6	57 6	41 0	38 6	57 6	41 0
Top gallant sail	32 6	43 2	22 0	30 3	43 2	22 0	27 6	40 0	22 0	27 6	40 0	22 0
Driver	47 0	62 6	32 6	47 0	62 6	36 0	45 0	60 0	32 0	45 0	60 0	36 6
		63 6				63 6			54 0			58 6

not surprising that their weights plot as a straight line on a graph against tonnage. The weights of anchors and cables also vary directly with tonnage.

Men and their possessions

These ships had big crews and the weight of the men and their sea chests was considerable (see Table A5.8). They had to be fed, too, and the next set of figures in that table show the food allowed for a man in two weeks. Water was carried at one gallon (10lb) per man per day.

To conclude, a table from Harvey[4] is given (Table A5.10) with some impressive figures which illustrate both the size and the complexity of the wooden warship.

Stability and hydrostatics

The need for adequate stability, both as power to carry sail, and to limit heel in a beam wind, was well understood. Excess heel would reduce the maximum elevation of guns on the lee side and bring the gun ports too close to the water; this was particularly important to a fleet which always sought the windward position in battle.

The significance of metacentric height (GM) as a measure of stability, at least for small angles, was also recognised. Metacentric height can be calculated

4. Ibid.

Table A5.7 **Areas of Sails and Positions of their Centres of Effort**

Names of the sails	*120 guns* *Area of the sails (sq ft)*	*Centre of effort: Above the load line (ft*	*in)*	*From the centre of flotation: Afore (ft*	*in)*	*Abaft (ft*	*in)*	*80 guns* *Area of the sails (sq ft)*	*Centre of effort: Above the load line (ft*	*in)*	*From the centre of flotation: Afore (ft*	*in)*	*Abaft (ft*	*in)*	*74 guns* *Area of the sails (sq ft)*	*Centre of effort: Above the load line (ft*	*in)*	*From the centre of flotation: Afore (ft*	*in)*	*Abaft (ft*	*in)*
Jib	2,132	73	0	135	0	–	–	1,989	73	0	131	0	–	–	1,950	67	0	118	0	–	–
Fore course	3,210	52	0	76	0	–	–	3,537	50	6	73	0	–	–	3,120	45	9	67	2	–	–
Top sail	3,577	98	0	77	3	–	–	3,600	98	0	73	0	–	–	3,221	91	6	67	2	–	–
Top gallant sail	1,334	141	0	77	9	–	–	1,205	141	0	73	0	–	–	1,144	131	0	67	2	–	–
Main course	4,305	53	6	–	–	11	0	4,914	50	6	–	–	12	0	4,300	47	6	–	–	12	0
Top sail	4,740	104	6	–	–	11	6	4,704	105	6	–	–	13	0	4,140	99	6	–	–	12	4
Top gallant sail	1,761	152	0	–	–	12	6	1,682	153	0	–	–	14	0	1,469	143	0	–	–	12	8
Mizen top sail	2,300	92	6	–	–	70	6	2,314	92	6	–	–	65	6	1,962	84	6	–	–	65	0
Top gallant sail	836	126	6	–	–	71	6	806	126	6	–	–	67	0	737	116	4	–	–	65	9
Driver	2,457	60	6	–	–	102	3	2,825	53	0	–	–	95	0	2,243	49	0	–	–	94	6
Total area of the sails	26,652	–	–	–	–	–	–	27,576	–	–	–	–	–	–	24,286	–	–	–			
		(ft	*in)*						*(ft*	*in)*						*(ft*	*in)*				
The centre of effort of the sails, afore the centre of flotation		11	9⅝						9	1⅝						9	7¼				
Ditto above the load waterline		87	1¼						83	10⅞						78	5½				
Load draught of water: Forward		24	7						21	9						20	11				
Load draught of water: Aft		26	0						25	0						23	9				

Names of the sails	*Razée of 50 guns* *Area (sq ft)*	*Above (ft*	*in)*	*Afore (ft*	*in)*	*Abaft (ft*	*in)*	*52-gun frigate* *Area (sq ft)*	*Above (ft*	*in)*	*Afore (ft*	*in)*	*Abaft (ft*	*in)*	*46-gun frigate* *Area (sq ft)*	*Above (ft*	*in)*	*Afore (ft*	*in)*	*Abaft (ft*	*in)*
Jib	2,100	65	0	120	0	–	–	1,850	58	0	117	0	–	–	1,280	48	6	103	0	–	–
Fore course	3,654	45	0	67	2	–	–	2,993	39	9	65	0	–	–	2,457	37	6	56	0	–	
Top sail	3,221	93	0	67	2	–	–	3,221	85	0	65	0	–	–	2,241	76	4	56	0	–	
Top gallant sail	1,144	132	6	67	2	–	–	1,144	125	0	65	0	–	–	738	108	9	56	3	–	–
Main course	4,928	47	0	–	–	12	0	3,971	40	0	–	–	11	0	3,075	37	6	–	–	10	0
Top sail	4,140	102	0	–	–	12	4	4,140	90	0	–	–	11	6	2,790	81	8	–	–	10	3
Top gallant sail	1,469	145	0	–	–	12	8	1,469	133	6	–	–	12	0	972	118	3	–	–	10	6
Mizen top sail	1,962	83	0	–	–	65	0	1,962	74	6	–	–	62	0	1,369	68	9	–	–	55	0
Top gallant sail	737	116	0	–	–	65	4	737	106	4	–	–	63	0	549	96	9	–	–	55	9
Driver	2,421	44	0	–	–	92	0	2,243	40	6	–	–	90	3	1,783	38	0	–	–	67	6
Total area of the sails	25,776	–	–	–	–	–	–	23,730	–	–	–	–	–	–	17,254						
		(ft	*in)*						*(ft*	*in)*						*(ft*	*in)*				
The centre of effort of the sails, afore the centre of flotation		10	2⅜						9	0						8	1¾				
Ditto above the load waterline		76	6⅞						71	0⅜						62	6				
Load draught of water: Forward		20	3						21	5						17	6				
Load draught of water: Aft		21	6						25	5						19	2				

Table A5.8 **Summary of Weights**

Weight of the masts and yards, and of the spare gear, rigging and blocks; of the sails, cables and anchors; water, provisions and men; of the powder; gunner's, boatswain's and carpenter's stores; of the guns and shot and weight of the boats when fitted for foreign service.

Number of guns	120	80	74	Razée 50	52	46	Razée Corvette 26	28	Corvette 18	Brig 18	Brig 10	Schooner	Cutter
[The units are Tons, Hundredweights and Quarters]													
Lower masts and bowsprit	52 12 1	51 18 2	36 14 0	38 14 0	43 2 0	21 12 3	21 5 1	9 2 0	9 2 0	7 9 2	4 5 2	6 8 0	5 9 2
Top masts and yards aloft	37 1 3	37 1 3	27 11 0	27 11 0		18 12 3	18 12 3	8 15 2	8 15 2	7 3 1	5 15 1	1 18 2	2 12 0
Spare gear and booms	16 11 3	16 11 3	12 12 0	12 12 0	12 12 0	7 10 2	7 10 2	4 2 0	4 2 0	3 0 2	2 4 3	1 3 0	– – –
Standing, etc	29 6 0	28 6 0	26 19 0	28 10 0	25 4 0	14 13 0	14 13 0	12 10 0	12 18 0	5 0 0	3 5 0	2 2 0	
Running	18 2 0	17 4 0	16 18 0	17 15 0	16 5 0	11 7 0	11 7 0	6 10 0	6 16 0	4 10 0	2 16 0	1 8 2	3 13 0
Blocks	12 3 0	11 2 0	10 12 0	10 12 0	10 0 0	5 8 0	5 8 0	4 4 0	4 4 0	2 0 0	1 0 0	0 6 3	
Ship's sails	6 19 3	7 5 3	6 0 2	6 14 0	6 1 0	3 15 2	3 17 0	2 2 3	2 5 1	1 11 3	1 4 2	1 5 0	1 17 0
Spare sails	4 4 0	4 7 0	3 14 1	4 5 0	3 14 0	2 5 2	2 6 0	1 9 3	1 13 1	1 5 2	0 17 1	0 16 0	0 5 1
Hempen cables	32 10 0	29 15 0	25 4 0	25 4 0	25 4 0	13 1 0	9 13 0	6 19 0	6 19 0	4 1 0	1 16 0	0 8 1	– – –
Iron cables	37 3 0	36 11 0	30 17 0	30 17 0	30 17 0	26 2 0	26 2 0	15 18 0	15 18 0	10 8 0	7 1 0	6 6 3	3 9 0
Anchors	20 16 2	17 8 0	15 5 0	15 5 0	12 10 2	10 1 0	8 11 0	4 5 2	4 5 2	3 10 2	2 14 0	2 2 3	1 7 2
[The units are Tons and Hundredweights]													
Iron ballast and tanks	373 0	247 0	196 0	100 0	187 0	107 10	84 0	81 to 55	77 0	47 0	25 0	30 0	32 0
Water	410 15	385 0	260 9	175 0	220 0	110 0	106 0	55 5	50 0	32 0	19 0	11 0	4 5
Coals and wood	100 0	78 0	52 0	45 0	38 0	32 0	21 0	15 0	10 0	8 10	6 0	4 0	2 0
Provisions, spirits and slops	296 4	241 15	214 18	134 3	113 0	69 4	59 0	31 15	28 10	23 14	6 10	6 8	3 2
Men, chests, etc	102 6	78 0	65 0	48 0	45 0	27 3	20 0	18 2	14 7	14 7	8 14	4 12	2 15
Gunner's stores	39 12½	27 2	22 2	18 0	16 0	12 11	11 10	7 10	6 5	5 17	2 2	1 8	0 18
Boatswain's and carpenter's stores	54 0	51 15	48 0	46 0	39 0	31 0	31 0	16 0	14 10	12 5	8 7	4 2¼	4 12
Guns, etc	329 18	224 5	178 7	150 18	125 4	80 7	68 8	31 3	21 17	21 17	8 2¼	4 7	3 8
Powder, etc	33 5	25 0	20 16½	18 12	13 18	11 18¾	9 5	4 18¾	2 15	2 15	1 10	0 11½	0 11
Shot and cases	125 14	98 12	79 17	80 12	58 2	45 10	38 15	30 3	22 2	22 2	6 0	25 ½	2 10
Launch	5 8	5 2	5 2	5 2	4 3½	4 3½	– –	–	–	–	–	– –	– –
	2 No.	2 No.	2 No.	2 No.	2 No.	2 No.	2 No.					Yawl	
Cutter	1 3	1 3	1 3	1 2	1 3	1 3	1 3	0 14¾	0 10¾	0 10¾	1 3	0 16	0 16
						Com- modore	Cutter	2 Cutter gigs					
Barge	1 10	1 10	1 10	1 10	1 10	1 10	0 14½	1 6	0 8	0 8	– –	– – –	– –
Pinnace	1 10	1 10	1 10	1 10	1 5¼	1 10	1 10	1 5¼	1 5¼	1 5¼	– –	– – –	– –
Gig	– –	– –	– –	0 10¾	– –	– –	0 9½	– –	– –	– –	0 9	0 13	0 13¼
Jolly-boat	0 9¾	0 9¾	0 9¾	0 9½	0 9¾	0 9¾	– –	0 9¾	0 7¾	0 7¾	0 9¾	0 7¾	0 4½

directly; the sums are simple but tiresome without a computer. It is not clear why this calculation was not attempted in the first half of the century. GM can also be found from the results of an inclining experiment, in which the heel produced by moving a weight through a known distance is measured. It is usually stated that very few (two to four) such experiments were carried out in the first half of the century, but since several precise GMs are quoted, it is likely that there were more.

The following figures give a rough idea of the range of metacentric heights for the different classes.

Line-of-battle ships	4ft–6.5ft
Frigates	4ft–6ft
Sloops and brigs	5ft–6ft

Table A5.9 **Dimensions of Masts and Yards**

Names of masts, yards, etc		*120 guns* Length (Yds	In)	Diameter (In)	*80 guns* Length (Yds	In)	Diameter (In)	*74 guns* Length (Yds	In)	Diameter (In)	*Razée 50 guns* Length (Yds	In)	Diameter (In)	*52 guns* Length (Yds	In)	Diameter (In)
Lower masts	Fore mast	36	28	36¾	36	0	36	32	30	31¼	32	30	33½	30	6	31
	Main mast	39	32	40	39	22	39¾	36	0	36	36	0	36	33	6	34½
	Mizzen mast	27	8	24½	27	8	24¾	24	23	21⅝	26	16½	24	24	0	22½
Bowsprit		25	1	36⅞	23	35	36	22	0	34⅛	22	0	34⅛	21	18	31½
Fore	Topmast	20	34	20⅝	20	26	20¾	19	8	19¼	19	8	19¼	19	8	19¼
	Top gallant mast	10	12	10¾	10	0	10	9	22	9⅝	9	22	9⅝	9	22	9⅝
	Lower yard	30	13	21½	29	33	21½	28	4	19⅝	28	4	19⅝	28	4	19⅝
	Top sail yard	21	18	13¾	21	20	13⅞	20	18	12¾	20	18	12¾	20	18	12¾
	Top gallant yard	14	8	8⅝	12	34	8	13	12	8½	13	12	8½	13	12	8½
Main	Top mast	22	34	20⅝	23	0	20¾	21	22	19¼	21	22	19¼	21	22	19¼
	Top gallant mast	11	17	11⅝	11	18	11⅜	11	0	11	11	0	11	11	0	11
	Lower yard	34	28	24⅝	34	15	24¾	32	8	22⅝	32	8	22⅝	32	28	22⅝
	Top sail yard	24	20	15½	24	27	16	23	18	14⅝	23	18	14⅝	23	18	14⅝
	Top gallant yard	16	9	10	15	12	9⅜	15	10	9¼	15	10	9¼	15	10	9¼
Mizen	Topmast	16	17	13¾	16	28	14	15	32	13	15	32	13	15	32	13
	Top gallant mast	8	8	8⅝	8	8	8½	8	0	8	8	0	8	8	0	8
	Cross jack yard	24	20	15½	24	27	16	23	18	14⅝	23	18	14⅝	23	18	14⅝
	Topsail yard	16	12	10⅛	16	12	10⅛	15	13	9⅝	15	13	9⅝	15	13	9⅝
	Top gallant yard	12	3	6½	11	12	7	10	21	6⅛	10	21	6⅛	10	21	6⅛
Driver boom		23	7	13¾	23	13½	13⅞	22	27	12¾	22	27	12¾	22	7	12¾
Driver gaff		17	6	12⅝	17	13	12	16	35	11⅝	16	35	11⅝	16	35	11⅝
Jib boom		17	18	15¼	16	24	14½	16	0	14⅛	16	0	14⅛	16	0	14⅛
Sprit sail yard		21	18	13¾	21	20	13⅞	20	18	12¾	20	18	12¾	20	18	12¾

Table A5.10 **Selected Material Quantities required for each Class**

Number of guns		*120*	*80*	*74*	*Razée 50*	*52*	*46*	*Razée Corvette 26*	*28*	*Corvette 18*	*Brig 18*	*Brig 10*	*Schooner*	*Cutter*
Number of sheets of copper sheathing	28oz	1,166	1,800	1,472	1,329	1,350	1,000	850	790	850	797	580	652	550
	32oz	3,572	2,050	1,734	1,706	1,650	1,170	1,130	600	613	301	200	80	–
Number of treenails		64,458	35,103	27,019	25,380	23,500	20,826	17,300	14,540	13,050	11,193	8,316	7,100	3,250
Number of barrels of pitch		50	45	43	37	36	25	18	12	11	11	7	7	5
Number of barrels of tar		109	106	105	105	66	44	39	22	18	16	7	5¾	5
Number of gallons of linseed oil		400	400	400	400	320	282	256	96	60	48	32	23	11
Number of fathoms of rope from ¾in to 18in in circumference		30,250	32,400	27,152	29,200	28,700	20,728	21,370	19,031	19,350	10,709	7,335	–	–
Number of blocks		940	940	934	934	934	893	893	848	848	576	399	–	–
Number of yards of canvas in ship's sails		12,517	12,947	10,784	11,130	10,824	7,307	7,381	4,796	5,096	3,547	2,740	2,790	4,140
Number of yards of canvas in spare sails		7,584	7,844	6,650	6,876	6,690	5,066	5,140	3,322	3,720	2,847	1,916	1,750	589
[For each class the first figure is for bower anchors and the second for stream anchors]														
Number of hempen cables		5 1	5 1	5 1	5 1	5 1	4 1	3 1	3 1	3 1	2 1	1 1	0 1	– –
Number of iron cables		3 1	3 1	3 1	3 1	3 1	3 1	3 1	3 1	3 1	3 1	2 1	3 0	3 1

Note for naval architects

The position of the centre of buoyancy can be calculated from Morrish's formula:

CB below the wl = ⅓(T/2 + volume ÷ water plane area)

provided that the depth of the false keel is neglected.

The height of the metacentre above the centre of buoyancy BM is given by:

$$BM = I/V = k.B^2/T$$

where k for a typical ship is:

Ship	Number of guns	k
Nelson	120	.18
Caledonia	120	.17
Boyne	98	.16
Colossus	80	.15
San Domingo	74	.18
Ajax	74	.19
Euryalus	36	.20
Revolutionnaire	38	.20
Leda	36	.20

The metacentric height is an inadequate guide to safe stability for larger angles of heel, particularly for sailing ships. The GM of *Captain* was quite reasonable, but her righting moment did not increase with heel as it should and vanished at too small an angle.

5. W H White, *Manual of Naval Architecture*, London (1900).

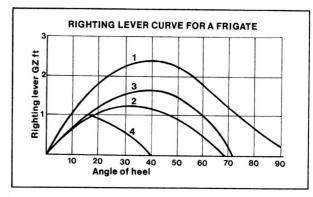

White[5] gives some information for a frigate in the form of a graph of GZ against angle of heel where GZ is righting moment ± displacement.

RIGHTING LEVER CURVE FOR A FRIGATE
1. 131ft x 40ft 7in x 17ft 4in draught, GM 6.2ft, displacement 1,055 load.
2. 131ft x 40ft 7in x 16ft 0in draught, GM 4.1ft, displacement 887 light.
3. 141ft x 38ft 8in x 16ft 7in draught, GM 4.5ft, displacement 1,075 load.
4. As 3., ports open.

Note that the righting moments are much smaller in the light condition than in the load as stores, water, etc, are consumed from low in the ship and the centre of gravity rises. To modern eyes, the curves seem quite satisfactory and this is confirmed by experience, since few ships were lost due to bad weather. The curve shown for the ship with gun ports open is not satisfactory; doors left open near the waterline are not safe in today's ships. It seems likely that White's curves 3 and 4 were produced for the inquiry into the loss of the *Eurydice* in 1878, blown over when her gun ports were open. (The dimensions are correct.)

A very useful figure is the weight which will increase the draught by one inch, shown in Table A5.11.

Table A5.12 shows how trim varied between the load and light condition.

Table A5.11 **Weights to increase Draught**

Class of ship	(Guns)	Displacement of one inch at the light line (Tons Cwt)		Displacement of one inch at the load line (Tons Cwt)		Displacement of one foot of the midship section at the light line (Tons Cwt)		Displacement of one foot of the midship section at the load line (Tons Cwt)	
	120	20	12	24	0	16	10	29	17
	80	17	12	21	11	15	18	26	13
	74	15	5	17	17	12	7	21	3
Razée	50	14	6	17	2	11	14	18	4
	52	12	18	16	2	8	9	17	6
	46	9	6	12	5	8	4	14	4
Razée corvette	26	8	18	11	10	6	10	12	15
	28	6	12	7	9	5	1	9	7
Corvette	18	5	13	7	0	3	10	7	5
Gun brig	18	4	10	5	13	3	11	6	10
	10	3	10	4	7	2	10	4	8
Schooner		2	13	3	10	1	13	3	6
Cutter		2	4	2	17	2	4	3	15
New class of ships									
London	92	20	4	23	9¾	16	0	27	2
Castor	36	11	12	14	7¼	9	14¾	12	12
Vernon	50	14	15	18	10½	10	14¾	19	12
Rover	18	5	4	7	5	4	2	7	2
Snake	16	4	8	5	14¼	4	0	6	12½

Table A5.12 **Trim**

Class of ships		Excess of after load draught above forward load draught (ft in)		Excess of after load draught above forward light draught (ft in)	
	120	1	5	2	4
	80	3	3	4	7
	74	2	10	4	1
	52	1	0	2	10
	46	1	8	4	9
	28	0	5	2	2
Corvette	18	0	7	1	10
Brig	18	3	3	4	10
Brig	10	1	1	2	5
Schooner	10	2	6	2	11
Cutter		6	10	6	6

It is but rarely that the load waterline is parallel to the keel, and the same may be said of the light waterline. In the different classes of ships which follow, the excess of the after load draught above the forward load draught is given in the second column, and similar differences in the light water draught are recorded in the last.

In every instance, excepting the cutter, the difference of the after and forward light water draughts exceeds the difference of the corresponding load water draughts.

With these notes (and the rest of the reports), together with Conway's three great books on the wooden fleet by Goodwin, Lees and Lavery, it should be possible to design and build a very good wooden warship and then take Harland's book as the guide to sailing it. Wouldn't it be fun?

Appendix 6

A Note on the Strength of the *Nemesis*

(See midship section in Chapter 7.)

The calculations outlined below, for engineers only, analyse the structure of HEICoS *Nemesis* using more modern methods than were available to Laird.

The bending moment on the *Nemesis* in waves can be estimated on the assumption that bending moment (BM) is equal to displacement x length ± constant, where the value of the constant is 25 for hogging (wave crest amidships) and 30 for sagging (wave crests at ends). For *Nemesis* the displacement would be about 620 tons and the length was 184ft. Values of the constants based on figures in White.[1]

The drawing of the structure amidships is based on the description given by Creuze.[2] From this it is possible to calculate the second moment of area (the strength of the structure). In the calculation, the following assumptions are made, based on:[3]

1. ⅝ of the wood is effective in tension, all in compression.
2. Wood 1⁄16 strength of iron.
3. ⅞ of iron effective in tension, due to rivet holes. This was the normal practice in riveted ships but later work shows that it was a pessimistic assumption.

The calculations give a second moment of area (I) of 9,200in²ft² but since Creuze is not entirely clear and some structural members may not have been mentioned, a value of I of 10,000 is used. The neutral axis is 6ft below the upper deck, 7.5ft above the keel. Then:

$$\frac{\text{Stress}}{\text{Distance from axis}} = \frac{\text{Bending moment}}{\text{2nd moment of area}}$$

	Hogging	*Sagging*
Bending moment (tons/ft)	4,560	3,800
Stress (tons/sq in)		
Deck	2.7	2.3
Keel	3.4	2.9

These figures are quite typical of those used in wrought iron structures. *Nemesis* would not have cracked had it not been for the much higher local stresses at the square corners of the holes for the paddle box beams. The cracks which formed would have weakened the structure considerably, increasing the stresses, and she was fortunate to survive a further gale in this state.

1. W H White, *Manual of Naval Architecture*, London (1900).
2. A F B Creuze, 'On the *Nemesis*', *Journal of the United Services Institution*, May 1840.
3. White, op cit.

Appendix 7

Fouling and Corrosion

Marine life, both animal and vegetable, will form on solid objects close to the surface of the sea. This growth of barnacles and weeds adds considerably to the drag on a ship moving through the sea. Even as late as the Second World War, fouling increased the frictional drag by about ¼ per cent per day in temperate waters and ½ per cent in the tropics.

In the late eighteenth century this problem was largely solved when copper sheathing was introduced. This protected the wooden hull from boring worms (*Teredo*), but was also an effective anti-fouling material, as the copper slowly dissolved in the sea water forming salts which are toxic to most forms of fouling. Typically, one would expect a sheathed ship, a few months out of dock, to have a speed advantage of about 1½ knots over an unsheathed ship. Since the Royal Navy was well ahead of other navies in the use of copper sheathing they had an important speed advantage for a few years; for example, the capture of six Spanish ships off Gibraltar in 1780.[1]

There were only a few problems with wooden ships. The rush of water over the copper, particularly near the bow, wore it away quite quickly, needing expensive replacement. The Board asked Sir Humphry Davy, the scientist, to investigate the problem and he found that fastening blocks of zinc to the copper would stop the erosion, the zinc rather than the copper sheet disappearing. Unfortunately, this treatment also prevented copper from killing the fouling and after trials in 1828 on the *Samarang* it was not used.

Two different metals connected together in salt water form an electric battery, and one will be preserved at the cost of rapid damage to the other, this being the basis of Davy's work. This problem became more severe with the introduction of paddle steamers; *Elfin*, *Geyser* and

1. R J B Knight, 'The introduction of copper sheathing into the RN 1779–86', *Mariner's Mirror*.

Penelope were among those which suffered from early corrosion of the iron frame of the paddle wheels, close to the copper of their sheathing.[2]

It was clear that this electrolytic corrosion would prevent the use of copper sheathing on iron hulls. Eventually, in the late 1860s a technique was developed in which an iron hull was clothed in a tight wooden sheath and copper fastened to the wood, care being taken that the nails did not reach the iron. This scheme worked, but it was heavy and expensive. There were similar problems where copper pipes were fastened to iron hulls which contributed to the short life of *Grappler* and, possibly, to the loss of *Megaera*.

Even by itself, iron will rust in sea water. It was soon found that red lead paint, properly applied, would protect wrought iron from rusting but this had no antifouling action. Iron ships in home waters had to be docked at least every twelve months to remove a layer of shells and weed.[3] In the Mediterranean and Black seas, ships were docked every six months and in the Indian Ocean docking was needed every four months, unless they spent some time in fresh water which would kill much of the fouling. The chief engineer of the East India Company at Bombay, A Cursetjee, reported that when *Indus* docked he removed barnacles 12in thick and 18in long.

The *Pekin* of the P&O line left England in February 1847 and was docked in Bombay in October. Captain Gribble said, 'I can compare her to nothing else than a half tide rock. The barnacles were 9in long, the second strata being complete, with a feathering coral formation sprouting from cluster to cluster. The *Pekin*, though a fast ship, had her speed reduced by fouling to 6 knots per hour'.

There were many inventors who claimed to have invented a good anti-fouling compound. In January 1848 the P&O company arranged for one of their ships, the *Ripon*, to be painted with patches of anti-fouling from ten different inventors. After some months she was docked and it was apparent that none of them was effective.

The Royal Navy was most interested in the work of W J Hay, chemist and lecturer at the RN College, Portsmouth. Hay mixed a paint with copper oxide suspended in linseed oil, which was first tried on the *Rocket* in May 1845, followed by the *Fairy* in September and the *Undine* in May 1847. *Undine* was docked after five to six months and it was reported that the starboard side, painted with red lead, was 'very foul with grassy weeds and slime', while the port side with Hay's compound was clean, except for a few spots where the paint had rubbed off. A similar trial was held on the unique iron sailing ship *Recruit*. After a voyage to the Tagus and back, the side painted with Hay's compound was clean while the other was covered with 'bushels of Lepus Anatifra'.[4]

Hay was later to claim that the problem of fouling was a more important factor than resistance to gunshot in ending the first iron ship programme.[5] This was certainly an exaggerated viewpoint, but it is clear from correspondence with Symonds that the Board were fairly concerned over fouling of iron ships. Hay persevered in his work and persuaded the Admiralty to build a laboratory for him in Portsmouth Dockyard which he ran for many years with the title of Admiralty Chemist. After many changes of name, this laboratory still exists in the yard. By the time the next generation of iron warships was built, commencing with the *Warrior*, Hay's compound was the standard anti-fouling paint.

2. W J Hay, 'The protection of iron ships from oxidation and fouling', *Trans INA*, vol 4 (1863).

3. J Bourne, *A Treatise on the Screw Propeller*, London (1852).

4. Hay, op cit.

5. Ibid.

Appendix 8
Notes from Dupuy de Lôme

Mémoire Sur La Construction Des Bâtiments en Fer by Dupuy de Lôme (Paris 1844), a very detailed and useful report, is extremely difficult to locate in the UK and though it has already been quoted extensively, some further extracts on cost may be of interest.

The author points out that Glasgow could build iron ships more cheaply than Liverpool due to lower wages and the greater use of the cheaper grades of iron.

Table A8.1 **Wages**

	Liverpool £ s d			Glasgow £ s d		
Foreman per month	9–10			7		
Carpenter per day		5			4	
Smith per day		5			4	
Plater per day		4	9			
Riveter per day		3	6		3	
Driller per day		3			2	
Apprentice per week		2–5			2–3	

Table A8.2 **Cost of Iron**

	Staffordshire	Low Moor	Coalbrookdale	Clyde
Plates (l/ton)	10	20–10	11	10
Angles	10			10
Rivets	11	16		10
Coke	Liverpool £21, Glasgow £14 per ton			

Overall, Laird's cost was £40 per ton of hull weight, Glasgow £33. Of Laird's total, £12 was material cost and the remaining £28 was labour, wastage, overheads and profit. He quotes a wastage of 24 tons in 830 for the *Great Britain*.

The Strength of Ships – Wood and Iron

The wooden walls of Nelson's day may have had a 'heart of oak' but they were weak ships. In a seaway, they would flex and bend – 'working' as it was known. Morgan (1827) measured a frigate bending 1½in as it changed tack. The relative movement between the timbers would further weaken the joint and soon water would get in, causing rot and even more working. It was often said that wooden ships were strong because they would flex in a seaway and some modern writers have copied this statement. It could hardly be further from the truth; it was the working of wooden ships which made them weak and led to the need for early repairs.

The principal loading on a ship comes from the uneven distribution of weight and buoyancy. In calm water the weight of the heavy guns and their supporting structure at the ends of the ship would be greater than the support given by the buoyancy and the ends would tend to droop – hogging. The designer would do his best to limit these loads by adopting fairly full shapes for the bow and stern, far more full than desirable for speed, and would also keep the ship short. In the hogging situation just described, the deck would be in tension – pulled, the bottom would be compressed and the sides would be squeezed out of shape, squares becoming diamonds.

In a seaway, the situation is even more complicated. With a wave crest amidships and troughs at the end the ship would be hogging, but the out of balance forces would be much increased, as would distortion of the hull. Wave crests at bow and stern would increase the buoyancy, while the trough amidships would reduce the buoyancy and the ship would tend to sag in the middle. It was this alternate hogging and sagging which made the ship 'work'.

In a wooden ship it was the distortion of the sides of the hull which was the major problem. Seppings's analogy of a five-bar gate without the diagonal bar is a good one. Resistance to this change of shape came from friction between the planks which, up to a point, could be increased by hard caulking. Seppings's diagonal trusses were a great improvement but the rows of gun ports still weakened the side structure.

Most of these problems are overcome in an iron hull, as the material is inherently stronger, can be shaped to give strength for light weight and, most important, the strength of a riveted joint between the edges of the plates is almost as strong as the plates themselves.

Weight and strength

Modulus of elasticity is a measure of deflection caused by a particular load and is therefore related to stiffness, an aspect in which the superiority of iron is apparent.

The above figures were those used in the late nineteenth century and are probably much the same as those accepted as good practice earlier in the century, and

Table A9.1 **Weight and Strength**

Material	Wt/cu ft (lb)	Tensile strength (1,000lb/sq in)	Compressive strength (1,000lb/sq in)	Modulus of elasticity (1,000,000lb/sq in)
British oak	54	8–10	7.6–10	1.45
Danzig oak	52	4–13	6.8–8.7	1.19
Danzig fir	36	2.2–4.5	7–9.5	1.96
Elm	35	5.5–13.5	5.8–10	0.7
Pitch pine	40	4.6–7.8	6.5–9.8	1.23
Teak	48	3.3–15	6.3–12	2.4
Wrought iron	480	21	28	

rather higher than would be used today. The first important point to note is the variability in the strength of all timbers. A carefully selected test piece might reach the higher value, but the strength of a structure depends on its weakest link, the lower figure.

A good piece of structural timber, an inch square, could take a pull of about 4 tons before breaking, while an inch bar of iron should take 21 tons. The densities are in the ratio of 54lb/sq in for the wood and 480lb/sq in for iron. Thus the iron is about five times as strong, but nine times as heavy, showing that in simple tension timber is lighter for the same strength.

In practice, this is not correct. It is never possible to work to the ultimate strength of any material, particularly one exposed to alternating loads. When allowance was made for imperfections in the material itself and the way in which it was used, experience showed that iron in tension could be used at about one-fifth of its ultimate strength, but wood only at one-tenth. In compression, wood does rather better and an oak strut can be taken to ½ ton/sq in and iron to 3 tons/sq in.

The bending of a beam will put one side in tension and the other into compression, so that for a square section beam the guidelines above still apply. However, iron can be shaped to take the load much more efficiently. An iron beam of I section, 12in deep with 6in flanges, all ½in thick, will weigh 40lb/sq ft and will resist a bending moment of 192 tons-inches. An oak beam to take the same bending moment will be 14½in square and weigh 75.6lb/ft, nearly twice as much. (With modern adhesives, laminated wood beams can also be shaped for light weight but at high cost.)

In calculating the strength of an iron structure, it was customary to reduce the total area of material resisting tension by one-eighth to allow for the effect of rivet holes. (Later work showed that this was pessimistic.) The ends of planks were not fastened to each other at all (only the keel was scarphed) and the butts were arranged so that there were three intact planks between two consecutive butts in the same space, so that only three out of four planks were effective in taking the load. The strength was further reduced by the holes for bolts and treenails so that only five-eighths of the wood was effective.

Overall, the load-bearing part of an iron hull probably weighed about two-thirds of that of a corresponding wooden hull. Since much of the hull of a warship does not carry the principal loads (eg, minor bulkheads) the saving of weight in practice was less, say 15–20 per cent. In addition, the beams and frames took up less space and the capacity would increase by up to 20 per cent. Iron hulls were more durable; though they do rust, this was a small problem compared with the rotting of a wooden hull. The rigidity of the iron hull, due to its firm connections, became essential for high power, screw steamers.

However, wrought iron itself was variable and unreliable, as shown by tests made by John Bird of the Admiralty Research Establishment (Dunfermline) on samples taken from the *Warrior* during her restoration.

Table A9.2 **Plate Strength – Longitudinal Direction**

Sample	0.2% proof N/mm²	UTS	Elongation (%)	Reduction of area (%)
1	220	284	11	1
2	212	253	8	2

The same properties were then measured at right angles to the plane of a 4½in armour plate for twelve samples.

Sample	0.2% proof N/mm²	UTS	Elongation (%)	Reduction of area (%)
Mean	121	149	5.1	2.25
Range max-mm	170–99 (40)	195–111 (43)	10–3	1–3

Note: the figures in brackets show values for one particularly bad test piece.

The impact strength measured by the energy absorbed in breaking a test piece with a sharp V notch in it is given in Table A9.3. It is very relevant to resisting gun shot.

Table A9.3 **Impact Strength**

Temperature (°C)	–20	0	+15	40	100	140
Absorbed energy (Joules)	11	11	17	24	26	25

These last figures show why wrought iron could resist shot in warm climates, but not when it became cold.

Wrought iron was not a very good material from which to build warships, but until about 1880 steel was even more unreliable.

Appendix 10

A Technical Note on the *Rattler* and *Alecto* Trials

(Note: only enough information is given for a naval architect to repeat the sums using standard methods.)

This note looks at the trials from a hydrodynamicist's viewpoint; this is almost irrelevant since the great virtues of the screw lay in other aspects. The hydrodynamicist will look at three aspects:

a. The reliability of the data
b. A comparison of the results with modern expectation
c. What conclusions can be drawn on the performance of the hull, propeller and machinery

Results

The valuable trials were 1, 9 and 11 in Bourne's listing.

Trial	V (knots)	N (rpm) engine x 4	ihp	Thrust (tons)	(thp)
1	9.2	95	335	3.89	214
9	8	84	205	2.75	185
11	6	68	127	2.15	108

Graphs of T/N^2 and of N to base V plot fairly well as straight lines confirming the validity of the data, though the measured thrust at the lowest speed is on the low side. The meter was probably sticking a little.

There is evidence from Admiralty records that even the early propellers were similar in efficiency to modern designs of similar geometry. The propeller data are read from the AEW 1953 series for a screw of BAR (blade area ratio) = 0.2, pitch = lift and diameter 10ft.

Using these results, the thrust identity wake can be deduced:

$$\text{Wake fraction } w = \frac{V_S - V_A}{V_S} = \frac{J' - J}{J'}$$

where J is the advance coefficient corresponding to K_T for the ship.

Rattler wake fraction

Speed (knots)	9.2	8	6
Wake w	0.13	0.07	0.12

Rather less precisely, the resistance of the hull can be deduced from the Taylor-Gertler series using:

$$C_P = 0.78, \quad C_V = 0.003, \quad \text{wetted surface} = 6{,}790\text{sq ft}$$

Thrust is much greater than the resistance deduced. This is due to the combined effects of interaction (thrust deduction), roughness and errors.

If it is assumed that all the difference is in interaction, the thrust deduction factor t comes out at 0.36, a high but not impossible figure.

The hull efficiency corresponding is 0.73, again not impossible. It is clear that the hull/propeller efficiency of *Rattler* was low, from her failure to defeat *Alecto* more decisively. When *Rattler* towed *Alecto* bow first, the thrust was 4.6 tons and this had to overcome the resistance of *Alecto* and the augmented resistance of *Rattler*. This leads to even higher figures and suggests that

Alecto's drag was increased considerably due to the impingement of *Rattler*'s slipstream. In the famous tug of war, the slipstream of the propeller would impinge directly on *Alecto*, while that of the paddles might pass to the sides of *Rattler*, giving her an added advantage.

Note: A fairly full set of calculations on which this note is based has been deposited in the libraries of RINA; Science and Maritime Museums; Froude's Museum, Haslar; Naval Library; World Ship Society.

Appendix 11
The Battle of Eckenfjorde 1849

The Battle of Eckenfjorde on 5 April 1849 was one of the few occasions in which shells were used at sea prior to the Crimean War. The Danish sailing liner, *Christian VIII*, supported by two steamships, *Geyser* and *Hecla*, were in action with two Prussian shore batteries, one of which, the northern, had two 8in and two 24pdrs, while the southern had four 18pdrs firing red-hot shot.

The action began at about 0800hrs when the *Christian VIII* was in action with the northern battery. She was set on fire by shell, but this was soon extinguished. Her return fire was rather ineffective because her ports were too small to allow her guns to train prop-

erly. Later in the day, one of the steamers had her starboard paddle wheel put out of action and the *Christian VIII* was trapped, bow to the north battery and stern to the south. At about 0600hrs fires were started aft by red-hot shot which soon became uncontrollable.

As well as showing that red-hot shot were still more effective than shells, this was the only occasion on which a steamer was immobilised by damage to a paddle wheel.

Based on an eye witness account by Lieutenant Colonel Stevens RMA, in the Royal Artillery Institute, Woolwich.

Appendix 12
The Gun Boat Builders

Class	Gleaner	Dapper	Albacore	Cheerful	Clown	Total
Builder						
Pitcher, Northfleet	4	12	34		4	54
Deptford Dockyard	2	2		1		5
Green, Blackwall		2	12			14
White, Cowes		2	2			4
Thompson, Rotherhithe		2				2
Laird, Birkenhead			10	4		14
Wigram, Blackwall			14			14
Mare, Blackwall			6			6
Patterson, Bristol			2			2
Smith, North Shields			6		2	8
Fletcher, Limehouse			5			5
Hill, Bristol			3			3
Briggs, Sunderland			4	2		6
Devonport				2		2
Sheerness				1		1
Westbrook, Blackwall				2		2
Pembroke				4	2	6
Joyce, Greenwich				2		2
Young, Limehouse				4		4
Miller, Liverpool					2	2
Total	6	20	98	20	12	156

Appendix 13
The Attack on Kronstadt

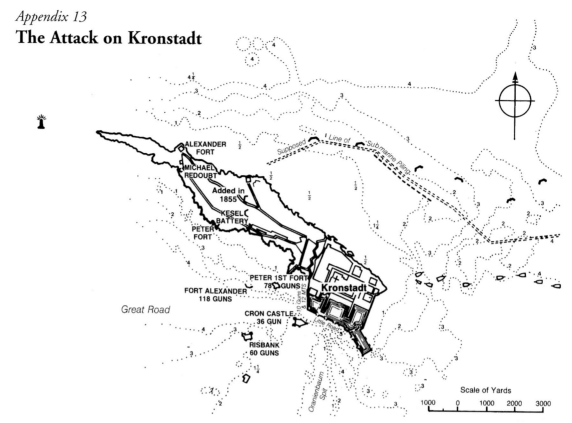

The defences of Kronstadt. Captain Sulivan devised an ingenious scheme using all the new technology of the fleet to overcome these formidable defences.

The plan outlined by Sulivan for an attack on Kronstadt is an impressive preview of a Second World War assault using a combination of all arms. The massive granite forts protecting the deep channel to the south were as invulnerable to attack in 1856 as they were in earlier years. Sulivan planned a bombardment from the shallow waters to the north.

The Russians had taken a number of precautions against such an attack. Their first line of defence comprised their gun boats. They had twenty-three 'fine screw gun boats, larger, I think, than ours, with some three heavy guns each, with a range equal to the heaviest gun we have, and yet they have only the machinery of railway engines to fit in them.' (Sulivan) The engines were built by the American Locomotive Co, which operated the St Petersburg–Moscow railway. (Their English engineer, Baird, refused to assist.) Other views on the Russian gun boats were less flattering.

Sulivan was confident that the Anglo-French gun boat force could keep the Russian boats at a distance. However, the obstacles erected by the Russians were formidable. They consisted of a considerable number of 20ft x 8ft coffer dams of timber, filled with stones, with 15ft gaps between them. Sulivan and his brother, later Admiral G L Sulivan, intended to make a detailed survey of the obstructions in a double paddle canoe wearing specially designed oilskin suits, lined to keep out the cold, and with pockets for lead and line. G L Sulivan had worked as a diver, placing demolition charges under the beached gun boat *Jasper* in the Sea of Azov, and similar techniques would have been used at Kronstadt.

The mining of *Merlin* and *Firebrand* showed that the approach was defended by these infernal machines, but the sweeping operations undertaken in 1855 had been successful. Once a gap had been cleared, the armoured batteries would move through and destroy the field gun batteries defending the north side. The forts at each end would be kept under fire from liners, probably the second batch of blockships, which were armed with coastal attack in mind.

With the opposing batteries out of action, a large number of mortar vessels would move in and bombard the dockyard, arsenal and ships at anchor, firing over the island. There is a suggestion that some of the armoured batteries would engage the southern forts by direct fire, with the ships moored in the blind arcs of the forts. The force which Sulivan saw as necessary was:

Batteries	8
Mortar vessels	30
Gun boats	30
Steam frigates	4

There would have been a strong force of troops available to land and occupy Kronstadt should Russian resistance collapse, but it does not sound as though Sulivan thought this likely. Overall, the plan should have worked and caused great damage to Russian installations. Sulivan probably overstates his case in suggesting that the leaked plans for the attack were a prime factor in persuading the Russians to accept peace terms. It is also far from clear as to the extent to which Sulivan had obtained acceptance of his plan. It is another example of the willingness of many seamen officers to utilise new technology in war.

Notes on Individual Dockyards

Portsmouth

The home of the Navy, Portsmouth was the biggest, both in area and in number of employees, throughout the era. Bentham's docks and Marc Brunel's block mills were followed by a programme of roofing the slips. From 1814 wooden roofs were used, but from 1844 iron sheds were built. In 1843 the new seven-acre steam basin and factory was started and completed, fourteen days ahead of schedule, in May 1848. In their construction, 1,200 convicts and 1,050 free labourers were employed. The basin was closed by a ship-shaped caisson 81ft long, built by Fairbairn. The entrance was found to be too narrow and the caisson was buried, to be rediscovered in 1984.[1]

There were two manually operated cranes, lifting 7½ tons and 15 tons respectively, and a 'swan neck' steam crane lifting 15 tons. There were two docks: No 7, specially wide to take paddlers and later joined to No 10 to take larger ships such as *Warrior*; and No 8 dock, longer and narrower for screw ships.

The new basin was dominated by the steam factory, now No 2 Ship Shop, 600ft long and two storeys high. On the ground floor were the heavy turning shop, erecting shop, punching and shearing shop, boiler shop and extension. Above were the millwright's shop, light turning and fitting shop and the pattern store. An iron and brass foundry was also opened in 1848 and a separate iron foundry in 1845, followed by a new smithy in 1852, using some material from the Great Exhibition. Although the new facilities were intended for refitting work only, it is clear that at least two sets of new machinery were built in the yard. Five new slipways were added between 1838 and 1845, all roofed.[2]

Master Shipwrights[3]

Name	Date appointed
N Diddams	Nov 1802
J Nolloth	Jan 1823
R Blake	Feb 1835
J Hepburn	Jul 1836
J Fincham (1st SNA)	Oct 1844
R Abethell (1st SNA)	Jul 1852
R Cradock	Apr 1862

Chief Engineer

A Murray	1846–62

Plymouth, Keyham and Devonport

The breakwater enclosing Plymouth Sound was built between 1810 and 1838. The magnificent anchorage so enclosed was supported at first by the original yard, known as Plymouth Dock, now South Yard. The dockyard town was renamed Devonport in 1824, but the

dockyard only took that name in August 1843 during a visit by the Queen.

In the early 1840s it was decided that the existing yard was too small for the new docks required by the bigger ships entering service and to accommodate a steam factory. Some 72 acres of land were purchased at Keyham and the contractor, G Baker, began work in 1844 with a coffer dam 1,600ft long and 26ft wide along the river front. A Nasmyth steam pile-driver was used to drive timbers up to 66ft long, taking three or four months for the complete job. The foundation stone of the basin was laid in 1849 and it was officially opened in October 1853 when HMS *Queen* was taken into the basin.[4]

There were two basins, the south, which was 650ft x 560ft and the north, which was longer and narrower. There were three docks in the south basin, 318ft x 80ft. All the usual dockside equipment was provided including steam cranes, one of 40 tons capacity and two lifting 20 tons. The cost of £1½ million was about twice the estimate.[5]

The steam factory was designed by C Barry, and built alongside the north basin in the form of a quadrangle surrounding an open space 780ft x 350ft and is an impressive sight today. As well as offices, a drawing office and a store, there was a boiler shop, iron foundry, engine erecting shop, turning shop, fitting shop and, below ground, cells for the convicts who built the yard. The Keyham Yard was independent of Devonport, even working different hours. The two yards were linked by a tunnel in 1857, but only in 1876 did they become a single dockyard.

Master Shipwrights

Name	Date appointed
T Roberts	Jun 1813
E Churchill	Sep 1815
T Roberts	Jun 1830
T F Hawkes	Jul 1837
W Edye	Dec 1843
J P Peake (1st SNA)	Jan 1859

Pembroke

This yard was very different in character from the other home yards, as it was solely a building yard and not concerned with refit work. It was opened in October 1815 as the Pater yard with temporary facilities, and gradually took a larger and more permanent form, with the name Pembroke Dock coming in 1830. To a considerable extent, the original labour force was drafted from Plymouth and Portsmouth when complements were reduced after the war.

Although many ships were built there in the first half

1. *Discovery of the Steam Basin Caisson*, Portsmouth City Council (1985).

2. E C Riley, *The Evolution of the Docks and Industrial Buildings in Portsmouth Royal Dockyard*, Portsmouth City Council (1985).

3. The lists of master shipwrights were supplied by J David Brown, Head of Naval Historical Branch.

4. K V Burns, *The Devonport Dockyard Story*, Liskeard (1980).

5. G Dicker, *A Short History of Devonport Dockyard*, Plymouth (1980).

of the century and, indeed, up to the First World War, it was never extended to take bigger ships and was closed in 1923.

Master Shipwrights	
Name	Date appointed
T Roberts	Jun 1813
J Peake	Jun 1830
T F Hawkes	Oct 1832
W Edye	Sep 1837
F J Laire (1st SNA)	Feb 1844
R Abethell (1st SNA)	Oct 1844
W Rice (1st SNA)	Jul 1852
O W Lang	Apr 1853
H Cradock (1st SNA)	Jan 1859

Chatham

Samuel Bentham had employed Marc Brunel to modernise the yard between 1810 and 1813, leaving it well equipped for many more years. With the other Thames yards, Chatham built many of the early steamships. Chatham was the first dockyard to build an armoured ship, *Aetna*, and later the first iron-hulled ship, *Achilles*, though long after commercial yards had been building such ships. Three iron-framed covered slips were built in 1848 and a fourth soon after, clad in corrugated iron. With the slightly earlier slips at Portsmouth, these were the first large-span iron buildings, well in advance of the more famous big train sheds.[6] The yard is closed, but the historic area remains, with numerous eighteenth- and nineteenth-century buildings as a monument to the pioneer age of the modern Navy as well as to the splendour of the great age of steam.

Master Shipwrights	
Name	Date appointed
G Parkin	Jun 1813
W Stone	Feb 1830
J Fincham (1st SNA)	Apr 1839
F J Laire (1st SNA)	Oct 1844
S Read (1st SNA)	May 1848
O W Lang	Oct 1858

Sheerness

Sir John Rennie had planned a major modernisation in 1810 which was completed in 1823 at a cost of £2½ million. The main feature was a basin 300yds x 150yds. There was a new sea wall, mast pound and three dry docks. There were many new buildings, often using timbers from old warships as foundations. Many of the early steamers were built at Sheerness and a small steam factory was set up in the Crimean War.

Master Shipwrights	
Name	Date appointed
H Canham	Aug 1813
J Nolloth	1817
O Lang	Jan 1823
J Seaton	Jul 1826
J Fincham	Feb 1835
J Atkins	Apr 1839
W Henwood (1st SNA)	Jan 1859

Woolwich

There was a steady building programme until the yard closed in 1869. It should be noted that there were two master shipwrights called Oliver Lang, father and son, and both were outstanding. The father was a strong supporter of the first School of Naval Architecture, though he educated and trained his son himself using a similar approach.

Woolwich was much more famous for its steam factory, the first to be built. It was a substantial and impressive building, showing the Admiralty's appreciation of the need to look after its steamships. The status of the chief engineers was only slightly less than that of the master shipwright. In 1843 the senior staff and their annual pay were:

		£
Chief engineer	T Lloyd	650
Assistant	A Murray	400
Foremen	J Kingston (inventor of the Kingston valve)	225
	J Dinnen	225

The factory also had an important role in training naval engineers (see E C Smith, 'The Engineer's Button', *Engineering*, 28 January 1944). It was close to both the Admiralty and Somerset House and hence able to maintain contact with the senior men. Since the centre of the marine engineering industry was on the Thames, there was an interchange of both ideas and staff with Woolwich. Murray came in when Fairbairn's yard closed, while Humphrys left to set up his own business. Another chief engineer, Atherton, was a Cambridge Wrangler, far removed from the mechanic image. Overall, the factory played a major part in keeping the Navy in the vanguard of technical progress.

Master Shipwrights	
Name	Date appointed
E Sison	Jul 1801
H Canham	1817
O Lang	Jul 1826
N Tinmouth	Jul 1836
W M Rice (1st SNA)	Apr 1853
G Turner	Jul 1859

6. P MacDougall, *The Chatham Dockyard Story*, Rochester (1981).

Chief Engineers	
P Ewart	?Killed in an accident
T Lloyd	1842
C Atherton	1847
E Humphrys	1849
C Atherton	1851
J Trickett	1862

Deptford

Deptford built the first naval steamships, *Congo* and *Comet*, under Oliver Lang, but its position, so far from the sea, was inconvenient and it was closed in 1832. It reopened as a stores depot five years later, and from 1843 until it finally closed in 1869 it was a busy building yard.

Master Shipwrights	
Name	*Date appointed*
W Stone	Aug 1813
(C Long)	Jan 1830
C Wilcox	May 1848
H Chatfield (1st SNA)	Oct 1853
J I Fincham	May 1860

The post of master shipwright was not filled when William Stone moved to Chatham; the senior assistant master, Charles Long, acted until 1848.

Overseas

The only overseas yard to build a ship was Malta with the *Melita*; the remainder were used for repairs and refit only. Yards which had master shipwrights were:

Malta	Cork	Bombay
Jamaica	Antigua	Quebec
Gibraltar	Cape of Good Hope	Trincomalee
Bermuda	Halifax, NS	Kingston, Ontario.

Index